D0985477

Books by Tom McComas and James Tuohy

Lionel: A Collectors Guide & History
Vol. I: Prewar O Gauge
Vol. II: Postwar
Vol. III: Standard Gauge
Vol. IV: 1970-1980
Vol. V: The Archives
Vol. VI: Advertising & Art
Great Toy Train Layouts of America
Collecting Toy Trains

Price and Rarity Guides

3-Rail Guide, No. 1 (1996 edition)
American Flyer S Gauge 1946-2000)
Lionel Prewar: 1900-1943 No. 1
Lionel Postwar: 1945-1969 No. 1
Lionel Postwar: 1945-1969 No. 2
Lionel: 1970-1989
Lionel: 1970-1992
Lionel: 1901-1995
Lionel: 1901-1996
Lionel: 1901-1997
Lionel: 1901-1998
Lionel: 1901-1969 (1999 edition)
Lionel Illustrated: 1970-1999
Lionel Illustrated: 1970-2000
Lionel Illustrated: 1901-2002
M.T.H. Guide, No. 1 (1999 edition)
M.T.H. Guide, No. 2 (2001 edition)
Lionel Illustrated: 1900-1969 2005 Edition
Lionel Illustrated: 1900-1969 2011 Edition

TM Videos

1991 Lionel Video Catalog
1992 Lionel Video Catalog
23rd Annual LCCA Convention
American Flyer 2
A Lionel Christmas, Part 1
Fun & Thrills With American Flyer
Great Toy Train Layouts of America, Parts 1-6
Holiday Music
How To Build A Toy Train Layout
I Love Big Machines, Parts 1 and 2
I Love Cat Machines, Parts 1-4
I Love Christmas
I Love Toy Trains The Music Video
I Love Toy Trains, Parts 1-12 + Final Show
I Love Toy Trains 90-min. Editions 1-3
Lionel: The Movie 1-3
No Game Today
The Great Montana Train Ride
The History of Lionel Trains
The Magic of Lionel, Parts 1-4
The Making of the New Lionel Showroom Layout
Atlas 21st Century Track System
A Century of Lionel Trains
All About Cowboys
All About John Deere
Baby Trains
Great Lionel Layouts, Parts 1 and 2
Great MTH Layouts, Parts 1 and 2
I Love Lionel
Lionel Fastrack
Lionel Legends 1 and 2
Oh No!
OO-HO
Richard Kughn
The Re-Making of the Lionel 1949 Showroom Layout
The Layouts of Clarke Dunham
The Station at Citicorp
Toy Train Accessories, Parts 1 and 2
Toy Train Revue Video Magazine, 1-12
Toy Trains & Christmas Memories
Toy Trains and Christmas, Parts 1-3
Toys of the Past
Celebrity Train Layout Series
I Love Toy Trains Music DVD
Great Train Story
All About John Deere Parts 1-4
John Deere Country Parts 1-3
John Deere Action Parts 1-2
Earth Mover Action
John Deere Heaven
Fun on the Farm
Lionel Nation Parts 1-5
World Class Hi-Rail Layouts
A Lionel Christmas, Part 2

Magazines

Toy Train Revue Journal

Webzine

www.toytrainrevue.com

LIONEL®
Price & Rarity Guide

1900 - 1969
2011 Edition

ISBN: 978-1-932291-97-1
Published by TM Books & Video, Inc.
Box 279
New Buffalo, Michigan 49117
1-219-879-2822

Printed in the United States of America
First printing October, 2010

Lionel®

Price & Rarity Guide

1900 - 1969

2011 Edition

by
Tom McComas
and
Joseph Stachler

For Miss Havens

Contents

Original TCA and TTOS Grading Standards

Mint	Brand new. Unmarred, all original and unused with original box and all appropriate contents.
Like New	Free of any blemishes, nicks or scratches; original condition throughout, very little sign of use.
Excellent	Minute nicks or scratches. No dents or rust.
Very Good	Few scratches, exceptionally clean; no dents.
Good	Scratches, small dents, dirty.
Fair	Well-scratched, chipped, dented, rusted or warped.
Poor	Beat-up, junk condition, some usable parts.

Condition	Add or subtract to listed price
Prewar 1901-1929	
Mint Boxed	+125% or more
Like New	+50%
Excellent	25%
Very Good/Good	**Price Listed**
Fair	-50%
Prewar 1930-1943	
Mint Boxed	+100% or more
Like New (with box)	+80%
Like New (no box)	+50%
Excellent	**Price Printed**
Very Good/Good	-50%
Fair	-60% or more
Postwar 1945-1969	
Mint Boxed	+100% or more
Like New (with box)	+80%
Like New (no box)	**Price Printed**
Excellent	-25%
Very Good/Good	-50%
Fair	-60% or more

READ:
This guide includes 32 pages of color photographs. To see these photos on your computer, and to see some photos we couldn't fit in, go to our website and click on "TM Guide Photos."

We try to constantly improve our database so if you know of a legitimate item we missed, or if we have something incorrect, let us know.

Our website – www.tmbv.com
Email – info@tmbv.com

We kept The original TCA and TTOS grading standards because we like them better than the new, more complicated, grading standards.

Introduction

We printed our last Lionel Prewar/Postwar guide in 2005. We stopped publishing guides because prices didn't change much from year-to-year and we were busy producing videos. But we kept getting emails, phone calls, and personal pleadings at meets for us to publish another guide. We asked, "Why another TM Guide?" Typical responses:

1) Better organized – by category in numerical order
2) More variations
3) No ringers
4) Index in the back makes it easy to find an item
5) Prices more accurate, and...
6) Color pictures.

We discussed the idea. Is another guide necessary? We knew prices were down. Did we want to be the bearer of bad news? Does the collecting community really want the truth? Can they handle the truth? Our decision: yes, let's publish another guide and let the chips fall where they may. So, Mr. Collector, fasten your seat belt, you're in for a bumpy ride. Since our last guide, a perfect storm of negative factors has resulted in a gradual drop in prices. As we interviewed collectors all around the country, it became clear – prices are down (see Market Repot on page 61)

Thanks for purchasing the TM Guide and good luck.

Acknowledgements

The best thing about this hobby is the people you meet. For example, in putting this guide together we talked to knowledgeable train collectors all over the country – most we've known for years and none of whom we would have ever met if it weren't for the trains. It's been fun. The mutual enthusiasms and joys of sharing a mutual fondness for a toy that is both historical, memory evoking, and still fun to play with. So thanks, trains.

John La Lima was a major contributor to Postwar. Lou Palumbo also helped along with Rogers Piercy, Floyd Kenlay, and the misguided Don Zarobsky (who spends most of his time cheering for Notre Dame, the Cubs, and the Bears). John Potter shared his knowledge, humor, and Prewar trains to photograph. Craig Chidester and Shannon worked long into the night sharing information they had gathered after years of hunting. Jim Flynn contributed his extensive knowledge about the Early Period and also sent excellent photographs. Dick Kuehnemund, OO scholar, sent the photos of the unassembled kits and got us on the right track in the OO segment. Dick Kughn, always eager to help, contributed some insight into his deal with Lou and Carl of Madison Hardware. Also thanks to Jenna Egan who put our videos in the Lionel catalog. David Dansky, Fritz von Tagen, Ken Bianco, and Tony Wallis – wise trainmen all. Ron Grossman contributed both wit and insight to our *Century of Lionel* video. We welcome his column.

Robin Coe is our miracle worker with Photoshop and InDesign. She kept asking us to get the book started early so we wouldn't have to put in a week of 20-hour days at the end. Nice thought, Robin, but it never happens. Now that the book is at the printers, you can go home.

Others who contributed include RJ and Jodi Walpole, Bonnie Gross, Tony Pirkel, Dane Lowry, the Countess Albertini, Tom, Chris, Marc, and Patrick Also to Jack and Jeff, who promised to give up smoking. And, of course, the lovely Charyl, who manages somehow to keep the TM ship afloat and sailing steadily onward.

Michael Childress contributed nothing to this book but he helps edit our DVDs, and there's some space left, so I thought I would mention his name.

About This Guide
Getting Started

Take time to read this section. Our format is easy but you have to understand it. Items are listed in the text by category, F3s under Diesels, etc. Within their category, the catalog number for each item is listed in numerical order. Prewar and Postwar items are also listed by numerical order in the index.

Sample entry:

1234	**Roadname** 54-56		
	1. Gray-red/blue	(3)	900
	2. Gray-red/yellow	(4)	700▲

The number on the left in boldface type is the catalog number. Next is the road name of the item followed by the years in the catalog. The number in parenthesis is the Rarity Rating based on a 1 to 5 scale. 5 is rare. 1 is common.

Prices

The number in boldface on the right is the asking price based on grading standards established by the TCA and TTOS (see chart opposite page 1).

Visit our website (**www.tmbv.com**) for: Postwar Mint pricing, Postwar boxes, Postwar HO, Modern HO, Standard Gauge and Large Scale.

Postwar

Price based on Like New condition without the box. To determine value of items in better or worse condition, see chart opposite page 1

Prewar

Price based on Excellent condition without the box for items made in 1930 and after. For item made up through 1929, price based on items in very good condition without the box. To determine value of items in better or worse condition, see chart opposite page 1.

We chose these grades for the various eras because we feel it is reasonable for a collector to assemble a collection in the condition we selected. If you have an item in a grade different from the one printed, check the chart opposite page 4 to see how much to add or subtract from the printed price.

How to Find an Item

If you know the catalog number – go to the index, the catalog numbers are listed in numerical order. The page the item is on is printed to the right. If you don't know the catalog number – look for the category on the contents page or the Quick Reference to find the category.

Variations

We list only collectible variations (those worth more than the normal production version).

Colors

The dominant exterior color is to the left of the slash. The color of the type is to the right of the slash. Two exterior colors are separated with a hyphen. Example: a car with a white body, red roof and red type would be white-red/red.

Trend Arrows

▲ Indicates item is in demand and the price is going up. ▼ Indicates demand is down and the price is falling. No Trend Arrow indicates no discernible trend, one way or another.

? Indicates we are looking for information on this item or proof this item exists. If you have information, send to info@tmbv.com.

Well-done restorations bring a VG price.

Determining Prices

Lionel collectors and experts are selected from all parts of the country. They are sent our list and asked to assign an asking price and rarity rating for each item within the limits of their expertise. We also observe prices at meets, eBay "sold" prices, auctions, "buy-sell" sections in club magazines and hobby stores. The prices and rarity ratings in this book are a consensus of all those factors.

We urge the reader to remember that this is a guide and the actual selling price will always depend on a number of factors, including how motivated the buyer and seller are, the location, and the economic climate. The skills of the buyer at bargaining, and the seller at promoting also affects the price. It is impossible to combine all these factors and arrive at one definitive price. That is why we call this book a guide. It gets you in the ball park, even takes you to your section, but you have to find your own seat.

Determining Rarity

In addition to value, we also ask our experts to list an indication of how hard an item is to find. Rarity is an important element of collecting and we feel our Rarity Ratings add greatly to the usefulness of this guide. While it is generally true that the higher the price, the rarer the item, it is by no means an inflexible truth. There are items that turn up with regularity but are in such great demand that they cost dearly (GG-1s for example). Conversely, some items are hard-to-find, but have a low price tag because collectors are not that interested in them.

Our system goes from 1, the most common, through 5, the rarest and most desirable. The rarity of an item is affected by quantity produced and desirability. Some Prewar and Postwar items were produced for a short time and in low quantity, which explains their rarity today.

5 Items that are high-priced, very difficult to find, and in great demand. Such as: *517 caboose with black roof, 2023 with gray* nose, 2332 GG-1 in black.

4 A regular production item, but produced in lower numbers than normal. Good chance it will turn up at a large meet. *Examples:* 2341 Jersey Central FM, 225E in gunmetal, 6517 Erie.

3 Items that are gaining in collector popularity and are getting hard to find. *Examples: Dark green 253, 3360 Burro crane*

2 Medium-priced rolling stock and small steam engines that are easy-to-find and lack the appeal and collector value of the more glamorous, higher-priced items: *Examples: 603 orange passenger cars, 2055 steamer, 2023 UP Alco.*

1 Low-priced, common items that are usually made of plastic and have little collector or intrinsic value. *Examples: 152 crossing* gate, 6465 Sunoco tank car.

5P Prototypes of which there are one, or two made.
Examples: 213 lift Bridge, brown Burro Crane

5X Pre-production mock-ups, factory mistakes, paint samples, or special items of which fewer than 100 were made.

Example: 6464-100 1954

Note: A Rarity Rating with a plus sign (+), as in 3+, is an indication of a rarity that is more than a 3 but less than a 4.

Variations

We list only major variations that are worth more than the normal production version. Major variations are those which can be readily seen, exist in sufficient numbers so as to be attainable, and are accepted as legitimate collectible variations by the majority of experienced collectors. Major variations usually have to do with body type, exterior color and the size, color or placement of graphics. An example would be the 6464 Rutland boxcar with a solid shield.

We do not list minor variations. Minor variations are not worth more than the normal production version. They are not easily recognizable and are ignored by the majority of experienced collectors. Examples would be slight changes of color, different body molds, or different types of doors, trucks, frames or couplers – all of which can be easily changed.

Prewar Trim and Colors

In most cases, we use the color names established by the TCA in their fine book on Prewar Lionel (available through the TCA, Strasburg, PA). In general, Lionel used dull colors (maroon, gray, Mojave) up to 1924, and bright colors (orange, cream, green) from 1924 to 1936. After 1936, the trend was to more realistic appearing trains, and colors became subdued again.

Trim refers to handrails, journals, number plates, brakewheels, window inserts and other small decorative pieces added to the item. Brass plates were used until 1935, when a combination of brass and nickel was used. In 1938, plates changed to nickel. Nickel journals were used until 1929 or 1930, when they changed to copper. Copper was used until 1934 or 1935, when the journals changed back to nickel. From 1939 through 1942, journals were both nickel and black oxidized.

Warning: Trim can easily be switched. So can trucks, couplers, roofs, door guides and bases of accessories. Example: 813 cattle cars exist with the orange roof from a 814 boxcar. It is unlikely a major variation is going to surface suddenly that has gone undetected by thousands of collectors for over 70 years. Best to have a healthy skepticism about unusual color schemes and odd combinations of trim.

Many fine reproductions and repaints have been created of the more desirable locos and cars. Some are not identified as reproductions. If you have doubt, seek the help of an experienced collector.

Abbreviations and Symbols:

*	Indicates less than the normal sampling used to determine the price or no known sales.
alum	Aluminum
ASF (trucks)	Strong-Arm truck
blk	Black
bj	Black journals
bnt org	Burnt Orange
brn	Brown
crm	Cream
D	Dummy
D-C	Distance Control
DD	Double Door
DG	Door guides
dk	Dark
DL	Directional lights
DSS	Department Store Special
E	Automatic Reverse Unit
EC	Electrocouplers
ECP	Electrocouplers Plus
EH	Electronic horn
ERU	Electronic reverse unit
ESOS	Electronic Sound of Steam
fc	Fixed couplers
FG	Firebox glow
FM	Factory mistake
grn	Green
HL	Headlight
hs	Heat stamped
LH	Left hand switch
litho	Lithographed
lt	Light

mar	Maroon
MB	1955 Door
MR	Manual reverse
MT	Magne-Traction
MSOS	Mechanical Sound of Steam
N-D	Non-derailing switch
NDV	No difference in value
NIB	No individual box. Item came in set box.
nj	Nickel journals
NM	Announced but never made
ob	Original box
Obvs	Observation
oc	Operating Couplers
op	Operating
org	Orange
PDM	Pullmor Direct Motor
PF	Possible fake
PM	Pullmor Motor
U	Uncataloged
rd	Red
RH	Right-hand switch
rs	Rubber stamped
RT	Rubber Tire
SB	1953 Door
SG grn	Stephen Girard Green
SM	Service Manual
SMT	Sprung Metal Trucks
SS	Service Station
SSS	Service Station Special
TL	Tail Lights
TT	Traction Tire
Tus	Tuscan
T&W	Indicates tender comes with or without whistle
U	Uncataloged
VAD	Value Added Dealer
W	Whistle
WL	Warning Light
X	Indicates different from normal production-higher couplers, different trim, color, etc.
YED	Year-end deal
yell	Yellow
2PR	Two-position reverse
3PR	Three-position reverse
4W	Four-wheel trucks
4WPT	Four-wheel plastic trucks
4WT	Four-wheel die-cast trucks
6W	Six-wheel trucks
6WT	Six-wheel die-cast trucks

Road Name Abbreviations

ACL	Atlantic Coast Line
ACY	Akron, Canton & Youngstown
AT&SF	Atcheson, Topeka & Santa Fe
B&A	Boston & Albany
BAR	Boston & Aroostook
BN	Burlington Northern
B&LE	Bessimer & Lake Erie
B&M	Boston & Maine
B&O	Baltimore & Ohio
CCC&STL	Cleveland, Chicago, Cincinnati & St. Louis
C&IM	Chicago & Illinois Midland
C&NW	Chicago & North Western
C&O	Chesapeake & Ohio
CIRR	Chatahoochie Industrial Railroad
CN	Canadian National
CN&L	Columbia, Newberry & Laurens
CP & CP Rail	Canadian Pacific
CPR	Canadian Pacific Railroad
D&H	Delaware & Hudson

D&RGW	Denver and Rio Grande West
DT&I	Detroit, Toledo & Ironton
DT&S	Detroit, Toledo & Shoreline
EMD	Electro Motive Division of GM
FEC	Florida East Coast
GM&O	Gulf, Mobile & Ohio
GN	Great Northern
GTW	Grand Trunk Western
IC	Illinois Central
ICG	Illinois Central Gulf
L&C	Lancaster & Chester
LL	Lionel Lines
L&N	Louisville & Nashville
LV	Lehigh Valley
MKT	Missouri, Kansas & Topeka
MP	Missouri Pacific
MPA	Maryland and Pennsylvania
NKP	Nickel Plate Road
NJZ	New Jersey Zinc
NP	Northern Pacific
N&W	Norfolk & Western
NYC	New York Central
NY,NH&H	New York, New Haven & Hartford
ON	Ontario Northland
PC	Penn Central
P&E	Peoria & Eastern
PFE	Pacific Fruit Express
PL&E	Pittsburgh & Lake Erie
PRR	Pennsylvania Railroad
RF&P	Richland, Fredericksburg & Potomac
RI	Rock Island
SCL	Seaboard Coast Lines
SP	Southern Pacific
SP&S	Spokane, Portland & Seattle
TAG	Tennessee, Alabama & Georgia
TP&W	Toledo, Peoria & Western
UP	Union Pacific
WM	Western Maryland
WP	Western Pacific

Organization Name Abbreviations

ADTCA	Atlantic Division of TCA
CLRC	Chicagoland Lionel Railroader Club
D-TTCA	Detroit-Toledo Chapter of TCA
EDTCA	Eastern Division of TCA
FPTCA	Fort Pitt Division of TCA
GLTCA	Great Lakes Division of TCA
GTCA	Gateway Chapter of TCA
IETCA	Inland Empire Train Collectors Association
LCOL	Lionel Central Operating Lines
LCCA	Lionel Collectors Club of America
LCAC	Lionel Collectors Association of Canada
LOTS	Lionel Operating Train Society
LRRC	Lionel Railroaders Club
LSDTCA	Lone Star Division of TCA
MDTCA	Midwest Division of TCA
METCA	Metropolitian New York Div. of TCA
NLOE	Nassau Lionel Operating Engineers
NETCA	New England Division of TCA
PNWTCA	Pacific Northwest Division of TCA
RMTCA	Rocky Mountain Division of TCA
SDTCA	Southern Division of TCA
S-STCA	Sacramento-Sierra Chapter of TCA
TCA	Train Collectors Association
TTOM	Toy Train Operating Museum
TRTCA	Three Rivers Chapter of TCA
TTOS	Toy Train Operating Society
VTC	Virginia Train Collectors
WMTCA	Western Michigan Chapter of TCA

Market Report – Fall 2010

The train market is down about 20%. However, we have seen rare and top-condition items command higher-than-ever prices. So there is a downward trend but with exceptions because there is still crazy money out there being spent on boxed, rare trains in top condition. Boxed sets are also strong because demand is high and supply low.

The Economy
Unemployment is at 10%. The stock market is as unpredictable as a summer sky over Kansas and the cost of living is up. We're fighting two wars and our deficit makes Pikes Peak look like a molehill. In this environment, it's tough to justify many toy train purchases. On the bright side, it's a buyer's market, and top quality trains still are a sound investment. There are many good buys out there.

Reproductions
It was nice to see Lionel and MTH kiss and make-up but those MTH reproductions with the Lionel name have impacted the Prewar market. Excellent early 400Es used to go for $4000-$5000 now sell in the $3000-$4000 range. Union Pacific sets were $1200-$1500, now $800-$1000. Scale 700Es, were $7500. Now $4000. Items in below Very Good condition have been negatively impacted even more.

We personally like the reproductions. To be able to film a brand new, Ives Prosperity Special or Lionel Blue Comet running down the track (with smoke) is a big kick. But owners of original Ives Prosperity Specials and Lionel Blue Comets don't get the same kick. They feel they have been kicked as they watch the value of their toy trains drop.

Supply
The heart of the toy train hobby has always been guys who grew up in the fifties. That's when Lionel was the largest toy company in the world, peaking in 1953 with sales of almost 33 million. But that was a long time ago. Many of those kids from the 50s have gone to the big hobby shop in the sky and there's not enough younger guys joining the hobby to make up for those exiting the hobby. So more trains are for sale with fewer enthusiasts to buy them. When supply exceeds demand, prices fall. Exceptions are top-collectible and top-condition boxed items–their supply has not exceeded demand. The "on any given day" law can also affect an item's price.

What's the "on any given day" law? On any given day, at any auction, all it takes is two collectors wanting the same item to inflate the value to uncharted territory (examples: see 112 and 113 stations below). These unheard of prices are usually the result of passion for the item and/or the ego of the bidder. Mix passion, ego, and a rare item and the job of the price guide publisher becomes complicated. And, with the number of auctions (on-site and on-line) more than doubling over the last year, the auction venue has thrown an impossible-to-calculate wildcard into the pricing mix. So what do we do when we hear a crazy price being paid for an item? We recognize the abnormal conditions (ego, rare item, mint, boxed) that generated the exorbitant price, and factor it in accordingly. Let's say we hear a mint-boxed N&W 646 steamer sold for $6000 at auction. How does that $6000 price affect us? We might add $50.

Biggest Hits
Like new and excellent items without a box are taking the biggest hit. Examples: LN Illinois Central F3 AB/black lettering was listed in our 1991 Postwar guide at $1400. $700 in this guide. LN Jersey Central FM $3500 in the 91 guide. $1200 in this guide.

On the upside, very early Lionel Manufacturing-era (3-rivet trucks, knobby roofs, thin rims), mint-boxed Postwar and Prewar sets, and mint-boxed accessories are still commanding top prices. Even common items command crazy prices if they are truly mint. Examples: a 112 Lionel City station (with lights) recently sold for $800. A 113 Lionel City station (no lights) sold for $1800. Both were mint in the box. Lucky to get $250 in excellent with no box.

The new virtual world has impacted the way trains are bought and sold. It used to be meets, hobby stores, auctions, and mail order. For today's buyers and sellers, e-Bay and on-line auctions have dramatically changed things. We are guessing here, as we have seen no statistics, but those two venues account for more than half of the collectible trains changing hands today.

Collector Jim Flynn on Internet sales, "Items sell differently in different venues. An item may not achieve the desired price or even get the opening bid, then sell for many times the opening price if re-listed a few months later. An item may sell on the Internet that generated no interest at a national train show, and vice-versa. There are still many dedicated collectors that buy with passion, while others buy purely based on price. Often we receive low-ball offers on an item, with economic or other justification from the prospective buyer. Then, a few days later, the item will sell for full price. Timing plays a big part."

"Ten years ago," says Postwar dealer Rogers Piercy, "we bought and sold everything at meets. Today, we buy and sell everything on eBay or auctions. I don't even bother going to meets. Why deal with 200 guys with fishhooks in their pockets when you can sell the world on the Internet. It's incredible. We have customers in France, Spain, Italy, Australia, Japan, the Netherlands – even Saudi Arabia. My little post office wonders what the heck I am selling."

With the market soft, prices down, and supply plentiful, this is a great time to buy. Layout building is on the rise and "runners" can be had at very reasonable prices. This is good because lower prices will generate interest with new and younger collectors and the key to the hobby's future is getting more folks involved. After all, the trains were made to be played with, not sit on shelves. TCA and other clubs have recognized this, and started Kids Club activities at meets. The TM kid videos have sold almost three million copies, most going to folks outside the hobby.

Starter sets are another opportunity to expand the hobby that are not being exploited to their fullest potential. None of the manufacturers are doing anything to take the starter set buyer from a temporary small layout around the tree – which everyone is bored with in about 20 minutes – to building a permanent layout. The idea would be to take that first-time set buyer from a one-and-done at Christmastime only guy to a permanent layout guy who would be buying add-ons for the entire year. How to do it? – include a DVD in each set showing how the entire family can get involved in building a layout. It's creative, hands-on, educational, and fun. Oh, by the way, in the interest of full disclosure, we produce DVDs.

Most of the new, younger guys entering the hobby are operators. They have been attracted by the sophisticated electronics, features like station calls, realistic whistle and horn sounds, and the scale look of the new trains. They are not interested in rare variations of 6464 boxcars. They are not interested in collecting at all. They want trains to run. This has further dissipated the market for rare prewar and postwar items as the number of folks interested continues to shrink.

Background

In the early 80s, guys who grew up in the 50s were reaching their peak earning years. They wanted to re-live their childhoods and buy all the trains that didn't appear under their Christmas tree in the 1950s. Suddenly, the market for toy trains exploded. In 1975, there were 8000 members of the TCA. In 1985, there were 20,000 members. Weekend train meets, attended by thousands, were held all over the country. Demand skyrocketed and so did prices. This trend continued through the 90s and into the new century.

The six collector guidebooks TM published between 1972 and 1980 played a role in this boom. They were the first books to include color pictures of Lionel trains, a history of the company, and at the end of each chapter, a pecking order as to which were the most collectible items in each category. For the first time those interested could read the history of the Lionel company, see color pictures of the trains, and be told which trains were the

continued on page 200

Prewar 1900-1942

Accessories

Note: "O" designates item made for O Gauge.
"N" designates Standard Gauge.

2	**Figure Set** (seated) 10-18	(5)	300
023	**Bumper** 15-33		
	1. Black 15-26	(2)	30
	2. Red 27-33	(3)	30
23-65N	**Bumper** 15-33	(3)	65
025	**Illuminated Bumper** 29-42		
	1. Cream/red stripes 29-32	(4)	60
	2. Black 33-42	(1)	40
25-50N	**Illuminated Bumper** Black/yellow-red, 27-42	(3)	50
27N	**Lighting Set** for early cars, 11-23	(4)	75
35	**Boulevard Lamp** 40-42 and Postwar		
	1. Aluminum	(2)	40
	2. 92 Gray	(3)	60
43	**Bild-A-Motor Gear Set** Std Gauge, 29	(4)	125▼
043	**Bild-A-Motor Gear Set** 29	(4)	100▼
43	**Pleasure Boat** White/vermilion/cream top, 33-36 with display stand	(4)	550▼
44	**Racing Boat** White/green/dark brown top, 35,36 with display stand	(5)	600▼
45	**Gateman** Green/ivory/vermilion roof, 35,36		
045	1. Blue gateman	(2)	75▼
	2. Brown gateman	(5)	100▼
45N	**Gateman** (Same as 45/045) 37-42		
	1. Silver crossing post, 37-40	(1)	50▼
	2. Gray crossing post, 41,42	(4)	100▼
46	**Single Arm Crossing Gate** 38-42 add $50 for original latern		
	1. Green/aluminum gate	(2)	75▼
	2. Green/gray gate	(4)	100▼
47	**Double Arm Crossing Gate** 38-42 add $100 for 2 original laterns		
	1. Green/aluminum gate	(2)	125▼
	2. Green/92 gray gate	(4)	175▼
48W	**Whistling Station** lithograph, 37-42	(2)	60
49	**Airport** 58" diameter cardboard base, 37-39 w/color lithograph	(5)	650▼
50	**Airplane** with pylon and controls, 36	(3)	500▼
50	**Paper Train** 43,44 Price listed is for complete set unassembled in box	(4)	400▼
51	**Airport** Square cardboard airport, 36,38 color lithograph	(5)	600▼
52	**Street Lamp** Aluminum, 33-41	(4)	150▼
53	**Street Lamp** 31-42		
	1. Light mojave	(3)	50
	2. Light ivory	(3)	75
	3. Aluminum	(4)	150
54	**Small Double Gooseneck Lamp** 29-35		
	1. Pea green	(3)	75▼
	2. State brown	(5)	140▼
	3. Green	(4)	75▼
	4. Maroon	(5)	110▼
55	**Airplane** w/pylon and controls, 37-39	(4)	500▼

No.	Item	Rarity	Price
56	**Park Lamp Post** 24-42 and Postwar		
	1. Dark gray	(3)	**50**
	2. Gray	(3)	**50**
	3. Mojave	(3)	**75**
	4. Green	(1)	**50**
	5. Pea green	(2)	**50**
	6. Copper	(5)	**300**
	7. Aluminum	(5)	**150**
57	**Broadway Lamp Post** 22-42		
	1. Gray	(3)	**50**
	2. Yellow	(4)	**60▼**
	3. Orange	(3)	**50▼**
	Note: All three colors exist with the following celluloid printed lamp shades in either silver or black lettering. Silver lettering is harder to find:		
	a. Broadway & Main	(1)	
	b. Broadway & 21st Street	(4)	
	c. Fifth Avenue & 21st Street	(5)	
	d. Fifth Avenue & 42nd Street	(4)	
	e. Broadway & Fifth Avenue	(2)	
	f. Broadway & 42nd Street	(2)	
	g. Broadway & 42nd Street & Fifth Avenue & 21st Street (add 50%)	(5)	
58	**Small Gooseneck Lamp** 22-42, 46-50 (Postwar carry-over)		
	1. Maroon	(3)	**40**
	2. Green	(3)	**40**
	3. Pea green	(3)	**50**
	4. Aluminum	(5)	**100**
	5. Cream	(3)	**70**
59	**Gooseneck Lamp** 20-36		
	1. Dark green	(2)	**35**
	2. Olive green	(2)	**50**
	3. State brown	(5)	**100**
	4. Pea green	(2)	**35**
	5. Mojave	(5)	**60**
	6. Maroon	(5)	**60**
	7. Red	(5)	**200**
60N	**Telegraph Post** 20-35		
	1. Gray/maroon	(2)	**45**
	2. Peacock/red	(3)	**50**
	3. Apple green/maroon	(3)	**40**
060	**Telegraph Pole** O gauge, 29-42 w/track extension arm		
	1. Orange/maroon	(2)	**25**
	2. Peacock/red	(3)	**40**
	3. Gray/light red	(4)	**45**
61	**Large Gooseneck Lamp** 14-32, 34-36		
	1. Black	(5)	**100▼**
	2. Dark green	(3)	**60▼**
	3. Olive green	(3)	**60▼**
	4. Maroon	(2)	**60▼**
	5. Mojave	(4)	**60▼**
62	**Semaphore** single arm, 20-32		
	1. Dark green/yellow	(4)	**50**
	2. Pea green	(2)	**40▼**
	3. Apple green	(4)	**50▼**
63	**Semaphore** single arm Black/orange/dk grn, 15-20	(4)	**40▼**
63	**Twin Street Lamp** Aluminum, 33-42	(4)	**200▼**
64	**Semaphore** double arm Black/orange/dk grn, 15-21	(4)	**60**
64	**Highway Lamp** Green, 40-42 and Postwar	(3)	**60**
65	**Semaphore** single arm, Black/cream/orange, 15-26 illuminated		
	1. Notched arm	(4)	**40▼**
	2. Unnotched arm	(5)	**50▼**

66	**Semaphore** double arm Black/orange/dk grn, 15-28	(5)	**75**
67	**Large Twin Gooseneck** 15-32		
	1. Dark green/large shade	(5)	**125▼**
	2. Dark green/small shade	(3)	**75**
	3. State brown	(4)	**100**
68	**Warning Signal** 20-39	(1)	**10**
068	**Warning Signal** 25-42	(1)	**25**
69	**Warning Bell** 21-35		
069	(Also in white, dk green, orange & red NDV)		
	1. Maroon/brass/black	(3)	**30▼**
	2. Olive green/black/brass	(2)	**30▼**
69N	**Warning Bell** Red or aluminum. NDV, 36-42	(3)	**50▼**
70	**Accessory Set** O & Std gauge, w/box, 21-25	(5)	**1100**
	1-59 Lamp Post, 2-62 Semaphores,		
	1-68 Warning Signal		
71N	**Set of Six 60 Telegraph Poles** w/box, 21-31		
	1. Gray/maroon	(2)	**400▼**
	2. Peacock/red	(3)	**450▼**
	3. Apple green/maroon	(4)	**500▼**
071	**Set of Six 060 TelegraphPoles** w/box, 29-42		
	1. Orange/maroon	(3)	**450**
	2. Green/red	(3)	**450▼**
	3. Gray/light red	(4)	**500▼**
76	**Block Signal** illuminated, 23-29		
076	1. Mojave	(2)	**80**
	2. White	(3)	**100**
76	**Watchman's Shack** with Ringing Bell, 39-42		
	1. Red/white/orange	(4)	**150▼**
	2. Same with gray post	(5)	**300▼**
77	**Crossing Gate** 23-35		
077	1. Black/black-white/unlit	(4)	**50▼**
	2. Black/red-white/unlit	(3)	**45▼**
	3. Dark gray/black-white/lit	(3)	**45▼**
	4. Dark green/green-white/lit	(3)	**45▼**
	5. Pea green/black-white/lit	(3)	**45▼**
77N	**Crossing Gate** Black/red, lighted, 36-39	(3)	**50▼**
78	**Block Signal** 24-32 (premium for solid castings)		
078	1. Maroon base/mojave	(3)	**75▼**
	2. Orange base/cream	(4)	**100▼**
79	**Railroad Crossing Signal** 28-40		
	1. Cream 28-34	(3)	**125▲**
	2. Aluminum 36-40	(4)	**150▲**
80	**Racing Car Set** One orange or red car, 12-16	(5)	**2000*▼**
	two figures, 36" diameter track circle w/starting post		
80	**Operating Semaphore** 26-35		
080	1. Black/mojave	(3)	**50▼**
	2. Terra cotta/mojave	(4)	**70▼**
80N	**Operating Semaphore** Red/alum/orange, 36-42	(3)	**95▼**
81	Same as **Racing Car Set** 80		
	w/30" diameter track circle		
82	**Operating Semaphore** 27-35		
082	1. Peacock/cream/number plate	(4)	**125▼**
	2. Peacock/cream/no number plate	(4)	**100▼**
	3. Green/aluminum/no number plate	(3)	**75▼**
82N	**Operating Semaphore** Grn/aluminum/black, 36-42	(2)	**125**
83	**Traffic Control Signal** 27-42		
	1. Mojave/cream/white	(4)	**200▼**
	2. Red/cream/flesh	(3)	**100▼**
	3. Light red/cream/white	(3)	**150▼**
	4. Two-tone green	(4)	**200▼**
84	**Two Race Sets** 12-16		*****
84 & 084	**Operating Semaphore** manual, 27-32	(4)	**125▼**
	Dark green/cream/orange		

85	**Racing Car Set** one 80 and one 81 racing car, 12-16		*
85	**Telegraph Post** with extension arm, 29-42		
	1. Orange/orange/maroon	(2)	**60**
	2. Aluminum/aluminum/red	(4)	**75**
	3. Gray/gray/red	(4)	**80**
86	**Set of Six 85 Telegraph Poles** 29-42		
	1. Orange/orange/maroon	(2)	**300▼**
	2. Aluminum/aluminum/red	(4)	**400▼**
	3. Gray/gray/red	(4)	**400▼**
87	**Railroad Crossing Signal** 27-42		
	1. Mojave/orange	(4)	**175▼**
	2. Dark green/pea green	(5)	**325▼**
	3. Dark green/yellow	(4)	**275▼**
87	**Rheostat** for racing car sets U?	(5)	**?**
89	**Flag Pole** Ivory 23-34	(2)	**140▼**
90	**Flag Staff and Flag** 27-42	(3)	**150**
092	**Signal Tower** 23-28		
	1. White/red/mojave	(3)	**125▼**
	2. Terra cotta/red/mojave	(4)	**225▼**
	3. Lt. Terra cotta/pea/ivory	(3)	**125▼**
	4. Terra cotta/pea/mustard	(3)	**125▼**
92	**Floodlight Tower** 31-42		
	1. Terra cotta base/pea green tower 31-34	(3)	**175▼**
	2. Red base/aluminum tower 35-40	(2)	**150▼**
	3. Red base/gray tower 40-42	(4)	**275**
93	**Water Tower** 31-42 and Postwar		
	1. Terra cotta/pea green tank	(3)	**125**
	2. Aluminum/aluminum tank /decal	(2)	**75**
	3. Gray/aluminum tank/decal	(4)	**150**
	4. Gray/gray tank/decal	(5)	**400**
94	**High Tension Tower** 32-42		
	1. Terra cotta base, dark gray tower 32-34	(4)	**350▼**
	2. Red/aluminum tower 35-40	(3)	**270▼**
	3. Red/gray tower 41,42	(5)	**350▼**
96	**Manual Coal Elevator** Alum/yel/red roof, 38-40	(4)	**250**
97	**Remote Control Coal Elevator** w/controller, 38-42		
	1. Alum/yellow/red roof	(3)	**250**
	2. Gray/yellow/red roof	(4)	**350**
097	**Telegraph Post Set** with six 060 poles, 34, 35 Pea green/pea green-red	(3)	**350**
98	**Elevated Coal Storage Bunker** 39,40 Aluminum/yellow/red roof	(4)	**450**
99	**Train Control Block Signal** 32-35		
099	1. Black/ivory/black	(2)	**75▼**
	2. Red/ivory/black	(2)	**75▼**
	3. Black/light mojave/red	(2)	**75▼**
99N	**Train Control Block Signal** Red/alum/red, 36-42	(2)	**75▼**
100-104	**Bridge Center Span & Approaches** 20-31 Std. Gauge, Pea grn/cream and olive grn/cream. NDV		
100	Two Approaches	(2)	**40**
101	Two Approaches, one Center Span	(3)	**150▼**
102	Two Approaches, two Center Spans	(3)	**150▼**
103	Two Approaches, three Center Spans	(4)	**200▼**
104	Center Span	(2)	**50**
105-110	**Bridge Center Span and Approaches** 20-31 O-Gauge, Pea green/cream		
105	Two Approaches	(3)	**30**
106	Two Approaches, Center Span	(3)	**100▼**
108	Two Approaches, two Center Spans	(3)	**125▼**
109	Two Approaches, three Center Spans	(3)	**150▼**
110	Center Span	(3)	**50**
111	**Lamp Assortment** (complete) 20-31		
	1. Wooden lamp boxes	(5)	**1500▼**
	2. Cardboard lamp boxes	(4)	**800▼**

112	**Single Window Station** Cream/green, 31-35 no outside lights (NB)	(3)	500▲
113	**Single Window Station** Cream/green, 31-34 outside lights	(4)	400▼
114	**Double Window Station** Cream/green, 31-34 no *Automatic Train Control*	(4)	800▼
115	**Single Window Station** Ivory/red, 36-42 outside lights, *Auto Train Control*	(4)	400▼
116	**Double Window Station** *Automatic Train Control*		
	1. Cream/green, 35,36	(4)	1500▼
	2. Ivory/red, 36-42	(4)	1400▼
117	**Single Window Station** Ivory/red, 36-42 No outside lights, *Automatic Train Control*	(3)	360▼
118	**Tunnel** metal, no light, 20-32 Prem for solid lining	(1)	50
118L	**Tunnel** illuminated, 27	(5)	100
119	**Tunnel** no light, 20-42 Premium for solid lining	(1)	60
119L	**Tunnel** illuminated, 27-33	(5)	125
120	**Tunnel** 20-27 Premium for solid lining	(3)	125
120L	**Tunnel** illuminated, 27-42	(1)	200
121	**Lionel City Station** Salmon/pea green, 20-26 no lights	(3)	250
	Note: Lionel City Stations come with or without departure board. NDV		
122	**Lionel City Station** interior light, 20-31		
	1. Salmon/pea green	(3)	300▼
	2. Terra cotta/pea green	(3)	300▼
123	**Lionel City Station** Salmon/pea green, 20-23 interior light	(3)	550
123	**Tunnel** 90 degree curve O gauge, 33-42	(3)	450
124	**Lionel City Station** interior light, 1920-30, 33-36 plus two exterior corner lights		
	1. Brown/pea green	(3)	400▼
	2. Burnt orange/pea green	(3)	400▼
	3. Salmon/pea green	(3)	400▼
	4. Terra cotta/pea green	(3)	400▼
	5. Tan/red	(4)	450
125	**Track Template** 38	(5)	5
125	**Lionelville Station** 23-25 Brick lithograph/pea green no lights	(3)	200▼
126	**Lionelville Station** w/inside light, 23-36		
	1. Crackle red/maroon/mojave	(3)	225▼
	2. Crackle red/pea green/mojave	(3)	225▼
	3. Brick litho/pea green/flat light gray	(3)	175▼
	4. Mustard/light red/green	(4)	350▼
127	**Lioneltown Station** w/interior light, 23-36		
	1. Ivory/red/mojave	(2)	150
	2. White/light red/mojave	(3)	200
	3. White/light red/mustard	(3)	225
	4. Mustard/maroon/gray	(4)	250
	5. White/red/green base	(5)	400
128	**Lionel City Station & Terrace Platform** 28-42 129 Platform in combination with:		
	1. Lionel City Stations 121, 122 & 124, 28-30	(4)	2000▼
	2. Single Window Stations 112 & 113, 31-36	(4)	2200▼
	3. 115 Single Window Station 37-42	(4)	3000▼
129	**Terrace Station Platform** 28-33,35-42		
	1. Lt mojave/pea grn lattice gold light posts, 28-33	(4)	1500▼
	2. Cream/cream, aluminum light posts, 35-42	(5)	2200▼
130	**Tunnel** 90 degree curve O gauge, 24-26	(5)	1000▼
130L	**Tunnel** Same as 130 but illuminated, 27-33	(5)	1200▼
131	**Corner Display Platform** Part of set 198, 24-28	(4)	450▲
132	**Corner Display Platform** Part of set 198, 24-28	(4)	450▲

133	**Heart Shaped Display Platform** 24-28 Part of set 198	(4)	**450**
134	**Oval Shaped Display Platform** 24-28 Part of set 198	(4)	**450**
134	**Lionel City Station** 124 Tan/red, 37-42 *Automatic Train Control*	(4)	**600**
135	**Circular Platform** Part of set 199, 24-28	(4)	**375**
136	**Large Elevation** Part of set 199, 24-28	(4)	**375**
136	**Lionelville Station** w/interior light, 37-42 *Automatic Train Control*		
	1. Mustard/red/green	(4)	**350**
	2. Yellowish cream/red/green	(3)	**275**
137	**Lioneltown Station** w/interior light, 37-42 *Automatic Train Control*		
	1. White/red/mustard	(3)	**250**
	2. White/red/light mojave	(3)	**225**
	3. White/red/92 gray	(5)	**300**
140L	**Tunnel** O or Standard gauge 90 degree curve, 27-32	(4)	**2200**
152	**Crossing Gate** 40-42 and Postwar		
	1. Red base/aluminum gates	(1)	**50**
	2. Red base/gray gates	(3)	**75**
	3. Red base/white gates	(5)	**100**
153	**Block Signal** 40-42 and Postwar		
	1. Green/alum post/orange	(1)	**45**
	2. Green/gray post/orange	(3)	**100**
154	**Highway Crossing Signal** 40-42 and Postwar		
	1. Red or orange base/silver post 40	(5)	**150▼**
	2. Black/aluminum 40 and Postwar	(2)	**35**
	3. Black/gray 41,42	(3)	**75**
155	**Freight Shed** illuminated, 30-42		
	1. Terra cotta/maroon 30-42	(3)	**300▼**
	2. Red/gray 40-42	(4)	**400▼**
156	**Illuminated Station Platform** 39-42		
	1. Green base/vermilion roof/silver posts	(3)	**125▼**
	2. Green base/vermilion roof/gray posts	(4)	**175▼**
157	**Hand Truck** 30-32		
	1. Dark red	(2)	**40**
	2. Red	(3)	**80**
158	**Station Platform** Set Two 156 Platforms, 40-42 one 136 Station in set box	(5)	**1200**
161	**Baggage Truck** 30-32		
	1. Pea green RS *Lionel Lines*	(3)	**90**
	2. Pea green no RS	(3)	**75**
	3. Green no RS	(2)	**50**
162	**Dump Truck** *Note: Bins can be switched*, 30-32		
	1. Yellow/green bin	(4)	**90**
	2. Orange/blue bin	(3)	**75**
	3. Orange/peacock bin	(2)	**50▼**
163	**Freight Station Set** w/two-157 Handtrucks, 30-42 one-161 Baggage Truck, one-162 Dump Truck		
	1. Large box illustrated display insert	(4)	**350▼**
	2. Small box no insert	(3)	**450▼**
164	**Remote Control Log Loader** 40-42		
	1. Green/cream/aluminum/light red	(3)	**275▼**
	2. Green/cream/92 gray/light red	(4)	**350▼**
165	**Magnetic Crane** 40-42		
	1. Aluminum superstructure	(3)	**275▼**
	2. Gray superstructure	(4)	**350▼**

184	**Bungalow** Illuminated, 23-32		
	1. Ivory/dark green/gray	(5)	**75▼**
	2. Flesh/orange/gray	(4)	**75▼**
	3. Cream/red/gray	(4)	**75▼**
	4. White/apple green/gray	(4)	**75▼**
	5. Yellow/red/gray	(4)	**75▼**
	6. Lithograph	(3)	**125**
185	**Bungalow** not Illuminated, 23,24		
	1. Ivory/dark green/gray	(5)	**100▼**
	2. Flesh/orange/gray	(4)	**100▼**
	3. Cream/red/gray	(4)	**100▼**
	4. White/apple green/gray	(4)	**100▼**
	5. Yellow/red/gray	(4)	**100▼**
	6. Lithograph	(2)	**100**
186	**Bungalow Set** Five 184 Bungalows, 23-32		
	1. Large box illustrated display insert	(4)	**2000***
	2. Small box no insert	(4)	**1900***
187	**Bungalow Set** Five 185 Bungalows, 23,24 w/box and insert	(4)	**1750***
189	**Villa** 23-32		
	1. Ivory/dark gray/pea green	(4)	**300▼**
	2. Ivory/maroon/pea green	(3)	**200▼**
	3. Sand/peacock/terra cotta	(4)	**300▼**
	4. Lt mustard/apple grn/gray	(4)	**325▼**
191	**Villa** 23-32		
	1. Brick litho/ pea green/mojave	(4)	**300▼**
	2. Terra cotta/pea green/mojave	(3)	**375**
	3. Red crackle/pea green/mojave	(3)	**400▼**
	4. Cream/red/Hiawatha gray	(4)	**450**
	Note: 184,185,189, and 191 come in many different variations. For a complete list refer to the TCA's book on prewar Lionel.		
192	**Villa and Bungalow Set** w/box and insert, 23-32		
	1. Two 184 and two 191 villas in assorted colors, 1923 only	(4)	**4000***
	2. Two 184, one 189 villa, and one 191 villa in assorted colors, 24-32	(4)	**4000***
193	**Accessory Set** w/box and insert, 27-29 (in 1927 pieces came in seperate sale boxes in set box w/o inserts) One each: 069 Warning Bell, 076 Block Signal, 077 Automatic Crossing Gate, 078 Automatic Train Control Signal, 080 Semaphore	(5)	**1200**
194	**Box Set** w/box and insert, 27-29 (in 1927 pieces came in seperate sale boxes in set box w/o inserts) Contains 1 each of 69, 76, 77, 78, 80	(4)	**1000***
195	**Illuminated Terrace** 27-30 Contains 90 flag, 184 bungalow, two 56 lamp posts, 189 villa, and 191 villa	(5)	**2500***
196	**Accessory Set** O & Standard gauge, 27 Two 58 Lamp Posts, six 60 Telegraph Poles, 62 Semaphore, 68 Warning Signal, 127 Station	(5)	**1100***
198	**Large Platform Set** 24-28	(4)	**2500**
199	**Small Platform Set** 24-28	(4)	*
200	**Manual Turntable** 28-36		
	1. Pea green/red center/brass	(3)	**150▼**
	2. Black/red center/brass	(4)	**300▼**
205	**LCL Containers** (set of three) 30-38 Hinged doors, brass trim, dark green	(4)	**275▼**
208	**Tool Set** 34-42		
	1. Dark gray painted chest	(3)	**200▼**
	2. 92 gray	(4)	**300▼**
	3. Silver painted chest, w/hoe, sledge hammer, pick, shovel, axe, and rake	(3)	**200▼**

No.	Description	Rarity	Value
209	**Set of 4 Barrels** Std. Gauge, 30-42		
	1. No box	(3)	**50▼**
	2. With box	(4)	**250▼**
0209	**Set of 6 Barrels** O gauge, 30-42		
	1. No box	(2)	**50**
	2. With box	(4)	**250**
270	**Girder Bridge** O-Gauge, Dk red, red NDV, 31-42	(3)	**50**
	1. Brass plate	(3)	**50**
	2. Nickel plate	(3)	**50**
	3. Decal	(4)	**200**
271	**Girder Bridge** Two of 270, w/box, 31-42	(4)	**200**
272	**Girder Bridge** Three of 270, w/box, 31-42	(5)	**350**
280	**Steel Girder Bridge** Std. Gauge, 31-33 Red, pea green, olive green, green. NDV	(3)	**125**
280X	**280 Bridge** modified to fit O gauge track, 36-42	(4)	**250▲**
281	**280 Bridge Span** Std. Gauge, set of 2, w/box, 31-33	(4)	**350▼**
282	**280 Bridge Span** Std. Gauge, set of 3, w/box, 31-33	(4)	**650▼**
300	**Hellgate** O or Standard gauge, 28-42		
	1. Pea green/cream/orange	(4)	**650▼**
	2. Aluminum/ivory/red	(5)	**800▲**
308	**Set of Yard Signs** w/box, 40-42 and Postwar	(2)	**75▼**
313	**Bascule Bridge** O-Gauge, 40-42 and Postwar		
	1. Aluminum bridge	(3)	**270▼**
	2. Gray bridge	(4)	**350▼**
314	**Girder Bridge** O-Gauge, U40-42 and Postwar		
	1. Aluminum	(1)	**25▼**
	2. Gray	(3)	**40▼**
315	**Trestle Bridge** w/red warning light O-Gauge, 40-42		
	1. Aluminum	(3)	**150**
	2. Gray	(4)	**200▼**
316	**Trestle Bridge** O-Gauge, U42		
	1. Aluminum	(3)	**75**
	2. Gray	(4)	**125**
435	**Power Station** 26-38		
	1. Mustard/mojave/gray	(3)	**300▼**
	2. Cream/terra cotta/gray	(4)	**500▼**
	3. Mustard/terra cotta/gray	(3)	**400▼**
	4. Cream/light mojave/green	(4)	**1000▼**
436	**Power Station** 26-37		
	1. Terra cotta/mustard	(3)	**500▼**
	2. Same as 1 with *Edison Service* sign over door rather than the common *Power Station*	(5)	**2000▲**
	3. Cream/terra cotta	(3)	**300▼**
	4. Cream/light mojave/green	(4)	**800▼**
437	**Switch Signal Tower** 26-37		
	1. Burnt orange/mustard/peacock roof	(3)	**550▼**
	2. Terra cotta/cream/pea green roof	(4)	**650▼**
	3. Cream/orange roof	(5)	**4000***
438	**Signal Tower** 27-39		
	1. Orange/red/pea green, no switches, 27	(4)	**500▼**
	2. Same with knife switches, 28-35	(3)	**300▼**
	3. Orange/maroon/pea green	(3)	**300▼**
	4. White/red/silver, 36-39	(4)	**500▼**
439	**Panel Board** 28-42		
	1. Crackle maroon/white	(3)	**175▼**
	2. Maroon/black panel	(3)	**150▼**
	3. Red/black	(3)	**150▼**
	4. Aluminum/white	(4)	**200▼**
440	**Signal Bridge** 32-35		
0440	1. Gray/maroon/terra cotta, 32-34	(2)	**300**
	2. Aluminum/red/red, 35	(4)	**350**
440C	**Panelboard** for 440 or O440, 32-35 Mentioned in catalog but number never listed	(4)	**175▼**

440N	**Signal** 36-42		
	1. Aluminum/red/red	(2)	**275**
	2. Gray/red/red	(4)	**600**
441	**Weighing Scale** 27-40 Cream/crackle maroon/pea geen w/brass weights	(5)	**750▼**
442	**Landscaped Diner** 610 Ivory/red, 38-42 passenger car on wood base	(3)	**250▼**
444	**Roundhouse Section** Terra cotta/pea green, 32-34	(5)	**1700▼**
455	**Electric Range** 30,32,33	(4)	**1800**
550	**Set of Six Standing Figures** 32-36	(4)	**300**
	In original box w/insert	(4)	**400**
551	**Engineer** (oil can spout usually broken off) 32		
	1. Powder blue	(3)	**30**
	2. Medium blue	(3)	**30**
552	**Conductor** 32		
	1. Navy uniform	(3)	**25**
	2. Black uniform	(3)	**25**
553	**Porter** Navy uniform, with step box, 32	(3)	**40**
554	**Male Passenger** 32		
	1. Brown overcoat	(3)	**25**
	2. Gray overcoat	(4)	**30**
555	**Female Passenger** 32		
	1. Maroon overcoat	(3)	**25**
	2. Brown overcoat	(3)	**25**
	3. Green overcoat	(4)	**30**
556	**Red Cap** 32	(3)	**30**
812T	**Tool Set**	(3)	**150**
840	**Power Station** 28-42		
	1. Cream/orange/mojave floor, 28-34	(4)	**2000▼**
	2. Cream/orange/gray floor, 35-42	(5)	**3000▼**
910	**Grove of Trees** 32-42	(4)	**550**
911	**Illuminated Country Estate** 32-42 Wood base covered with shrubbery and trees around 191 villa, many variations. NDV		
	1. Terra cotta/pea green/mojave	(3)	**900▼**
	2. Crackle red/pea green/mojave	(4)	**100▼**
	3. Yellow/red/gray	(3)	**900▼**
912	**Illuminated Suburban Home** 32-42 Wood base covered with shrubbery and trees around 189 villa, many variations. NDV		
	1. Mojave/white/dark gray	(3)	**800▼**
	2. Gray/ivory/apple green	(4)	**900▼**
	3. Terra cotta/white/pea grn	(3)	**800▼**
	4. Ivory/cream/mojave	(5)	**900▼**
	5. Light mustard/apple green/gray	(4)	**850▼**
913	**Illuminated Landscaped Bungalow** 32-42 Wood base w/shrubbery and trees around 184 bungalow		
	1. Lithographed	(3)	**600▼**
	2. Cream/red/mojave	(3)	**600▼**
	3. Ivory/red/gray	(3)	**600▼**
	4. Ivory/apple green/gray	(3)	**600▼**
	5. Yellow/red/gray	(4)	**600▼**
914	**Park Landscape** Wood base with trees, 32-36 shrubbery, and garden urn with flowers	(3)	**750▼**
915	**Tunnel** 90 degree curve Standard gauge, 32-34	(5)	**700▼**
915	**Tunnel** 90 degree curve, 35 O gauge, slightly smaller than previous 915	(5)	**400**
916	**Tunnel** 90 degree curve O gauge, handpainted, 32	(4)	**350**
916	**Tunnel** 90 degree curve, 33-42 Slightly smaller than previous 916	(4)	**300**
	In Macy's box	(5)	**700**

917	**Mountain** O or Standard gauge, 32-36 Handpainted scenic hillside	(5)	**1500▲**
918	**Mountain** O or Standard gauge, 32-36 Handpainted scenic hillside	(5)	**1500▼**
919	**Sack of Grass** 32-42	(3)	**40**
920	**Illuminated Scenic Park** Two sections, 32,33 two 189 villas, two 191 villas, and two 184 bungalows	(5)	**2500▼**
921	**Illuminated Scenic Park** 32,33 Two 920 end sections, and one 921C center section	(5)	**4500▼**
921C	**Illuminated Center Section** 32,33 Contains one 189 villa, 191 villa, 184 bungalow, 910 grove of trees and 914 park landscape or 922 illuminated lamp terrace.	(5)	**2000▼**
922	**Lamp Terrace** (56 lamp/copper) 32-36	(5)	**600**
923	**Tunnel** O or Standard gauge, 33-42	(4)	**600▼**
924	**Tunnel** 90 degree turn 072 gauge, 35-42	(4)	**750▼**
925	**Lubricant** 35-42	(1)	**10**
927	**Ornamental Flag Plot** 37-42	(3)	**325▼**
1022	**Tunnel** 90 degree turn, 35-42 Lionel Jr. and small O gauge	(3)	**200**
1023	**Tunnel** Handpainted, 34-42 Lionel Jr. and small O gauge	(3)	**75**
1045	**Operating Watchman** 38-42 and Postwar		
	1. Black uniform	(4)	**75**
	2. Brown uniform	(3)	**60**
	3. Blue uniform/silver post	(2)	**50**
	4. Blue uniform/gray post	(4)	**75▼**
1500	**Locoscope** 39 (must be complete with box) Viewer in the shape of a steam locomotive with thirty-nine black & white pictures on 16mm film	(4)	**400**
1560	**Station** Lithograph Clockwork Sets, 33-37		
	1. Terra cotta base	(3)	**40**
	2. Dark green base	(4)	**50**
1569	**Accessory Set** 34-37 Four 1571 Telegraph Poles, 1572 Semaphore, 1573 Warning Signal, 1574 Clock, 1575 Gate	(4)	**400▼**

Track, Transformers & Switches

Miscellaneous Track Accessories

OTC	**Lockon** 23-36	(1)	**2**
RCS	**Remote Control Track** 38-42	(1)	**15**
UTC	**Universal Lockon** 36-42	(1)	**5**
030	**Curved Silent Track Bed** 31-39	(4)	**30**
031	**Straight Silent Track Bed** 31-39	(4)	**30**
032	**90 Degree Silent Track Bed** 31-39	(4)	**30**
033	**45 Degree Silent Track Bed** 31-39	(4)	**30**
034	**Switch Silent Track Bed** (Pair) 31-39	(4)	**50**
41	**Accessory Contactor** 37-42	(2)	**10**
153C	**Track Contactor** 41-42	(1)	**10**
159	**Block Control Actuator** with box, 40-42	(4)	**100**

O Gauge Track, Crossings & Switches

1/2 0C	**One-Half Section Curved Track** 34-42	(4)	**5**
0C	**Curved Track** 15-19	(1)	**2**
0C	**Curved Track** 20-42	(1)	**2**
1/2 OS	**One-Half Section Straight Track** 32-42	(2)	**5**
0S	**Straight Track** 15-42	(1)	**2**

OSS	**Straight Track** w/2 insulated rails, 22-42	(4)	**10**
011	**N-D Distant Control Switches** (Pair) 33-37		
	1. Pea green 33	(4)	**50**
	2. Black 34-37	(2)	**50**
011L	**N-D Distant Control LH Switch** 33-37		
	1. Pea green 33	(4)	**25**
	2. Black 34-37	(2)	**25**
011R	**N-D Distant Control RH Switch** 33-37		
	1. Pea green 33	(4)	**25**
	2. Black 34-37	(2)	**25**
012	**Distant Control Switches** (Pair) 27-33	(2)	**30**
012L	**Distant Control LH Switch** 31-33	(2)	**15**
012R	**Distant Control RH Switch** 31-33	(2)	**15**
013	**Switches and Panel Board** 29-31	(5)	**150**
	One pair 012 switches w/439 illuminated panel board		
020	**90 Degree Crossing** 30-42		
	1. Pea green 30-33	(2)	**5**
	2. Black 34-42	(1)	**5**
020X	**45 Degree Crossing** 30-42		
	1. Pea green 30-33	(3)	**7**
	2. Black 34-42	(1)	**7**
021	**Illuminated Manual Switches** (Pair) 22-37		
	1. Unpainted w/o insulated frogs 22	(5)	**50**
	2. Unpainted with insulated frogs 23-26	(3)	**25**
	3. Pea green 27-33	(2)	**25**
	4. Black 34-37	(1)	**25**
021L	**Illuminated Manual LH Switch** 15-21,31-37		
	1. Unpainted w/o insulated frog 15-21	(5)	**25**
	2. Pea green 31-33	(3)	**10**
	3. Black 34-37	(1)	**10**
021R	**Illuminated Manual RH Switch** 15-21,31-37		
	1. Unpainted w/o insulated frog 15-21	(5)	**25**
	2. Pea green 31-33	(3)	**10**
	3. Black 34-37	(1)	**10**
022	**Unlighted Manual Switches** (Pair) 22-26		
	1. Unpainted w/o insulated frogs 22	(5)	**40**
	2. Unpainted with insulated frogs 23-26	(5)	**40**
022L	**Unlighted Manual LH Switch** Unpainted, 15-21 without insulated frog	(5)	**20**
022R	**Unlighted Manual RH Switch** Unpainted, 15-21 without insulated frog	(5)	**20**
022L	**Remote Control LH Switch** 38-42	(1)	**25**
022R	**Remote Control RH Switch** 38-42	(1)	**25**
042	**Manual Switches** (Pair) 38-42	(1)	**50**
042L	**Manual LH Switch** 38-42	(1)	**25**
042R	**Manual RH Switch** 38-42	(1)	**25**

O-27 Track, Crossings & Switches

1013	**Curved Track** 33-42	(1)	**3**
1018	**Straight Track** 33-42	(1)	**3**
1019	**Remote Control Track** 38-42	(1)	**10**
1021	**Remote Control Track** 38-42	(1)	**10**
1024	**Manual Switches** (Pair) 36-42	(1)	**20**
1024L	**Manual LH Switch** 37-42	(1)	**10**
1024R	**Manual RH Switch** 37-42	(1)	**10**
1025	**Illuminated Bumper** 40-42	(1)	**40**
1121	**Remote Control Switches** (Pair) 37-42	(1)	**25**

O-72 Track, Crossings & Switches

711	**Remote Control Switches** (Pair) 35-42	(3)	**200**
711L	**Remote Control LH Switch** 35-42	(3)	**100**
711R	**Remote Control RH Switch** 35-42	(3)	**100**
720	**90 Degree Crossing** 35-42	(3)	**20**
721	**Manual Switches** (Pair) 35-42	(4)	**150**
721L	**Manual LH Switch** 35-42	(4)	**75**
721R	**Manual RH Switch** 35-42	(4)	**75**
760	**16 pcs of 761** (72" circle) w/box, 35-42	(4)	**100**
761	**Curve Track** 35-42		
762	**Straight Track** 35-42		
762S	**Insulated Straight Track** w/lockon and wires, 35-42		

O-72 T-Rail Track, Crossings & Switches

730	**90 Degree Crossing** 35-42	(4)	**40**
731	**Remote Control Switches** (Pair) 35-42	(4)	**300**
731L	**Remote Control LH Switch** 35-42	(4)	**150**
731R	**Remote Control RH Switch** 35-42	(4)	**150**
771	**Curved Track** U35-42	(4)	**15**
772	**Straight Track** 6-ties, U35-42	(4)	**20**
772S	**Straight Track** 40-42 Two rails insulated for operating accessories	(4)	**75**
773	**T-Rail Fish Plate Set** 100 screws, 36-42 100 nuts, 50 plates, wrench	(5)	**75**

OO Gauge Track, Crossings & Switches

OO-31	**Curved Track** 2-rail, 39-42	(4)	**20**
OO-32	**Straight Track** 2-rail, 39-42	(5)	**50**
OO-34	**Curved Track** 2-rail, 39-42	(4)	**20**
OO-51	**Curved Track** 3-rail, 39-42	(3)	**20**
OO-52	**Straight Track** 3-rail, 39-42	(4)	**25**
OO-54	**Curved Track** 3-rail, w/elect connections, 39-42	(3)	**25**
OO-61	**Curved Track** 3-rail, 38	(3)	**20**
OO-62	**Straight Track** 3-rail, 38	(4)	**25**

OO61, OO62 In 38, track came with spring clip below center rails. From 38-42, track came w/o spring clip and with different pins.

OO-63	**Curved Track** 3-rail, 1/2 section, 38-42	(5)	**30**
OO-64	**Curved Track** with electrical connections, 38	(3)	**25**
OO-65	**Straight Track** 3-rail, 1/2 section, 38-42	(5)	**30**
OO-66	**Straight Track** 3-rail, 5/6 section, 38-42	(5)	**40**
OO-70	**90 Degree Crossing** 38-42	(3)	**50**
OO-72	**Switches** 3-rail, pair, 38-42	(4)	**300**
OO-72L	**Switch** 3-rail, 38-42	(4)	**150**
OO-72R	**Switch** 3-rail, 38-42	(4)	**150**

Standard Gauge Track & Switches

S	**12" Straight Track** 3 ties, 07,08	(5)	**10**
S	**14" Straight Track** 3 ties, 08-30	(3)	**4**
S	**14" Straight Track** 4 ties, 31-42	(2)	**2**
SC	**14" Straight Track** 15-22 with electrical connections, 3 ties	(4)	**10**
20	**90 Degree Crossing** 09-42		
	1. Depressed center	(4)	**5**
	2. Fibre center and solid metal base	(2)	**5**
	3. Bakelite center and solid metal base	(2)	**5**
20X	**45 Degree Crossing** 28-32	(3)	**10**

21	**90 Degree Crossing** 1906	(4)	**10**
21	**Manual Switch** Illuminated		
	1. No fibre rails, 15-22	(3)	**20**
	2. Fibre rails, 23-25	(4)	**25**
22	**Manual Switch** not Illuminated, 06-22		
	1. Cast iron switch stand, 06-15	(3)	**20**
	2. Stamped steel switch stand, 16-22	(2)	**20**
22	**Manual Switch** with fibre rails, 23-25	(3)	**20**
23-65	**Bumper** 15-33	(3)	**65**
25-50	**Bumper** Black/yellow-red, 27-42	(3)	**50**
210	**Pair of Switches** Right and left hand, 26-42		
	1. Green base 26-33	(3)	**30**
	2. Black base 34-42	(2)	**30**
210L	**Manual Switch** Left hand, 26-42	(2)	**20**
210R	**Manual Switch** Right hand, 26-42	(2)	**20**
220	**Pair of Manual Switches** Not Illuminated, 26	(2)	**15**
222	**Pair of Distance Control Switches** 26-32 w/controllers Illuminated	(3)	**100**
222L	**Left-Hand Distance Control Switch** 26-32 Illuminated	(2)	**45**
222R	**Right-Hand Distance Control Switch** 26-32 Illuminated	(2)	**45**
223	**Pair of N-D Switches** Illuminated, 32-42		
	1. Green base	(4)	**175**
	2. Black base	(4)	**175**
223L	**Left-Hand N-D Switch** Illuminated, 32-42	(4)	**75**
223R	**Right-Hand N-D Switch** Illuminated, 32-42	(4)	**75**
225	**439 Control Panel** w/222 switches, 29-32	(4)	**375▼**

Transformers and Controllers

Note: All transformers are for 110 volt, 60 cycle current, unless otherwise noted.

A	**Transformer** 22-37		
	1. 40 Watts, 22-31	(3)	**15**
	2. 60 Watts, 32-37	(1)	**25**
B	**Transformer** 17-38		
	1. 50 Watts, 17	(4)	**15**
	2. 75 Watts, 18-38	(1)	**15**
C	**Transformer** 75 Watts, 25-40 cycle, 22-37	(5)	**15**
F	**Transformer** 40 Watts, 25-40 cycle, 30-37	(5)	**20**
H	**Transformer** 75 Watts, 25-40 cycle, 38-39	(5)	**15**
J	**Transformer** 100 Watts, 4 current, U36 selection: 90-250 volt/40-133 cycle	(5)	**15**
K	**Transformer** 15-38		
	1. 200 Watts, cast iron case slate top, 15-19	(3)	**50**
	2. 150 Watts, sheet-metal case & top, 20-38	(1)	**25**
L	**Transformer** 14,35-38		
	1. 75 Watts, brass case slate top, 14	(4)	**20**
	2. 50 Watts, black sheet-metal case & top, 35-38	(1)	**15**
	3. 50 Watts, red sheet-metal case & top	(4)	**15**
N	**Transformer** 50 Watts, 42	(3)	**15**
Q	**Transformer** 75 Watts, 39-42	(2)	**15**
R	**Transformer** 100 Watts, 39-42	(1)	**20**
rx	**Transformer** 100 Watts, 25-40 cycle,	(4)	**35**
T	**Transformer** 15-38		
	1. 75 Watts, 15-17	(4)	**15**
	2. 150 Watts, 18-21	(5)	**45**
	3. 110 Watts 22	(5)	**20**
	4. 100 Watts, 23-38	(1)	**25**
U	**Transformer** 50 Watts, 33	(3)	**45**

V	**Transformer** 150 Watts, 39-41	(2)	**150**
W	**Transformer** 75 Watts, 39-42	(3)	**25**
Z	**Transformer** 250 Watts, 39-42	(4)	**250**
65	**Whistle Controller** 35	(4)	**15**
66	**Whistle Controller** 36-39	(1)	**10**
67	**Whistle Controller** 36-39	(1)	**10**
81	**Controlling Rheostat** 27-33	(2)	**15**
88	**Battery Rheostat** 15-28	(3)	**50**
91	**Circuit Breaker** 30-42	(1)	**35**
95	**Controlling Rheostat** 34-42	(2)	**15**
96C	**Control Button** 38-42	(1)	**15**
167	**Whistle Controller** 40-42	(1)	**10**
167X	**Whistle Controller** OO 40-42	(3)	**25**
168	**Magic-Electrol Controller** 40-42	(3)	**50▲**
169	**Teledyne Controller** 40-42	(3)	**50▲**
170	**Direct Current Reducer** 220 Volt, 14-38	(5)	**100**
171	**Direct Current Inverter** 115 Volt, 36-42	(3)	**100**
172	**Direct Current Inverter** 220 Volt, 37-42	(5)	**100**
1012	**Station Transformer** 30-32	(4)	**50**

Winner Lines Transformers

1017	**Station Transformer** 33	(3)	**70▲**
1027	**Station Transformer** 34	(2)	**70▲**
1028	**Transformer** 25 Watts, 35	(3)	**25**
1029	**Transformer** 25 Watts, 36-37	(1)	**10**
1030	**Transformer** 50 Watts, 36-37	(1)	**15**
1037	**Transformer** 40 Watts, 41-42	(1)	**10**
1038	**Transformer** 30 Watts, U37	(3)	**10**
1039	**Transformer** 35 Watts, 38-40	(1)	**10**
1040	**Transformer** 60 Watts, 39	(1)	**20**
1041	**Transformer** 60 Watts, 40-42	(1)	**15**
1229	**Transformer** 25 Watts, 220 volt, U36	(5)	**25**
1230	**Transformer** 50 Watts, 220 volt, U36	(5)	**25**
1239	**Transformer** 30 Watts, 220 volt, U38	(5)	**25**

Clockwork Trains

1536	**Mickey Mouse Circus Train Outfit** 35	(5)	**5000***
	1508 Commodore Vanderbilt engine and 1509 stoker tender with diner, animal car, and band car all numbered 1536. Complete set includes cardboard Mickey Mouse barker, circus tickets, auto, gas station, sign, and circus tent. Price is for set in original box.		
1100	**Mickey Mouse Handcar** 35-37		
	1. Red base	(4)	**590▼**
	2. Maroon base	(5)	**800▼**
	3. Apple green base	(4)	**1000▼**
	4. Orange base	(5)	**1500▼**
1103	**Peter Rabbit Chickmobile Handcar** U35-37		
	1. Yellow with flanges (track version)	(5)	**450▼**
	2. Same no flanges (floor version)	(5)	**750▼**
1105	**Santa Claus Handcar** 35,36		
	1. Green base	(5)	**1400▼**
	2. Red base	(4)	**1400▼**
1107	**Donald Duck Rail Car** 36,37		
	1. White house/red roof	(4)	**800▼**
	2. White house/green roof	(4)	**600▼**
	3. Orange house/green roof	(5)	**900▼**

Locomotives

1506	**0-4-0** Black/red, 35 1509 Mickey Mouse stoker tender, 1515 tank, 1517 caboose, set no. 1532	(4)	**400▼**
1506L	**0-4-0** Black/red, 33,34 Same as 1506 with 4-wheel 1502 tender 3 1811 Pullman cars, set no. 1525	(3)	**125**
1508	**0-4-0 Mickey Mouse** Red, 1509T, 35 *(see Mickey Mouse Circus Train)*	(5)	**750▼**
1511	**0-4-0** 1516T, 36,37		
	1. Black	(3)	**125**
	2. Red	(4)	**150**
1588	**0-4-0** Torpedo-type, 1588T, 36,37	(4)	**150**

The Gray Years 1941, 1942

During the years 1941-42, Lionel began to eliminate the use of aluminum paint on various parts of their accessories and rolling stock, and started to use gray paint instead. Commonly called 92 gray, this paint is a high gloss medium gray, and is very distinctive. The prevailing theory is that the aluminum used in the pigment was needed for the war effort in Europe. This may also explain the replacement of gunmetal paint with black on their steam engines at approximately the same time. The following is a list of the accessories and rolling stock which came in gray.

Accessories

35	**Boulevard Lamp**	(3)	**50▼**
45N	**Operating Gateman**	(4)	**150▲**
46	**Single Arm Crossing Gate**	(4)	**100▼**
47	**Double Arm Crossing Gate**	(4)	**175▼**
060	**Telegraph Pole**	(4)	**45**
071	**Telegraph Pole Set** w/box	(4)	**400▼**
76	**Watchmans Shack** w/gray posts	(5)	**300▼**
085	**Telegraph Pole** w/track connector	(4)	**80**
086	**Telegraph Pole Set** w/box	(4)	**500▼**
92	**Floodlight Tower**	(4)	**275**
93	**Water Tower**	(5)	**400**
94	**High Tension Tower**	(5)	**500**
97	**Coal Loader**	(4)	**350**
137	**Lioneltown Station**	(5)	**300**
152	**Crossing Gate**	(3)	**75**
153	**Block Signal**	(3)	**100**
154	**Highway Crossing Signal**	(3)	**75**
156	**Station Platform**	(4)	**175▼**
164	**Log Loader**	(4)	**375**
165	**Gantry Crane**	(4)	**500**
208	**Tool Set Box**	(3)	**400**
313	**Bascule Bridge**	(4)	**375▼**
314	**Girder Bridge**	(3)	**50**
315	**Trestle Bridge**	(4)	**200▼**
316	**Trestle Bridge**	(4)	**100▼**
440N	**Signal Bridge**	(4)	**400▼**
514R	**Refrigerator**	(5)	**750▼**
1045	**Operating Watchman**	(3)	**75▼**

Rolling Stock

620	**Floodlight Car**	(3)	**125**
654	**Tank**	(3)	**70**

820	**Floodlight Car** w/cast lights	(5)	**1200**
1630	**Passenger**	(4)	**75**
1631	**Passenger**	(4)	**75**
2620	**Floodlight Car**	(3)	**150**
2630	**Passenger**	(4)	**400**
2631	**Passenger**	(4)	**400**
2642	**Passenger** Tuscan/92 gray inserts	(4)	**150**
2643	**Observation** Tuscan/92 gray inserts	(4)	**150**
2654	**Tank**	(3)	**85**
2755	**Tank**	(4)	**250**
2820	**Floodlight Car** w/cast lights	(5)	**600▼**

Lithographed Cars

Note: Early versions have latch couplers, brass or nickel journals. Late versions have box couplers, black journals. Numbers changed in 1938 when couplers changed from manual to automatic.

4-Wheel, 6-inch Freight Series

1512	**Gondola** 31-33,36,37		
	1. Dark blue, *Winner Lines,* 31,32	(4)	**20**
	2. Dark blue no, *Winner Lines,* 31-33	(4)	**20**
	3. Light blue, *Winner Lines,* 31,32	(3)	**20**
	4. Light blue, no *Winner Lines,* 31-33	(3)	**20**
	5. Light blue/red, 36,37	(3)	**20**
	6. Light blue/red and yellow, 37	(4)	**20**
1514	**Box Erie** 31-37		
	1. Yellow/dark blue, 31-33	(3)	**25**
	2. Yellow/dark blue, *Lionel Lines* .33	(3)	**25**
	3. Yellow/light blue, *Lionel Lines* .34	(2)	**25**
	4. Yellow/light blue, *Lionel & Baby Ruth* .35	(2)	**25**
	5. Yellow/lt blue/red, *Lionel & Baby Ruth.* 36,37	(4)	**30**
	6. Yell/lt blue/red and yel, *Lionel & Baby Ruth,* 37	(4)	**30**
1515	**Tank** 31-37		
	1. Aluminum, *Winner Sunoco* ,31,32	(4)	**25**
	2. Aluminum, *Sunoco,* 31,32	(2)	**25**
	3. Aluminum,*Union Tank Lines,* 33	(5)	**75**
	4. Aluminum, *Lionel Lines & Sunoco,* 34,35	(2)	**25**
	5. Aluminum/red *Lionel Lines & Sunoco,* 36,37	(3)	**25**
	6. Alum/red & yell, *Lionel Lines & Sunoco,* 37	(4)	**25**
1517	**Caboose** 31-37		
	1. Dark red/brown, *Winner Lines,* 31,32	(3)	**20**
	2. Dark red/brown, no *Winner Lines,* 33	(2)	**20**
	3. Red/black, no *Lionel Lines,* 34	(4)	**20**
	4. Red/black, *Lionel,* 35	(2)	**20**
	5. Red/red/yellow, cupola stripe *Lionel,* 36,37	(3)	**20**
	6. Red/red & yellow/yellow stripe, *Lionel,* 37	(4)	**20**

8-Wheel, 8-inch 1600-2600 Freight Series

Note: X designates no journals

1677	**Gondola** either latch or box couplers, 33-35, 39-42		
	1. Peacock/copper or nickel journals, 33-35	(4)	**50**
	2. Dk orange/nickel journals, 39	(3)	**30**
	3. Dk orange/black journals, 40-42	(4)	**50**
1679	**Baby Ruth Box** 33-42		
	Either orange or brown doors and guides NDV		
	1. Yellow/dark blue, 33-35	(3)	**35**
	2. Yellow/medium blue, 36-39	(2)	**25**
	3. Yellow/turquoise, 37,38	(2)	**25**
	4. Yellow/light blue, 38,39	(2)	**25**
	5. Yellow/maroon, 39-42	(2)	**25**
	6. Yellow/brown, 39-40	(5)	**35**

1679X	**Baby Ruth Box** U36-42		
	1. Yellow/medium blue, 36,37	(4)	**25**
	2. Yellow/turquoise, 37	(4)	**30▲**
	3. Yellow/light blue, 38,39	(4)	**25**
	4. Yellow/maroon, 39-42	(3)	**25**
1680	**Tank** 33-42		
	1. Aluminum, 33,34	(4)	**25**
	2. Aluminum, *Sunoco,* 33,34	(3)	**25**
	3. Aluminum, *Sunoco & Lionel Lines,* 35-38	(2)	**35▲**
	4. Orange, *Shell,* copper or nickel journals, 39,40	(3)	**30**
	5. Aluminum, *Lionel Lines,* 40	(3)	**20**
	6. Silver, *SUNX* X *Sunoco & Lionel Lines,* 41,42 Nickel or black journals NDV	(3)	**25**
	7. Gray *SUNX* nickel or black domes, 42 nickel or black journals NDV	(4)	**20**
1680X	**Tank** U36,39,41,42		
	1. Alum, *Sunoco & Lionel Lines,* no journals, 36-39	(3)	**20**
	2. Orange, *Shell,* dummy box coupler, 39,40	(4)	**30**
	3. Silver, *SUNX,* dummy box coupler, 41	(4)	**20**
	4. Gray, *SUNX* ,nickel domes, dummy coupler, 42	(3)	**25**
1682	**Caboose** 33-42		
	1. Red/brown, 33-35	(3)	**30▲**
	2. Red/yellow/yellow stripe, 36	(3)	**30▲**
	3. Red/yellow/no stripe, 39-42	(3)	**30▲**
	4. Dark brown/brown,	(2)	**15**
1682X	**Caboose** no journals, U36-42		
	1. Red/yellow/yell stripe, 36	(5)	**35**
	2. Red/yellow/no stripe, 37-40	(3)	**30**
	3. Dark/brown/brown, 41,42	(3)	**15**
2677	**Gondola** Dk orange, 40-42	(2)	**75**
2679	**Baby Ruth Box** nj, bj, 38-42		
	1. Yellow/medium blue, 37,38	(2)	**45**
	2. Yellow/turquoise, 39,40	(3)	**45**
	3. Yellow/light blue, 39,40	(2)	**45**
	4. Yellow/maroon, 39-42	(2)	**35**
2680	**Tank** 38-42		
	1. Aluminum, *Sunoco & Lionel Lines,* 38,39	(2)	**30**
	2. Orange, *Shell,* 39,40	(2)	**40▲**
	3. Silver, *SUNX,* 41	(3)	**30**
	4. Gray, *SUNX,* nickel or black domes NDV 42	(4)	**35**
2682	**Caboose** front coupler only, 38-42		
	1. Red/yellow/no stripe, 38-40	(2)	**25▲**
	2. Dark brown/brown, 41,42	(3)	**25▲**
2682X	**Caboose** two couplers, 40-42		
	1. Red/yellow/no stripe, 40	(3)	**35▲**
	2. Dark brown/brown, 41,42	(4)	**35▲**

1700-2700, 9 1/2-inch Freight Series

1717	**Gondola** U33-40		
	1. Tan/orange, U33,34	(4)	**45**
	2. Tan/cream, U35	(4)	**35**
	3. Tan/orange, U35-40	(2)	**35**
	4. Tan/orange, U41,42	(4)	**45**
1717X	**Gondola** Tan/orange, U41,42	(4)	**45**
1719	**Box** Peacock/blue, U33-42		
	1. Copper journals, U33,34	(3)	**45**
	2. Nickel journals, U35-40	(3)	**45**
	3. Black journals, U41,42	(4)	**50**
1719X	**Box** Peacock/blue, U41,42	(4)	**50**
1722	**Caboose**		
	1. Orange/maroon, U33,34	(3)	**35**
	2. Red/maroon, U35	(4)	**50**
	3. Orange-red/maroon, U36-40	(2)	**35**
	4. Orange-red/maroon, U41,42	(3)	**35**

1722X	**Caboose** Orange-red/maroon, U41,42	(4)	**25**
2717	**Gondola** Tan/orange, U38-42		
	1. Nickel journals, U38,39	(3)	**35**
	2. Black journals, U41,42	(3)	**30**
2719	**Box** Peacock/blue, U38,39,U41,42		
	1. Nickel journals U38,39	(3)	**35**
	2. Black journals, U41,42	(3)	**30**
2722	**Caboose** Orange-red/maroon, U38,39,U41,42		
	1. Nickel journals, U38,39	(2)	**30**
	2. Black journals, U41,42	(3)	**30**

Lionel-Ives

1017	**Transformer Station** 32,33	(2)	**35**
1053E	**Complete Electric Railroad** 43 1/2" X 29 1/2", 33 Includes set 1052E, mountain, 913 country estate and decorated platform	(5)	*
1651	**Electric 0-4-0** Red litho/brown/black, Sets only, 33	(3)	**150**
	Set no.1050E with two 1690 Pullmans and one 1691 Observation	(3)	**350**
1661E	**Steam 2-4-0** 4-wheel 1661 lithograph tender, 33 Sets only	(3)	**250**
	Set no. 1051E with 1679 box car, 1680 tank car, and 1682 caboose	(3)	**450▼**
	Set no. 1052E with two 1690 Pullmans and one 1691 Observation	(4)	**175**
1677	**Gondola** Peacock, sold separately, 33-35	(4)	**150**
1678	**Cattle** Green/orange, lithograph, sold separately, 33	(5)	**350▼**

Lionel Jr.

1057E	**Distant Control Railroad** 34 43 1/4" X 29 1/2", Includes set no. 1056E, mountains, 913 bungalow	(5)	*
1066E	**Distant Control Railroad** 43 1/4" X 29 1/2", 35,36 Includes set no. 1065E, 913 bungalow, transformer, rheostat and curved tunnel	(5)	*
1681	**Steam 2-4-0** 4-wheel 1661 lithograph tender, 34,35 Sets only		
	1. Black/red frame, 34	(3)	**85**
	2. Red/red frame, 35	(4)	**100**
1681E	**Steam 2-4-0** 4-wheel 1661 litho tender, 34,35 Sets only, (same as 1681 with reversing E-unit)		
	1. Black/red frame, 34	(3)	**75**
	2. Red/red frame, 35	(4)	**100**
	Set no. 1056E with 2 1690 Pullmans and one 1691 Observation	(4)	**200**
	Set no. 1055E w/1679, 1680, 1682	(3)	**175**
1700	**Articulated Streamline Power Car** U35-37 Same as 1700E but no reverse. Used in uncataloged sets.		**300***
1700E	**Articulated Streamline Power Car** 35-37 Set 1065E 1701 Coach, 1702 Observation		
	1. Aluminum/light red, 35	(3)	**350▼**
	2. Chrome/red, 35	(2)	**300▼**
	3. *Hiawatha Orange* and gray, Set 1071E, 36 two 1701 Coaches, one 1702 Obs.	(4)	**1200▲**
	4. Chrome/red sides, 36,37 came both smooth and fluted, NDV	(3)	**300**
	5. Union Pacific yellow/brown	(5)	**2500▲**

Passenger Cars

2 1690 Pullmans 1691 Observation	8-wheel, 8", 33-40		
	1. Dk red/brown/yellow, brass handrails, 33-35	(2)	**35**
	2. Red/cream, underbellies nickel handrails, 36-39	(3)	**35**
	3. Red/cream, no underbellies nickel handrails, 40	(4)	**40**

1692	**Pullman 1693 Observation** 8", U37,38 Peacock cream inserts	(4)	**40**
1811	**Pullman** 4-wheel, Lionel Lines, 6", 33-37		
	1. Peacock/orange/cream, 33,34	(3)	**25**
	2. Gray/red/ivory, 35	(3)	**30**
	3. Red/cream, 36,37	(3)	**35**
1812	**Observation**		
	1. Peacock/orange/cream, 33,34	(4)	**50**
	2. Gray/red/ivory, 35	(4)	**50**
	3. Red/cream, 36,37	(4)	**50**
1813	**Baggage**		
	1. Peacock/orange/cream, 33,34	(5)	**100**
	2. Gray/red/ivory, 35	(5)	**100**

Winner Lines 30-32

Winner Lines never appeared on any car. The cars only came with or without LIONEL. Most cars came on black frames.

1010	**Electric** 0-4-0, Sets only, 31-32		
	1. Orange/green/cream (Engine only)	(3)	**100**
	2. Tan/green/cream (Engine only)	(3)	**100**
	3. Either w/2 matching 1011 Pullmans	(4)	**200**
1011	**Pullman Litho** 31-32		
	1. Orange/green/cream	(3)	**35**
	2. Dk orange/green/cream	(3)	**35**
1015	**Steam** 0-4-0, Black/orange/copper trim, 31,32 4-wheel 1016 black/orange tender, Sets only	(3)	**125**
1019	**Observation Litho** 31,32		
	1. Orange/green/cream	(4)	**75**
	2. Dk orange/green/cream	(3)	**35**
1020	**Baggage Litho** 31,32		
	1. Orange/green/cream	(5)	**100**
	2. Dk orange/green/cream	(3)	**35**
1030	**Electric** 0-4-0, Dk orange/grn/cream, Sets only, 32	(3)	**125**
1035	**Steam** 0-4-0, Sets only, 32		
	1. Black/red	(3)	**100**
	2. Black/orange	(4)	**100**
1512	**Gondola** lithograph, Sets only, 31,32		
	1. Blue with LIONEL printed	(2)	**30**
	2. Dark blue w/o LIONEL printed	(2)	**30**
1514	**Boxcar** lithograph, Sets only, 31,32		
	1. Yellow/dark blue/Eire markings	(3)	**35**
	2. Apple green doors/guides	(3)	**75**
	3. Black doors/guides	(5)	**100**
1517	**Caboose** lithograph, Dark red/brown/yellow, 31,32	(2)	**25**

O Gauge Electrics

Note: Cab color/trim/frame color if other than black

4	**0-4-0** 9 1/4", 28-32		
	1. Orange	(4)	**750▼**
	2. Gray/apple green stripe	(5)	**1200▼**
	Note: Hand reverse slot in cab. Exists with or without weights in frame. NDV		
4U	**0-4-0** *Bild-A-Loco* **4** in kit form, Orange, 28-32 9 1/4", with 8 sections of track. Price for complete kit with original box	(5)	**2000▲**
150	**0-4-0** (Early) *NYC* in oval, Dark green, 17 same body as 700 electric	(5)	**200**
150	**0-4-0** (Late) *NYC* in oval, 18-25		
	1. Dark green	(3)	**125**
	2. Brown	(4)	**200**
	3. Maroon	(3)	**125**
	4. Dark olive green	(3)	**125**
	5. Mojave	(5)	**400**
	6. Peacock	(5)	**400**
	7. Gray	(4)	**175**
	8. Olive green	(3)	**125**

152	**0-4-0** *NYC* in oval, 17-27		
	1. Dark green	(3)	**100**
	2. Dark olive green	(3)	**100**
	3. Dark gray	(3)	**100**
	4. Gray	(4)	**125**
	5. Peacock	(5)	**425**
	6. Mojave	(5)	**425**
	7. Pea green	(5)	**?***
153	**0-4-0** *NYC* in oval, Same as152 but w/reverse, 24,25		
	1. Dark green	(3)	**125**
	2. Dark olive green	(4)	**150**
	3. Gray	(4)	**150**
	4. Mojave	(5)	**350**
	5. Dark gray	(4)	**125**
	6. Peacock	(5)	**?***
	7. Olive green	(4)	**125**
	8. Glossy maroon	(5)	**?***
154	**0-4-0** *NYC* in oval, 17-23		
	1. Dark green	(4)	**150**
	2. Dark olive green	(5)	**250**
	3. Light olive	(5)	**350**
156	**4-4-4** *NYC* in oval, 17-23		
	1. Dark green	(5)	**700**
	2. Maroon	(5)	**700**
	3. Olive green	(5)	**800**
	4. Mojave	(5)	**1000▲**
	5. Apple green	(5)	**?***
	6. Gray	(5)	**900▲**
156	**0-4-0** *NYC* in oval, Dark green, 22	(4)	**1000▼**
156X	**0-4-0** *NYC* in oval, 23,24		
	1. Maroon (gloss or flat)	(4)	**500***
	2. Olive green	(4)	**550***
	3. Mojave	(4)	**500***
158	**0-4-0** *NYC* in oval, 19-23		
	1. Gray	(3)	**125**
	2. Black	(4)	**175**
	3. Green	(5)	**?***
203	**0-4-0 Armored Loco** gray, 17-21	(5)	**1500*▲**
	1. With two 702 gray supply cars	(5)	**2000*▲**
	2. With two 900 gray ammo cars	(5)	**2500*▲**
248	**0-4-0** 7 1/2" 27-32		
	1. Dark green/brass, RS, U26 strap or cast headlight NDV,	(4)	**225**
	2. Orange/brass, RS or etched NDV, U27	(2)	**125**
	3. Dark green/maroon, RS, U30	(3)	**225**
	4. Orange/peacock, RS	(2)	**125**
	5. Red/cream, RS	(2)	**125**
	6. Red/brass, RS	(3)	**225**
	7. Olive green/orange, RS U30	(5)	**350**
	8. Terra cotta/cream RS U31	(4)	**325**
	Note: 248 cataloged by Ives in 1928 and 1929. Designated 3260 and made in two colors,light blue and dark blue. Late 248 cabs may be found without handrails. NDV		
250	**0-4-0** (early) Dark green/brass, 8", 26 no reversing slot on top	(3)	**250**
250E	**0-4-0** (late) 8", reversing slot on top, U34 same as 252E with 250 number plates		
	1. Orange/brass/terra cotta frame	(4)	**450▼**
	2. Same as 1 but *E* is RS on door	(4)	**450▼**
	3. Terra cotta/brass/maroon or black frame	(3)	**150▼**
	4. Same as 3 but *E* is RS on door	(4)	**200▼**
251	**0-4-0** 10", 25-32		
	1. Gray/brass or red inserts NDV	(3)	**400▼**
	2. Red/brass or ivory inserts and with or without ivory stripe NDV	(4)	**450▼**

No.	Description	Rarity	Value
251E	**0-4-0** 10", 27-32		
	1. Gray/red or brass inserts NDV	(3)	**400▼**
	2. Red/ivory or brass inserts and with or without *ivory stripe.NDV*	(4)	**450▼**
	Note: Gray versions of 251 and 251E exist with either red or black lettering. NDV		
252	**0-4-0** 8", Same as 250 but with hand reverse, 26-32		
	1. Dark green/brass	(4)	**250**
	2. Peacock/brass	(2)	**125**
	3. Olive green/brass	(2)	**100▼**
	4. Terra cotta/brass/maroon frame with or without cream stripe NDV	(3)	**175**
	5. Orange/brass/terra cotta or black frame	(3)	**200**
	6. Maroon/brass/cream stripe, Macy or Hales DSS	(5)	**800▼**
252E	**0-4-0** 8", 33-35		
	1. Terra cotta/brass/terra cotta frame (easily faked)	(3)	**250▲**
	2. Terra cotta/brass/maroon frame	(2)	**225▲**
	3. Orange/brass/terra cotta frame	(2)	**225▲**
253	**0-4-0** 8", 24-32		
	1. Maroon/brass	(4)	**400**
	2. Red/brass	(4)	**450**
	3. Dark green/brass, strap headlight only	(3)	**200**
	4. Mojave/brass exists with cast or strap headlights NDV	(2)	**175**
	5. Peacock/orange with or without orange stripe	(2)	**150▼**
	6. Terra cotta/cream/maroon or black frame	(3)	**275▼**
	7. Pea green/orange with orange stripe, U30	(5)	**700*▼**
	8. Same as 7 but no orange stripe	(5)	**700*▼**
	9. SG green/cream/dark green frame	(3)	**225▼**
	10. Gray/brass, U23-26		*
	11. Red/orange U31	(4)	**375▼**
	12. Red/cream, U29	(4)	**375▼**
	13. Blue/brass U		*
	Note: Peacock and pea green versions exist with and without orange stripe. NDV		
253E	**0-4-0** 9", 31-36		
	1. Peacock/orange	(3)	**125▼**
	2. Terra cotta/cream/maroon frame	(4)	**300▼**
	3. SG green/cream/dark green frame	(4)	**325▼**
	4. SG green/cream/black frame	(3)	**225▼**
	Note: E is either rubber-stamped in black on door (1931 or 1932) or embossed in red on number plate. If on door, add $100.		
254	**0-4-0** 9 1/2", Brass inserts, 24-32		
	1. Dark green	(4)	**325▼**
	2. Mojave	(3)	**275**
	3. Olive green	(2)	**250▼**
	4. Pea green	(3)	**325▼**
	5. Pea green/dk green frame	(3)	**375▼**
	6. Red	(5)	**550▼**
	7. Apple green	(3)	**375▼**
	8. Orange	(5)	**500▲**
	Note: Variations exist having to do with red or orange celluloid inserts behind ventilators, different color hatches, and orange or red stripes. NDV.		
	Note: A rare export version exists with 1 headlight, no pantograph, 254 RS on ends, and underframe marked "Made in U.S. of America."		
254E	**0-4-0** 9 1/2", brass inserts and black frame, 27-34		
	1. Olive green/red stripe	(4)	**350▼**
	2. Olive green/no red stripe	(3)	**300▼**
	3. Pea green with or without orange stripe and orange hatches. NDV	(4)	**350▼**
	4. Orange	(5)	**500▲**
	Note: On most versions, the "E" is embossed in red on number plate. On some later versions, the "E" is rubber-stamped in black on the door. The rubber-stamped versions are rarer add $25 to $50.		

256	**0-4-4-0** 11 1/2", Orange only, 24-30		
	1. Nickel trim, RS *LIONEL* w/border, stamped HL	(5)	**1200▼**
	2. Same as 1 but no border	(3)	**750▼**
	3. Brass trim, RS *LIONEL* no border, diecast HL	(3)	**750▼**
	4. *Lionel Lines* on brass plate w/border, diecast HL	(4)	**1200▼**
	5. Same as 4/no border/larger letters	(3)	**750▼**
	6. Gray	(5)	**?***
450	**0-4-0** 9", Macy's Special DSS, U30		
	1. Red/brass	(5)	**900▼**
	2. Apple green/brass/dark green frame	(5)	**1000▼**
700	**0-4-0** *NYC* in oval, dark green, 15,16	(5)	**500▼**
701	**0-4-0** *NYC* in oval, dark green, 15,16		
	1. Iron wheels	(5)	**550**
	2. Diecast wheels	(4)	**450**
703	**4-4-4** *NYC* in oval, dark green, 15,16	(5)	**2000▼**
706	**0-4-0** Dark green, 15,16		
	1. *NYC* in oval	(5)	**500**
	2. Lettered *C.P.R.*	(5)	**500**
728	**0-4-0** *Quaker* 728, U15,16	(5)	*
732	**0-4-0** *Quaker*, U15,16	(5)	*
1651	**0-4-0** 9" Litho cab on 253-type frame, Red litho, 33 brown roof/black frame *Lionel Ives* markings, sets only	(3)	**150**

Steamers

Note: Gray versions in excellent or better condition of both sheet-metal and diecast locos are always harder to find than black versions.

260 Series Steamers

255E	**2-4-2** Gunmetal 263W, 35,36	(5)	**900▼**
260E	**2-4-2** 30-35, with *Chugger,* 33-35		
	1. Black/cream stripe, 260T 8 wheels	(4)	**750▼**
	2. Black/green frame, 260T 8 wheels	(3)	**650▼**
	3. Black/green frame, 260T 12 wheels	(4)	**750▼**
	4. Gunmetal 263T 12 wheels	(4)	**650▼**
	5. Gunmetal 263W, 1935	(4)	**800▼**
263E	**2-4-2** 36-39		
	1. Gunmetal 263W, 2263W	(3)	**650▼**
	2. Blue/dark blue 263W, 2263W, blue or red *cow-catcher. NDV*	(4)	**1100▼**

Diecast Steamers

204	**2-4-2** Same casting as 1684, U40,41		
	1. Gunmetal 1689W, 2689W	(4)	**125**
	2. Black 1689W, 2689W	(3)	**100**
224, 224E	**2-6-2** 38-42		
	1. Gunmetal, 2689W sheet metal tender	(2)	**175▼**
	2. Gunmetal, 2224W diecast tender	(4)	**2000▼**
	3. Black, 2224W diecast tender	(3)	**175▼**
	4. Black, 2224W plastic tender	(3)	**125▼**
	Note: Same casting used for 224, 229, 1664, 1666		
225, 225E	**2-6-2** Similar casting to Postwar 675, 38-42		
	1. Gunmetal 2225W, 2265W sheet metal tender	(3)	**225▼**
	2. Gunmetal 2235W, 2245W diecast tender	(4)	**2000▲**
	3. Black 2235W, 2245W diecast tender	(3)	**350▼**
	4. Black 2235W plastic tender	(2)	**225▼**
	5. Black 2225T, 2225TX, 2225W, 2225WX sheet metal tenders, uncataloged sets, 39,40	(4)	**325▲**
226E	**2-6-4** Black with red firebox light, 38-41		
	1. 2226T, 2226W	(4)	**650▼**
	2. 2226TX, 2226WX (lower coupler)	(4)	**650**
	3. Late version with 226 plate	(5)	**650▼**

Note: Tender lettering both silver and white: journals came both in nickel and black. NDV
Some 225s, 225Es, 226Es come with Lionel Lines plates rather than number plates. NDV

229	**2-4-2** 39-42		
229E	1. Gunmetal 2689T&W	(4)	**350**
	2. Black 2689T&W	(3)	**150**
	3. Black 2666T&W	(3)	**275**
238	**4-4-2** ***Pennsylvania*** Black 2225T&W U39-40	(4)	**425*▼**
	Note: 238s are usually gunmetal in cataloged sets and black in uncataloged sets		
238E	**4-4-2** ***Pennsylvania*** Gunmetal, 36-38		
	1. 265T&W 36,37	(3)	**350▼**
	2. 2265W 2225W 38	(4)	**450**
	3. High coupler, Sears DSS, 39, 40	(5)	**?***
250E	**4-4-2** ***Hiawatha*** 250W, 250WX, 250T, 35-42 2250T, 2250W	(5)	**2000**
264E	**2-4-2** ***Commodore Vanderbilt*** 35,36,U40 same as 265E but no eccentric rod		
	1. Red Comet 261T, 35	(5)	**650**
	2. Red Comet 265T, 36	(4)	**550**
	3. Black 265T, 36	(3)	**350**
	4. Black 265T, U40	(3)	**375**
265E	**2-4-2** ***Commodore Vanderbilt*** 35-40		
	1. Black 261TX, 35	(5)	**500**
	2. Black 265T&W	(3)	**350**
	3. Blue 265TW *Blue Streak* ,36-38	(4)	**1000**
	4. Gunmetal 265T&W 2225T&W, 36-38	(3)	**500**
	5. Chrome plated 265T, U35, 36		**5P**
	6. Black 2225T&W, 38-40	(3)	**450**
289E	**2-4-2** ***Lionel Lines*** same casting as 1689		
	1. Gunmetal 1689T&W, U36	(3)	**500▲**
	2. Black 1588W 1688T&W, U37	(4)	**675▲**
1664	**2-4-2** same casting as 1666, 38-42		
1664E	1. Gunmetal 1689W, 38,39	(3)	**150**
	2. Black 1689T&W 39-41	(2)	**85**
	3. Black 2666T&W plastic, 42 only (4) **75**		
1666	**2-6-2** same casting as 1664, 38-42		
1666E	1. Gunmetal 2689W 2689T&W, 38,39	(3)	**150**
	2. Black 2689T&W, 39-41	(2)	**135**
	3. Black 2666T&W plastic, 42	(3)	**125**
1668	**2-6-2** ***Lionel Lines*** 37-41		
1668E	1. Gunmetal 1689T&W, 37,38	(3)	**200▲**
	2. Black 1689T&W, 39-41	(2)	**125▲**
1684	**2-4-2** Same casting as 204, U41,42		
	1. Black	(3)	**100**
	2. Gray	(5)	**500**
1688	**2-4-2** same casting as 1666, 36-38 U37-42		
1688E	1. Gunmetal, 36-38, 1689T&W, U37-42	(3)	**125**
	2. Black 1689T&W, U40	(2)	**100**
1689E	**2-4-2** ***Lionel Lines*** same casting as 289E		
	1. Gunmetal 1689T&W, 36	(2)	**125**
	2. Black 1689T&W, 37	(2)	**100**

Hudsons

700E	**4-6-4** *New York Central* 700W, 37-42	(5)	**4000▼**
700E	**Walnut Display Board**	(4)	**1000▲**
700K	**4-6-4** *NYC* 700KW, 38-42		
	1. Original box/unassembled	(5)	**10000***
	2. Assembled, primer gray	(4)	**5000▲**
700EWX	**4-6-4** Same as 700E but with tinplate, U37,38 flanges and blind drivers	(5)	**4000*▲**
763E	**4-6-4** *New York Central* 37-42		
	1. Gunmetal 263W, 2263W oil, 37-40	(4)	**2000▼**
	2. Gunmetal 2226W, 2226WX coal, 40	(5)	**6500▲**
	3. Black 2226W coal, 41,42	(4)	**2000▼**

Sheet-Metal Steamers

249	**2-4-2** Gunmetal w/2235W DSS U	(5)	**?***
249	**2-4-2** 36-37 U38,39		
249E	1. Gunmetal 2225T&W 265T&W, 36	(4)	**350▲**
	2. Black 265T&W, 37	(3)	**275**
	3. Dull black 265T&W, 37	(5)	**325**
	Rare set: Gray 249 with 3 Ives 10-inch lithographed freight cars, U38	(5)	**550**
257	**2-4-0** Black only 30,U31,32		
	1. Orange stripe 257T	(3)	**300▼**
	2. No orange stripe 257T, 259T	(4)	**250▼**
	3. Ives plates, 31 only	(5)	**400▼**
	4. No orange stripe 257T crackle	(5)	**500▼**
258	**2-4-0** Black only 30		
	Same as 257 but with reverse lever in cab		
	1. Orange stripe	(3)	**350▼**
	2. No orange stripe, 258T	(4)	**300▼**
	3. Cream stripe	(4)	**250▼**
	4. Ives plates 31,32	(4)	**550▼**
	Came in 2 rare sets		
	a. U32 Passenger Set - Ives 258 with Ives 1695, 1696, and 1697 12-inch passenger cars	(5)	**2500**
	b. 1615X U32 Freight Set - Ives 258 with Ives 1707, 1708, 1709 and 1712 9 1/2 inch lithograph freight cars	(5)	**2000**
258	**2-4-2** U41		
	1. Gunmetal 1689T&W	(4)	**295▲**
	2. Black 1689T	(2)	**295▲**
	Note: Most 258s have number board on front. A few have the number rubber-stamped under the cab window. NDV		
259	**2-4-2** Black only 259T, 32	(3)	**125**
259E	**2-4-2** 33,34 36-38, U36-40		
	1. Black 259T 262T, 33,34	(3)	**225▲**
	2. Gunmetal 1689T 2689T, 36-38	(3)	**250▲**
	3. Black 1588TX UDSS, 36-40	(5)	**175**
	4. Black 1689T 2689T, U36-40	(3)	**150**
261	**2-4-2** Black 257T, 31 only	(3)	**275▼**
261E	**2-4-2** Black 261T, 35 only		
	1. Red stripe	(4)	**400▼**
	2. No red stripe	(4)	**500▲**
262	**2-4-2** Black 262T diecast, 31,32		
	1. Orange stripe	(5)	**650▲**
	2. No orange stripe, shiny	(3)	**325**
	3. No orange stripe, crackle finish	(5)	**500**
	4. No orange stripe, dull finish	(3)	**275**
	Note: Crackle tender shell will fit frames of 257T, 258T, 261T, and 262T		
262E	**2-4-2** Black 262T, 33,34		
	1. No stripe	(3)	**300▼**
	2. Orange stripe	(5)	**600**
	3. Red stripe	(5)	**?***
	4. **1663** with Ives plates, 31	(5)	**750**
	5. Black satin 265T&W, U35,36	(4)	**325▲**
	Rare: Headed 2 sets of Ives 1685 series pass cars:		
	a. Blue and silver	(5)	**1200▼**
	b. Vermilion	(5)	**1700▼**

Switchers

201	**0-6-0** ***Lionel Lines*** Large and small number, 40-42 versions, add $50 for small numbers.		
	1. 2201T	(4)	**650**
	2. 2201B	(4)	**700**
203	**0-6-0** ***Lionel Lines*** Large and small number, 40,41 versions, add $50 for large numbers.		
	1. 2203T	(4)	**500**
	2. 2203B	(4)	**600**
227	**0-6-0** ***Pennsylvania*** **8976** 39-42		
	1. 2227T, 227 on boiler	(4)	**750▼**
	2. 2227B, 227 on boiler	(4)	**900**
	3. 2227B, no 227 on boiler	(5)	**1000▼**
228	**0-6-0** ***Pennsylvania*** **8976** 39-42 Same as 227 but for use with 2800 series		
	1. 2228T	(4)	**800▼**
	2. 2228B	(4)	**1000▼**
230	**0-6-0** ***Pennsylvania*** **8976** 39		
	1. 2230T	(5)	**1400▼**
	2. 2230B	(5)	**1600▼**
231	**0-6-0** ***Pennsylvania*** **8976** 39		
	1. 2231T	(5)	**1100▼**
	2. 2231B	(5)	**1600▼**
232	**0-6-0** ***Pennsylvania*** **8976** 2232B, 40-42 *Magic Electrol*	(4)	**1250▼**
233	**0-6-0** ***Pennsylvania*** **8976** 2232B, 40-42 *Magic Electrol*	(4)	**1900**
701	**0-6-0** ***Pennsylvania*** **8976** 701T, 39-42 Built to NMRA scale standards	(5)	**2750▼**
1662	**0-4-0** ***Lionel Lines*** 2203T**,** 40-42	(3)	**295▼**
1663	**0-4-0** ***Lionel Lines*** 2201T, 40-42 Same as 1662 but with *Magic Electrol*	(4)	**100▼**

Passenger Cars

Note: Price listed is for EACH car. The locomotives that cars came with in sets are listed in parentheses.

529	**Pullman 530 Observation** 26-32 (152, 153, 252, 248, 259, 261)		
	1. Olive green/maroon	(2)	**50**
	2. Olive green/red	(2)	**50**
	3. Olive green/orange	(4)	**60**
	4. Terra cotta/cream/maroon frame	(4)	**75**
	5. Red brass/ Macy drumhead	(5)	**250**
600	**Pullman 601 Observation 602 Baggage** 33-42 (262E, 259E, 265E, 238)		
	1. Gray/red/ivory	(3)	**300▲**
	2. Blue/alum/alum	(4)	**450▲**
	3. Red/red/ivory	(4)	**350▲**
600	**Pullman** 4 wheels, 5 1/2", 15-25		
	1. Dark green	(5)	**125**
	2. Brown	(3)	**60**
	3. Maroon	(3)	**40**
	4. Orange	(3)	**45**
601	**Pullman 602 Baggage** 7", 8 wheels, 15-23		
	1. Dark green	(3)	**40**
	2. Orange	(4)	**75**
603	**Pullman** Orange, U22 Matches orange versions of 601 and 602,	(4)	**65**
603	**Pullman 604 Observation** 6 1/2", 8 wheels, 20-25		
	1. Orange with wood-grained doors	(2)	**50**
	2. Orange with maroon doors	(2)	**50**

603	**Pullman 604 Observation** 31-36 *(252, 259, 259E 264E* Red Comet*)* *Note: Same as 607, 608 but no lights.*		
	1. Red/black/cream	(2)	**60**
	2. Orange/terra cotta/cream	(2)	**75**
	3. SG green/dark green/cream, DSS	(4)	**125**
	4. Red/white with air tanks	(4)	**125▼**
	5. Red/white with underbellies	(4)	**100▼**
605	**Pullman 606 Observation** (251, 4U, 254E) 25-32		
	1. Gray/maroon/*NYC*	(3)	**175▼**
	2. Gray/maroon/*Lionel Lines*	(2)	**175▼**
	3. Gray/maroon/green stripe	(5)	**300▼**
	4. Gray/red U	(3)	**175▼**
	5. Red/ivory	(4)	**350▼**
	6. Orange/cream/cream doors	(4)	**225▲**
	7. Same with pea green doors, DSS, U	(5)	**350▼**
	8. Olive green/maroon U	(5)	**500▲**
607	**Pullman 608 Observation** illuminated, 26-37 (252, 253, 253E, 249E, 259E)		
	1. Peacock/orange/*Lionel Lines*	(3)	**50**
	2. Peacock/orange/*Illinois Central*	(5)	**200▲**
	3. SG green/dark green/cream	(3)	**125▼**
	4. Red/cream/DSS *Macy's*	(5)	**325▲**
	5. Maroon/cream/DSS *Macy's*	(5)	**325▲**
	6. Maroon/black/cream/DSS *Macy's* (no *Macy* markings)	(5)	**225▲**
	7. Rare DSS Set: Dark red 253 numbered 450 with red/cream 607,608 cars	(5)	**1500▲**
609	**Pullman 611 Observation** *Lionel Lines,* U35-37,40,41 (259E, 204) DSS, Blue/aluminum/aluminum, Same as 603	(4)	**125**
610	**Pullman 612 Observation** 8 1/2", 8 wheels, 15-24		
	1. Dark green/maroon	(3)	**65**
	2. Dark green/wood grained	(3)	**65**
	3. Maroon	(4)	**200**
	4. Mojave/maroon	(4)	**100**
	5. Mojave/wood grain	(4)	**100**
610	**Pullman 612 Observation** (body used for 442 diner) 26-30		
	1. Mojave/maroon/*NYC*	(2)	**75**
	2. Same as 1 w/*Illinois Central*	(4)	**1000▲**
	3. Mojave/red inserts *NYC*	(2)	**100**
	4. Olive green/maroon	(2)	**75**
	5. Olive green/red	(3)	**75**
	6. Olive green/orange	(3)	**100**
	7. Pea green/orange	(3)	**100**
	8. Red/aluminum/aluminum	(4)	**350▼**
	9. Terra cotta/maroon/cream, U33	(4)	**300▼**
	10. Light blue/alum/alum, DSS, U36,37	(5)	**250▲**
613	**Pullman 614 Observation 615 Baggage** 31-42 (262, 255 gray, 263E blue)		
	1. Terra cotta/maroon/cream	(4)	**200**
	2. Red/alum/aluminum, 35 only	(5)	**650▲**
	3. Blue/dark blue/ivory *Blue Comet*	(4)	**350**
	4. Blue/dk blue/ivory *Blue Comet w/1940's coupler*	(5)	**500**
629	**Pullman 630 Observation**		
	1. Dk green/maroon 4 wheels	(3)	**40**
	2. Orange/peacock 4 wheels	(3)	**40**
	3. Red/cream 4 wheels	(4)	**45**
	4. Red/cream 8 wheels	(4)	**100**
	5. Light red/cream DSS 4 wheels	(5)	**125**

710	**Pullman 712 Observation** (256, 260E, U251 red) 24-34		
	1. Orange/RS *Illinois Central* 4W	(5)	**750▲**
	2. Orange/RS *New York Central* 4W	(3)	**350**
	3. Orange/RS *Lionel Lines* 4W	(3)	**350**
	4. Red/ivory/green doors 4W or 6W	(3)	**500▲**
	5. Red/ivory/ivory doors U30 4W or 6W	(3)	**450**
	6. Blue/cream 6W	(4)	**600▲**
	Note: Add $100 for red with 6W trucks		
782	**Pullman 783 Pullman 784 Observation** 35-41 (250E) Hiawatha cars, Price listed is for all 3 cars	(3)	**1800▲**
1630	**Pullman 1631 Observation** Manual couplers, 38-42 no illumination		
	1. Light blue/aluminum	(2)	**95▲**
	2. Light blue/gray	(4)	**125▲**
1685	**Pullman 1686 Baggage 1687 Observation** U33-37 **Lionel-Ives** (262E, 259E, 261E, 249E, 265E, 264E, 263E)		
	1. Gray/maroon/cream, 6W	(5)	**600▲**
	2. Red/maroon/cream, 4W	(4)	**350**
	3. Dark red/maroon/cream, 4W	(4)	**350**
	4. Light blue/alum/alum, 4W	(4)	**550▲**
	5. Vermilion/maroon/cream, 4W	(4)	**350**
2600	**Pullman 2601 Observation 2602 Baggage** 38-42 Red/dark red/ivory (238, 225) +50% for 1940 cars	(4)	**450**
2613	**Pullman 2614 Observation 2615 Baggage** 38-42 (263E, 763E (4 car sets), 226E)		
	1. Blue/dark blue/cream, early trucks, 38-40	(3)	**300▼**
	2. Green/dk green/cream, late trucks, 40-42	(4)	**450▼**
	Note: Prototypes or color samples exist but blue version with late trucks or green version with early trucks never went into normal production		
2623	**Pullman** 41, 42 If steps broken deduct 50% (763E, 226E, 225E)		
	1. Irvington Tuscan	(5)	**750**
	2. Manhattan Tuscan, U	(4)	**750**
2624	**Pullman** Manhattan Tuscan (763E, 226E, 225E) U41,42	(5)	**3000**
2630	**Pullman 2631 Observation** automatic couplers, 38-42 no illumination (1666)		
	1. Blue/aluminum/aluminum	(2)	**200▲**
	2. Blue/gray/gray	(4)	**400**
2640	**Pullman 2641 Observation** automatic couplers, 38-42, Illuminated (1666)		
	1. Light blue/aluminum/alum	(3)	**250▲**
	2. Green/dark green/cream	(3)	**125**
2642	**Pullman 2643 Observation** Tuscan/Tuscan/gray 41,42	(4)	**150**

Passenger Sets

Note: Complete set in set box commands a higher price than total of components sold separately. Price listed is without box. Add 100% for box.

97	**251,** two 605s, 606, 25-30		
	1. Gray	(4)	**1800**
	2. Red 28,29	(5)	**3000**
144	**262, 262T,** two 613s, 614 Terra cotta, 31,32	(4)	**2500**
144E	**262E, 262T** 613, 614, 615 Terra cotta, 33,34	(4)	**1200▼**
146W	**225, 2245W,** 2600, 2601, 2602 Red, 39-40	(4)	**2500**
182E	**225E, 2265T,** 2600, 2601, 2602 Red, 38 only	(4)	**3200**
186W	**238E, 2265W,** 2600, 2601, 2602 Red, 38 only	(4)	**1500**
190W	**226E, 2226W,** 2613, 2614, 2615, 38-40		
	1. Blue 38,39	(4)	**2250**
	2. Green, 40	(5)	**3500**
194W	***Blue Comet*** **263E, 2263W,** 2613, 2614, 2615, 38,39	(4)	**2000**
234E	**259E, 262T,** 600, 601, 602 Gray, 34 only	(4)	**750**

241E	**260E, 260T,** two 710s, 712, 30-34		
	1. Red, 6-wheel trucks	(5)	**2100**
	2. Blue	(4)	**3500**
	3. Red, 4-wheel trucks	(4)	**2500**
246E	**262E, 262T,** 600, 601, 602 Gray, 33 only	(4)	**1200**
267	**4U,** two 605s, 606, 1930 only	(5)	**2500**
268	**256,** two 710s, 712, 25-28		
	1. *Lionel* RS border/cars *IC* markings	(5)	**2700**
	2. *Lionel* RS no border/cars *NYC* markings	(4)	**2200**
	3. Brass plate/cars *NYC* markings	(3)	**2200**
276W	**255E, 263TW,** 615, 613, 614 Red, 35	(5)	**4000▼**
283W	***Blue Comet* 263E, 263W,** 615, 613, 614, 36,37	(4)	**2250**
298W	**238E, 265W,** 600, 602, 601 Red, 36,37	(4)	**1200**
709W	***Rail Chief*** 700EW, 700W, 792 combination, 37-41 two 793 coaches, 794 observation	(5)	**7500**
748W	**763E, 2226WX,** Four 2623 *Irvington* 41,42, or *Manhattan* pullmans (known to come with both.)	(4)	**2100▼**
	***Union Pacific* M10000**		
752E Power Car, 753 Coach, 754 Observation			
	1. Yellow/brown, 34-36		
	a. M-10000 *Lionel Lines* RS black	(5)	*
	b. 752E *City of San Francisco* RS black	(5)	*
	c. 752E *Lionel Lines* RS in black	(4)	**1200▼**
	2. Aluminum, 34-36	(4)	**1200▼**
752W Power Car, 753 Coach, 754 Observation 35			
	1. Yellow/brown	(4)	**1300▼**
	2. Aluminum	(4)	**620▼**
752W Power Car, two 753 Coaches, 754 Observation			
	1. Yellow/brown, 36-41	(4)	**1700▼**
	2. Aluminum, 36	(4)	**1200▼**
755W	***Hiawatha*** 250E, 250TW, 782, 783, 784, 35-41		
	1. Thick casting/diecast trucks	(4)	**5000**
	2. Thin casting/stamped trucks	(4)	**5000**
766W	**763, 263W** Gray, two 613s, 614, 615 Blue cars, 37	(5)	**4500**
768W	**763,** two 2613s, 2614, 2615, 38-40		
	1. **2263W** Gray tender, Blue cars, 38,39	(4)	**4500**
	2. **2226W** Gray coalpile tender, Green cars, 40 only	(5)	**8500***
890W	**226E, 2226WX,** three 2623 Pullmans	(4)	**2500**
1048	**Passenger Car Set** two 2630, 2631, 1019 track, 38-40	(4)	**500***
1048X	**Passenger Car Set** two 2630, 2631, 41-42	(5)	**600***
1060	**Passenger Car Set** two 1690, 1691, 36-37	(4)	**500***
1576	**Passenger Car Set** 1811, 1812, 34-37	(4)	**450***
	Note: May have come with 2 1811, 1812, 1813 in 1935 add 1 to rarity.		

Passenger Streamline Sets

267E	**Flying Yankee** 35-41		
	1. 616W, two 617s, 618 All-chrome power car, 35 black roof	(4)	**1800**
	2. Same as 1 but power car w/dk gray nose, 36-41	(3)	**700**
	3. DSS, painted silver, red top, one 617 with 2 doors, smooth sides, U	(4)	**1700**
	4. Same as 3 but 617 has one door and ribbed sides	(4)	**1000**
	5. U35, 3 cars painted silver, black roof, sliding shoe pick-ups, smooth sides, coach car has 2 doors	(5)	**1200**
274W	**Commodore Vanderbilt** 35 265E, 265TW, 600, 601, 602	(4)	**1000**
279E	265E, 261TX, 619, 618 (**Silver Streak**) 35	(4)	**1800**
291E	**Red Comet** 264E, two 603s, 604, 35,36		
	1. With 261T, 1935	(4)	**2000**
	2. With 265T, 1936	(4)	**1600**

295E	**Blue Streak** 265E, 265TX, 619, 617, 618, 36,37		
295W	1. Blue/white stripe cars	(4)	**2200▲**
	2. Solid blue cars (came with black 265E only)	(5)	**4000▲**
299W	**UP's City of Denver** 36-39		
	636W, 2 637 coaches, 638 obvs		
	1. Medium brown/yellow/yellow vestibules	(3)	**1600▲**
	2. Dark brown/yellow/yellow-brown vestibules	(4)	**1500**
	3. Dark brown/yellow/yellow vestibules	(4)	**750**
	4. Green/dark green (only one 637 coach) DSS, U	(5)	**6500***

Rolling Stock

600 Series

620	**Floodlight** 37-42		
	1. Red/aluminum light	(2)	**95**
	2. Red/gray cast light	(3)	**150**
651	**Flatcar** w/4 stakes, 35-42		
	1. Green/nickel journals	(2)	**40**
	2. Green/black journals	(3)	**45**
652	**Gondola** 35-42		
	1. Yellow/nickel or black journals	(2)	**50**
	2. Orange/latch or box couplers	(3)	**60**
653	**Hopper** SG green, 34-40, U41,42	(3)	**80**
654	**Tank Car** 34-42		
	1. Aluminum/*Sunoco* decal	(2)	**50**
	2. Orange/*Shell* decal	(3)	**85**
	3. Light gray/*Sunoco* decal	(3)	**70**
	4. Light gray/*Sunoco* decal/black trim	(3)	**100**
655	**Boxcar** 34-42, U39,40		
	1. Cream/maroon/brass	(2)	**60**
	2. Yellow/brown/black journals, U39,40	(3)	**90**
656	**Cattle Car** 35-40		
	1. Light gray/red	(2)	**150**
	2. Lt gray/red/vermilion doors	(3)	**200**
	3. Orange/maroon RS	(4)	**200**
	4. Lt. gray/Tuscan/gray doors	(3)	**175**
657	**Caboose** 34-42		
	1. Dark red/cream	(1)	**30**
	2. Red/cream	(1)	**30**
	3. Red/white	(1)	**20**
	4. Red/Tuscan/white	(3)	**35**
	5. Nickel plates	(4)	**100**
659	**Dump** Dark green, 35-42	(3)	**100▲**

800 Series

Note: First versions of the 800 Series came with no journals (no holes punched in frame). These cars are rarer than later versions with journals (holes punched in frame). Became 2800 series in 1938 when couplers were changed from manual to automatic

800	**Boxcar** *PRR* and *Wabash,* 5 1/2", RS, 15-26		
	hook couplers no journals		
	1. Yellow orange/maroon	(5)	**100**
	2. Yellow orange	(3)	**60**
	3. Green	(5)	**150**
	4. Orange	(2)	**40**
801	**Caboose** 5 1/2", hook couplers, no journals, RS, 15-26		
	1. Brown/black *Wabash RR 4390*	(4)	**50**
	2. Brown/black *NYNH&H*	(5)	**400▲**
	3. Brown/black *Wabash RR 4890*	(3)	**40**
802	**Cattle** *Union Stock Lines,* 5 1/2", RS, 15-28		
	hook couplers no journals		
	1. Dark green	(4)	**70**
	2. Green	(3)	**60**
803	**Hopper** 23-34		
	1. Dark green RS no journals 23-28	(3)	**60**
	2. Peacock/brass 29-34	(2)	**50**

804	**Tank** 23-34, U35-40		
	1. Gray RS no journals 23-28	(3)	**40**
	2. Dark gray RS 23-28	(3)	**40**
	3. Terra cotta, RS, 23-28	(3)	**40**
	4. Aluminum/no decal, 29-34	(2)	**30**
	5. Alum/*Sunoco* decal, U34	(3)	**40**
	6. Orange/*Shell* decal/nickel, U39	(4)	**80**
	7. Orange/*Shell* decal, U40	(4)	**90**
805	**Boxcar** 27-34		
	1. Cream/orange	(5)	**200**
	2. Terra cotta/orange	(4)	**90**
	3. Orange/maroon	(4)	**85**
	4. Pea green/orange	(3)	**45**
	5. Pea grn/maroon no journals	(4)	**75**
	6. Pea green/orange, U31	(3)	**60**
806	**Cattle Car** 27-34		
	1. Pea green/terra cotta no journals, U27	(4)	**150**
	2. Orange/maroon no journals	(3)	**100**
	3. Orange/pea green	(2)	**75**
	4. Orange/orange, U31	(4)	**150**
807	**Caboose** 27-34,U35-39		
	1. Peacock/dark green/red nj, U27,28	(4)	**75**
	2. Dark red/peacock	(2)	**25**
	3. Red/cream	(3)	**30**
	4. Red RS/blk journals, U40,41	(4)	**50**
	5. Dull red/brown RS 42	(4)	**50**
	Note: Variations exist having to do with nickel trim, rubber stamping, brass and nickel journals, and different color shades. NDV		
809	**Dump** 31-34,U35-40		
	1. Orange	(4)	**125**
	2. Green	(3)	**75**
	3. Dark green, U35-40	(4)	**85**
810	**Derrick** 30-42		
	1. Terra cotta/maroon/peacock boom	(4)	**300▼**
	2. Same/brass knobs instead of nickel	(3)	**300▼**
	3. Yellow/red/green boom	(3)	**350▼**
811	**Flatcar** 26-40		
	1. Maroon/gold RS	(2)	**75**
	2. Aluminum/black RS	(3)	**100▼**
812	**Gondola** 26-42		
	1. Mojave	(3)	**70**
	2. Dark green	(2)	**50**
	3. Apple green	(4)	**100**
	4. Green, 36-40	(2)	**60**
	5. Green/brass	(4)	**120**
813	**Cattle Car** 26-42		
	1. Orange/pea green	(3)	**150**
	2. Cream/maroon	(4)	**350▼**
	3. Tuscan	(5)	**4500▲**
	Note: 813 and 814 come with both large and small door handles. NDV		
814	**Boxcar** 26-42		
	1. Yellow/brown/brass trim	(3)	**125**
	2. Yellow/brown/nickel trim	(3)	**150**
	3. Cream/maroon	(4)	**175**
	4. Cream/orange	(3)	**100**
	Note: Door guides usually match roof color but on cream/orange cars guides can be found in peacock add $150 or pea green add $75.		
814R	**Refrigerator** 29-42		
	1. Ivory/peacock/black frame	(3)	**250**
	2. White/blue/black frame nickel	(4)	**500**
	3. Ivory/blue/alum frame nickel	(4)	**700**
	4. Flat white/Tuscan/black frame HS	(5)	**3000**
	5. Same as 4 but w/nickel plates	(5)	**?***
	6. White/blue/aluminum frame brass	(4)	**600**

No.	Item	Rarity	Value
815	**Tank** 26-42		
	1. Pea green/maroon frame/no decal	(5)	**1200▲**
	2. Pea green/black frame/no decal	(2)	**125**
	3. Aluminum/*Sunoco* decal	(2)	**150**
	4. Aluminum/no decal	(4)	**150**
	5. Shell orange/*Shell* decal	(5)	**700▲**
816	**Hopper** 27-42		
	1. Olive green/brass	(3)	**225**
	2. Bright red/brass	(3)	**175▼**
	3. Dark red/brass	(4)	**175▼**
	4. Dark red/nickel	(4)	**325▲**
	5. Black/nickel	(5+)	**2500▲**
	6. Black/white RS	(5)	**1500▲**
	7. Orange, one known to exist	(5+)	*
	8. Dk green, one known to exist	(5+)	*
817	**Caboose** 26-42		
	1. Peacock/dk green/orange	(2)	**75▼**
	2. Peacock/dark green/brass	(3)	**125▲**
	3. Red/peacock/brass	(4)	**100▼**
	4. Red/brown/nickel plates	(5)	**950▲**
	5. Red/nickel/alum railing	(2)	**125**
820	**Boxcar** *Illinois Central* and *Union Pacific*, 15-26 5 1/2", hook couplers, no journals, RS		
	1. Yellow orange/brown	(5)	**100**
	2. Yellow/orange	(4)	**75**
	3. Orange	(3)	**60**
	4. Orange/maroon roof	(4)	**150**
	5. Dark olive green, *ATSF*	(5)	**?***
820	**Floodlight** RS, *Lionel Lines* ,31-42		
	1. Terra cotta/brass lights	(2)	**175**
	2. Terra cotta/nickel lights	(4)	**175▼**
	3. Green/nickel lights	(3)	**200▼**
	4. Green/gray diecast lights	(5)	**750▼**
821	**Cattle** *Union Stock Lines*, Green, 15,16,25,26 5 1/2", hook couplers, no journals, RS	(4)	**85**
	1. Dark pea green	(4)	**150**
	2. Light pea green	(3)	**85**
822	**Caboose** *NYC Lines* 5 1/2", hook couplers, RS, 15-26 no journals		
	1. Brown/black	(3)	**75**
	2. Maroon/black vertical ribs embossed outward, black or gold lettering	(3)	**75**
	3. Maroon/black vertical ribs embossed inward, black lettering	(3)	**75**
831	**Flatcar** 27-34, U35-40		
	1. Black/8 stakes/no journals	(4)	**225**
	2. Dark green/8 stakes	(4)	**200**
	3. Dark green/4 stakes	(2)	**25**
	4. Green/4 stakes, U35-40	(3)	**30**
900	**Ammunition Car** Gray, 17-21 matches 203 armored loco	(4)	**400**
901	**Gondola** 19-27 *Lake Shore* and *Pennsylvania*		
	1. Maroon	(3)	**60**
	2. Gray	(3)	**60**
	3. Light gray	(3)	**60**
	4. Dark green	(5)	**100**
	5. Olive	(5)	**100**
	6. Brown	(5)	**100**
	7. Dark olive green	(5)	**100**
	8. Dark gray	(3)	**60**
902	**Gondola** 27-34		
	1. Dark green	(5)	**50**
	2. Peacock/no journals	(5)	**35**
	3. Apple green	(3)	**40**

2600 Series

2620	**Floodlight** 38-42		
	1. Red/aluminum light	(2)	**150**
	2. Red/gray light	(3)	**150▼**
	3. Black/nickel light, 43	(5)	**400▼**
2651	**Flatcar** 38-42		
	1. Green	(2)	**60**
	2. Black, 42	(4)	**150▼**
2652	**Gondola** 38-42		
	1. Yellow	(2)	**60**
	2. Burnt orange	(3)	**80**
2653	**Hopper** 38-42		
	1. Stephen Girard green	(3)	**85**
	2. Black RS	(4)	**300▼**
2654	**Tank Car** 38-42		
	1. Aluminum/*Sunoco* decal	(2)	**50**
	2. Orange/*Shell* decal	(3)	**75**
	3. Gray/*Sunoco* decal	(3)	**85**
2655	**Boxcar** 38-42		
	1. Cream/maroon/nickel	(2)	**75▼**
	2. Cream/Tuscan, RS	(3)	**100▼**
2656	**Cattle Car** 38-42		
	1. Gray/red	(3)	**175▼**
	2. Burnt orange/Tuscan, RS	(4)	**350▼**
2657	**Caboose** 38-42		
	1. Red/cream	(2)	**35**
	2. Red/red/white RS	(3)	**40**
	3. Red/Tuscan/white,1 coupler	(3)	**50**
	4. Same as 3 with 2 couplers (2657X)	(4)	**80**
2659	**Dump** Green, RS, 38-42	(3)	**100▼**
2660	**Derrick** Cream/red 38-42		
	1. Green boom	(3)	**175▼**
	2. Unpainted black boom	(3)	**175▼**

2800 Series

2810	**Derrick** Yellow/red, 38-42		
	1. Early couplers and trucks	(4)	**275▼**
	2. Late couplers and trucks	(5)	**650▼**
2811	**Flatcar** Aluminum/black, RS, 38-42	(4)	**150▼**
2812	**Gondola** Green/nickel, 38-42	(2)	**75**
2812X	**Gondola** Burnt orange		
	1. Nickel trim, RS	(3)	**100▼**
	2. Nickel plates	(5)	**350▲**
2813	**Cattle Car** Cream/maroon, 38-42	(4)	**325▼**
2814	**Boxcar** 38-42		
	1. Yellow/brown	(4)	**250▼**
	2. Cream/maroon	(3)	**350▲**
	3. Burnt orange/Tuscan	(5)	**3000*▲**
2814R	**Refrigerator** 38-42		
	1. White/blue/black frame	(4)	**350▼**
	2. White/blue/alum frame	(4)	**475▼**
	3. Flat white/Tuscan/black frame, HS	(5)	**3500*▲**
2815	**Tank Car** 38-42		
	1. Aluminum/*Sunoco* decal	(2)	**200▼**
	2. Orange/*Shell* decals	(3)	**225▼**
	3. Orange/no *Shell* decal/decal lettering	(5)	**300▼**
2816	**Hopper** 38-42		
	1. Red/nickel	(3)	**275**
	2. Black, HS	(4)	**475▼**
2817	**Caboose** 38-42		
	1. Red/aluminum inserts	(3)	**125**
	2. Red/Tuscan/white, nickel	(5)	**750**
	3. Red/Tuscan/white, HS	(4)	**275**

2820	**Floodlight** 38-42		
	1. Green/nickel lights	(3)	**275**
	2. Green/gray, diecast lights	(5)	**800**

Operating Cars

3651	**Lumber** Black 39-42	(2)	**50▼**
3652	**Gondola** 38-42		
	1. Yellow/nickel plate	(2)	**50▼**
	2. Yellow/red, RS	(4)	**75▼**
	3. Yellow/black, RS	(3)	**65▼**
3659	**Dump** Black/red bin, 39-42	(2)	**75**
3811	**Flatcar** Black with logs, 39-42	(2)	**125▲**
3814	**Merchandise Operating Car** 39-42		
	1. Tuscan, *Lionel Lines,* RS	(4)	**450▲**
	2. Tuscan/decal	(3)	**200▼**
3859	**Dump** Black/red, 38-42		
	1. Early trucks and couplers	(3)	**125▼**
	2. Late trucks and couplers	(4)	**150**

Scale and Semi-Scale Freights

Note: Kit prices based on unassembled condition in original box.

714	**Boxcar** Scale, Tuscan, RS, *Pennsylvania* ,40-42	(4)	**400**
714K	**Boxcar Kit** Scale, 40-42	(5)	**1500**
715	**Tank Car** Scale, 40-42		
	1. Black, *Shell* decal, 40	(4)	**900**
	2. Black, *Sunoco* decal, 41, 42	(5)	**1100▲**
715K	**Tank Car Kit** Scale, 40-42		
	1. *Shell* decal	(4)	**1500**
	2. *Sunoco* decal	(5)	**1200**
716	**Hopper** Scale, RS, *B&O,* Black, 40-42	(5)	**650**
716K	**Hopper Kit** Scale, 40-42	(5)	**1500**
717	**Caboose** Scale, RS, *NYC,* Tuscan, 40-42	(4)	**750▲**
717K	**Caboose Kit** Scale, 40-42	(5)	**1500**
2672	**Caboose** *PRR,* Tuscan, 42	(3)	**75**
2755	**Tank Car** *Sunoco*, 41,42		
	1. Aluminum, 41	(3)	**140**
	2. Gray, 42	(4)	**225**
2757	**Caboose** *PRR,* Tuscan, 41,42	(2)	**60**
	Automatic coupler one end		
2757X	**Caboose** *PRR,* Tuscan, 41,42	(3)	**75**
	Automatic couplers both ends		
2758	**Boxcar** 41,42	(3)	**75**
2954	**Boxcar** Semi-scale, Tuscan, RS, *Pennsylvania,* 40-42	(4)	**350**
2955	**Tank Car** Semi-scale, 40-42		
	1. Lettered *Shell*	(4)	**250**
	2. Decal *Sunoco*	(5)	**350**
2956	**Hopper** Semi-scale, Black, 40-42	(5)	**300**
2957	**Caboose** Semi-scale, Tuscan, 40-42	(4)	**275**

Rolling Stock Outfits

Note: Must have original boxes (all interior and exterior packaging)

186	**Log Loader Outfit** 164, 3651, UCS, 40,41	(5)	**700*▼**
188	**Coal Loader Outfit** 97, 3659, UCS, 38-41	(5)	**700*▼**
801	**Freight Car Set** 2654, 2655, RCS, 38-40	(5)	**1000***
801X	**Freight Car Set** 2654, 2655, 41,42	(5)	**1000***
802	**Freight Car Set** 2814, 2815, RCS, 38-40	(5)	**1000***
802X	**Freight Car Set** 2814, 2815, 41,42	(5)	**2000***
808	**Freight Car Set** 27-34	(5)	**1400***
	One each: 803, 804, 805, 806, 807, 831		
818	**Freight Car Set** 812, 814, 815, 817, 35-37	(5)	**2000***

1049	**Freight Car Set** 2679, 2680, 1019, 38-40	(5)	**575***
1049X	**Freight Car Set** 2679, 2680, 41,42	(5)	**575***
1061	**Freight Car Set** 1679, 1680, 1682, 36,37	(5)	**600***
1577	**Freight Car Set** 1514, 1515, 1517, 34-37	(5)	**600***

OO Gauge Locomotives

001	**Hudson** 4-6-4 **5342** RS, 38 only		
	Scale fully detailed 3-rail (with draw bar pin & chain)		
	1. 001T no whistle	(4)	**600**
	2. 001W with whistle	(4)	**650**
	3. 001 39-42 w/spring draw bar pin, no whistle	(4)	**500**
	4. 001 39-42 w/spring draw bar pin, w/whistle	(4)	**525**
002	**Hudson** 4-6-4 **5342** RS, 39-42		
	Modified semi-detailed 3-rail		
	1. 002T no whistle	(4)	**500**
	2. 002W with whistle	(4)	**525**
003	**Hudson** 4-6-4 **5342** RS, 39-42		
	Scale fully detailed 2-rail		
	1. 003T no whistle	(4)	**500**
	2. 003W with whistle	(4)	**475**
004	**Hudson** 4-6-4 **5342** RS, 39-42		
	Modified semi-detailed 2-rail		
	1. 004T no whistle	(5)	**400**
	2. 004W with whistle	(5)	**425**
0081K	**Kit** containing 001 and 001T Information Requested		
0081KW	**Kit** containing 001 and 001W Information Requested		

Rolling Stock

0014	**Boxcar** Detailed 3-rail, 38-42		
	1. Yellow/maroon roof walk decal *Lionel Lines* 38	(4)	**250▲**
	2. Tuscan decal *Pennsylvania* 39-42	(3)	**100**
0015	**Tank** Detailed 3-rail, 38-42		
	1. *Sunoco* Silver, 38	(4)	**225**
	2. *Shell* Black, 39-42	(3)	**100**
	3. *Shell* Gray, 39-42	(3)	**100**
	4. *Sunoco* Silver 39-42	(5)	**125**
0016	**Hopper** Detailed 3-rail, 38-42		
	1. *SP* Gray, 38	(4)	**175**
	2. *SP* Black, 39-42	(4)	**175**
0017	**Caboose** Red, Detailed 3-rail, 38-42		
	1. *NYC* 39-42	(3)	**125▲**
	2. *PRR* maroon roofwalk 38	(4)	**150▲**
0024	**Boxcar** Tuscan, *Pennsylvania,* 39-42	(3)	**75**
	Semi-detailed 3-rail		
0025	**Tank** Semi-detailed 3-rail, 39-42		
	1. *Shell* Black 39-42	(3)	**75**
	2. *Sunoco* Black 41	(4)	**100**
0027	**Caboose** Red, NYC Detailed 3-rail, 39-42	(3)	**75**
0044	**Boxcar** Tuscan, *Pennsylvania* Detailed 2-rail, 39-42	(3)	**75**
0044K	**Boxcar Kit*** Tuscan, *Pennsylvania,* 39-42	(5)	**1000▲**
	Detailed 2 or 3 rail (w/box, unassembled)		
0045	**Tank** Black Detailed 2-rail, 39-42		
	1. *Shell* 39,40-42	(3)	**100**
	2. *Sunoco* 41	(4)	**120**
0045K	**Tank Car Kit*** Black Detailed 2 or 3 rail, 39-42		
	Shell, 39,40,42 (w/box, unassembled)	(5)	**1000▲**
0046	**Hopper** *SP* Black Detailed 2-rail, 39-42	(3)	**100**
0046K	**Hopper Kit*** *SP* Black Detailed 2-rail, 39-42	(5)	**1000▲**
0047	**Caboose** Red NYC Detailed 2-rail, 39-42	(3)	**100**
0047K	**Caboose Kit*** Red NYC Detailed 2-rail, 39-42	(5)	**1000▲**

**Kits must be in box and unassembled*

0074	**Boxcar** Tuscan *Pennsylvania,* 39-42 Semi-detailed 2-rail	(3)	**75**
0075	**Tank** Semi-detailed 2-rail, 39-42		
	1. *Sunoco* Silver, U39	(4)	**125**
	2. *Shell* Black, 39,40,42		*
	3. *Sunoco* Black, 41		*
0077	**Caboose** Red NYC Semi-detailed 2-rail, 39-42	(3)	**100**

Sets

0080	See page 203		
0080	**4-Car Set** 3-Rail, w/o whistle, 38-42 (OO1, OO14, OO15, OO16, OO17)	(5)	**1300***
0080W	**4-Car Set** 3-Rail, w/whistle, 39-42 (OO1, OO14, OO15, OO16, OO17)	(5)	**1300***
0082	**3-Car Set** 3-Rail, w/o whistle, 38-42 (OO2, OO24, OO25, OO27)	(5)	**1100***
0082W	**3-Car Set** 3-Rail, w/whistle, 39-42 (OO2, OO24, OO25, OO27)	(5)	**1100***
0090	**4-Car Set** 2-Rail, w/o whistle, 39-42 (OO3, OO44, OO45, OO46, OO47)	(5)	**1300***
0090W	**4-Car Set** 2-Rail, w/whistle, 39-42 (OO3, OO44, OO45, OO46, OO47)	(5)	**1300***
0092	**3-Car Set** 2-Rail, w/o whistle, 39-42 (OO4, OO74, OO75, OO77)	(5)	**1100***
0092W	**3-Car Set** 2-Rail, w/whistle, 39-42 (OO4, OO74, OO75, OO77)	(5)	**1100***

Standard Gauge

Electric Locomotives

Note: In general square cabs and thin rims are more desirable than round bodies and thick rims. The only exception is the 1911 with thick rims.

8	**0-4-0** 25-32		
8E	1. Maroon/brass	(3)	**200**
	2. Olive green/brass	(2)	**150**
	3. Mojave/brass	(2)	**200**
	4. Red/cream stripe/cream trim	(3)	**300**
	5. Red/no stripe/brass	(3)	**225**
	6. Dark olive green/brass U	(5)	**500**
	7. Maroon/cream stripe/cream trim U	(4)	**400**
	8. Pea green/yellow U	(5)	**425**
	9. Peacock/orange/orange stripe U	(5)	**500**
	10. Peacock/cream stripe/cream trim U	(5)	**500**
	11. Dark green/brass U	(5)	**500**
9	**0-4-0** ***NYC*** Dark green, manual reverse, 29	(5)	**2800**
9E	**0-4-0** ***NYC*** 28-30		
	1. Orange	(4)	**2200▼**
	2. SG two-tone green	(4)	**2000**
	3. Dark gray	(3)	**1200**
9U	**0-4-0** ***U-Build It*** **Kit** Orange, 28,29 Same as 9E but hand reverse		
	1. Unassembled in box complete	(5)	**12000***
	2. Assembled no box	(4)	**2800***
10	**0-4-0** ***CM&St.P*** 25-30		
10E	1. Mojave	(1)	**225**
	2. Gray	(1)	**200**
	3. Peacock	(1)	**225**
	4. Peacock/orange stripe	(3)	**350**
	5. Peacock/dark green frame cream stripe U	(4)	**450**
	6. Red/cream stripe U	(5)	**700**
	7. Red/no cream stripe U	(5)	**400**
	8. Tan U	(5)	**500**
	9. Olive U	(5)	**750**
	10. State brown/dk green frame/cream U	(5)	**750**
	11. Mojave/cream stripe	(5)	**250**

33	**0-6-0 Round Cab** (first versions) 13 only		
	1. Dk olive green/*NYC* oval	(2)	**600**
	2. Dk olive green/block *PRR*	(5)	**900**
	3. Dk olive green/red stripe	(4)	**700**
	4. Black	(4)	**700**
33	**0-4-0 Round Cab** (second versions) 13-24		
	NYC markings: common. *C&O* markings: rare.		
	1. Dark olive green	(2)	**150**
	2. Midnight blue DSS	(5)	**2000**
	3. Black	(2)	**175**
	4. Gray	(2)	**150**
	5. Maroon	(4)	**500**
	6. Red	(5)	**800**
	7. Peacock	(5)	**800**
	8. Dark green	(5)	**800**
	9. Red with cream striping	(5)	**600**
	10. Brown	(5)	**500**
	11. Mojave	(5)	**300**
	12. Pea green	(5)	**400**
	13. Black, FAOS DSS, 15	(5)	**3000***
34	**0-6-0 Round Cab** Dark olive green, 12, U13 RS block *NYC* or *NYC* oval	(4)	**900**
38	**0-4-0 Round Cab** RS *NYC* oval, 13-24 or block lettering		
	1. Dark olive green	(3)	**275**
	2. Black	(2)	**200**
	3. Maroon	(3)	**350**
	4. Dark green	(5)	**400**
	5. Mojave	(5)	**500**
	6. Peacock	(5)	**800**
	7. Gray	(5)	**350**
	8. Brown	(5)	**300**
	9. Red/cream stripe	(5)	**600**
	10. Red	(5)	**700**
	11. Dk olive green/RS *PRR*	(4)	**600**
	12. Black *62 FAOS* DSS	(5)	**1000**
42	**0-4-4-0 Square Cab** Dark green *NYC* oval, 12 or block lettering		
	1. Thin rims	(5)	**3500***
	2. Thick rims	(4)	**1750**
42	**0-4-4 Round Cab** *NYC* oval or block lettering, 13-23		
	1. Black	(2)	**450▼**
	2. Maroon	(5)	**2250**
	3. Dark gray	(3)	**700**
	4. Dark green	(3)	**825▲**
	5. Mojave	(4)	**1000**
	6. Peacock	(5)	**2400**
	7. Gray	(2)	**500**
	8. Olive green	(4)	**1200**
	9. Pea green	(5)	**2000***
	10. *61 FAOS* DSS, 15	(5)	**4500***
	Note: Odd colors turn up as a result of Lionel's policy of repainting trains which were sent in for repair.		
50	**0-4-0 Round Cab** 1924		
	Same as 38 but with Super motor		
	1. Dark gray	(2)	**175**
	2. Dark green	(3)	**225**
	3. Maroon	(4)	**400**
53	**0-4-4-0 Square Cab** Script *NYNH&H,* 12-14 oval or block *NYC*		
	1. Maroon	(4)	**1500**
	2. Brown	(4)	**1500**
53	**0-4-0 Square Cab** *NYC* oval, 15-19		
	1. Maroon	(2)	**800**
	2. Dark olive green	(4)	**1000**
	3. Mojave	(5)	**1200**

53	**0-4-0 Round Cab** *NYC* oval, Maroon, 20,21	(4)	**1000**
54	**0-4-4-0 Square Cab** Pedestal type headlight, 12 thick rim drivers	(5)	**3500**
54	**0-4-4-0 Round Cab** 13-24		
	Same as 42 but brass body, red spokes, and ventilators, red cab door window frames.		
	1. Single motor	(4)	**2800**
	2. Double motor	(5)	**3300**
318	**0-4-0** ***NYC*** 24-35		
318E	1. Dark gray	(2)	**400**
	2. Mojave	(2)	**350**
	3. Gray	(1)	**250**
	4. Pea green	(2)	**350**
	5. State brown/cream stripe	(4)	**750**
	6. State brown/no cream stripe	(4)	**750**
	7. Black (headed Coal Train)	(5)	**2000**
380	**0-4-0** ***CM&St.P*** 23-29		
380E	1. Mojave	(4)	**700**
	2. Maroon	(2)	**400**
	3. Dark green w/weighted frame	(4)	**550**
	4. Same w/o weighted frame	(3)	**450**
381	**4-4-4** ***CM&St.P*** 28-36		
381E	1. State green/apple green	(4)	**2500▼**
	2. State green/red	(5)	**4000**
381U	**4-4-4** ***U-Build-It Kit*** (in box) 28,29		
	1. Kit in box	(5)	**7500**
	2. Dark State green/381U plate	(5)	*
	3. Dark State green/381 plate	(5)	**4000▼**
402	**0-4-4-0** ***NYC*** 2 motors, 23-29		
402E	1. Mojave/strap headlight	(4)	**700**
	2. Mojave/cast headlight	(3)	**650**
	Note: Early 402s came with the E rubber-stamped on the door. These are rarer than those with the E on the brass plate. Add $50		
408E	**0-4-4-0** ***NYC*** 2 motors, 27-36		
	1. Mojave	(3)	**1200▼**
	2. Apple green	(3)	**1500▼**
	3. Dark green (State Set)	(5)	**8000▲**
	4. Tan (State Set)	(4)	**5000▲**
	5. Tan/dark brown roof (State Set)	(5)	**6500▲**
1910 1750	**0-6-0 Square Cab** *NYNH&H*, Dk olive green, 10,11		(4)
1910	**0-6-0 Round Cab** *NYC* oval, Dk olive green, 12	(3)	**1250**
1911	**0-4-0 Square Cab** *NYC* oval, 10,11 or block *NYNH&H*		
	1. Maroon	(5)	**2500**
	2. Dark olive green	(4)	**2000**
	Note: Add $200 for thick-rim version		
1911	**0-4-0 Round Cab** *NYNH&H* or block NYC, 12 Dark olive green	(3)	**1200**
1911	**0-4-4-0 Special Square Cab** block *NYC*, 11,12 Dark olive green	(5)	**2200▼**
1912	**0-4-4-0 Square Cab** Dark olive green, 10-12		
	1. Thin rim/script *NYNH&H*	(5)	**3500**
	2. Thick rim/block *NYC*	(4)	**3300**
1912	**0-4-4-0 Special Square Cab** 11 same as 1912 but made of brass	(4)	**6000***

Steam Locomotives

Note: Thin rims and split frames are more desirable than thick rims and solid frames.

No.	Description	Rarity	Value
5	**0-4-0** Black, no tender, 06-26		
	1. Thin rims	(4)	**1000***
	2. Thick rims	(3)	**600**
5	**Special 0-4-0** Thin rims, 06-11		
	1. 4w tender/10 series solid 3-rivet truck	(5)	**1800***
	2. 4w tender/10 series open 3-rivet truck	(4)	**1300***
	3. 8w tender 2 100 series trucks	(4)	**1000***
6	**4-4-0** Black/nickel trim, 8w tender, 06-23		
	1. Thin rims	(4)	**2000***
	2. Thick rims	(3)	**1500***
6	**Special 4-4-0** Thin rims, Brass/nickel, 08,09 8w tender	(5)	**2800***
7	**4-4-0** Brass/nickel, 8w tender, 10-23		
	1. Thin rims/open 3-rivet trucks	(5)	**4500***
	2. Thick rims/single rivet trucks	(4)	**3000**
51	**0-4-0** Thick rims,12-23 6w tender w/two 100 series trucks *Note: 5, 5 Special and the 51 are the same loco*	(3)	**1200***
384 384E	**2-4-0** 384T Black came w/or w/o green stripe, 30-32 and either brass or green window trim. NDV	(2)	**350**
385E	**2-4-2** 384T 385T, 33-39		
	1. Gunmetal/copper and brass 384T, 33	(4)	**600**
	2. Gunmetal/nickel 384T, 34	(4)	**600**
	3. Gunmetal/nickel Ives 385T, 35-39	(5)	**750**
	4. Gunmetal/chrome 39	(5)	**1000**
390	**2-4-2** 390T Black hand reverse, 29 only with or without orange stripe	(4)	**600**
390E	**2-4-2** 390T 390X, 29-31,33		
	1. Black/orange stripe	(3)	**650▼**
	2. Blue/cream stripe *Blue Comet*	(4)	**1400▼**
	3. Dark green/orange stripe-dark green stripe	(4)	**2250▼**
	4. Same as 3 with light green stripe	(5)	**2500▼**
	5. Black/red stripe	(3)	**1200▼**
392E	**4-4-2** 384T 392T 392W, 32-39		
	1. Black/brass and copper/384T with or without green stripe. NDV	(3)	**1200**
	2. Black/384T black crackle finish	(5)	**2500▲**
	3. Black/brass and copper/12w 392T	(5)	**2500**
	4. Black/nickel/12w 392T	(5)	**3500▲**
	5. Gunmetal/nickel/12w 392T	(4)	**1200▼**
400E	**4-4-4** 400T, 400W, 31-39		
	1. Black/brass and copper, brass boiler bands	(3)	**1600**
	2. Black/brass and copper, painted bands	(4)	**2000**
	3. Gunmetal/brass and copper, brass bands	(3)	**2200**
	4. Gunmetal/brass and copper painted bands	(4)	**4500**
	5. Gunmetal/nickel, painted boiler bands	(4)	**3500**
	6. Black crackle/brass	(5)	**7000***
	7. Black crackle/nickel	(4)	**4000**
	8. Blue/brass and copper	(4)	**3500▼**
	9. Light blue/nickel	(4)	**3500▼**
	10. Black/nickel	(5)	**4000▼**
1835E	**2-4-2** same as 385E, 34-39		
	1. Black/nickel/384T 34	(4)	**850▲**
	2. Black/nickel/1835TW 35-39	(3)	**700▼**

Passenger Cars

Early Passenger Cars

Note: Price listed is for EACH car

18,19,190 Series 06-27			
	1. Dark olive green/red window trim		
	a. High knobs	(5)	**1500**
	b. Low knobs	(5)	**1500**
	c. No knobs	(3)	**150***
	2. Yellow orange	(4)	**750**
	3. Dark orange	(4)	**600***
	4. Mojave	(4)	**700**
29	**Day Coach** 08-21		
	Early same body as No. 3 trolley 08,09	(5)	**1800***
	NYC & HRRR or *Pennsylvania RR*. Closed or open ends. Solid steps		
	Middle 10,11		
	High knobs or low knobs. *NYC&HRRR* perforated or 3-hole steps		
	1. Maroon/black trim	(5)	**2000***
	2. Dark green	(5)	**1800***
	Late Open clerestory 3-hole steps, 12-21 removable roof		
	1. Dark olive green/maroon stripe	(4)	**800***
	2. Dark olive green/no maroon stripe	(3)	**500***
31	**Combine** (See Late Additions page 203)		
32	**Baggage** (See Late Additions page 203)		
35	**Pullman 36 Observation** 12-26 (price for each car)		
	RS *NYC* common RS *C&O* or *NYNH&H* rare		
	1. Early Dk olive rib/sides, lg rail, pinhole steps	(5)	**?***
	2. Early dk olive rib/sides, lg rail, 3-hole steps	(4)	**250**
	3. Midnight blue rib or smooth sides DSS	(5)	**600**
	4. Dk olive smooth sides	(2)	**50**
	5. Orange smooth	(4)	**150**
	6. Maroon or Brown	(3)	**75**
180,181,182 Series 11-21			
	1. Maroon early	(5)	**225**
	2. Maroon late	(3)	**150**
	3. Brown	(4)	**175**
1910	RS 1910 and Pullman green, 09,10 open 3-rivet trucks 3 high knobs	(5)	**2200***

Large Classic Era Passenger Cars

Price listed is for EACH car

State Car Series 29-35

412	**Pullman CALIFORNIA**		
	1. State green/dark green/apple green	(4)	**1500▼**
	2. State green/dark green/cream	(5)	**5000▲**
	3. State brown/dk brn-tan vents/cream	(5)	**1900**
	4. State brown/solid dark brown/cream	(5)	**3000▲**
413	**Pullman COLORADO**		
	1. State green/dark green/apple green	(4)	**1800**
	2. State green/dark green/cream	(5)	**5000▲**
	3. State brown/dk brn-tan vents/cream	(5)	**1900**
	4. State brown/solid dark brown/cream	(5)	**2200**
414	**Pullman ILLINOIS**		
	1. State green/dark green/apple green	(5)	**2200**
	2. State green/dark green/cream	(5)	**5000▲**
	3. State brown/dk brn-tan vents/cream	(5)	**2000**
	4. State brown/solid dark brown/cream	(5)	**3000▲**
416	**Observation NEW YORK**		
	1. State green/dark green/apple green	(4)	**2000**
	2. State green/dark green/cream	(4)	**5000▲**
	3. State brown/dk brn-tan vents/cream	(5)	**2000**
	4. State brown/solid dark brown/cream	(5)	**3000▲**

418, 419, 431, 490 Series 23-32
Note: Most stamped New York Central or Lionel Lines. Illinois Central markings are rare.

418	**Pullman** 23-33		
	1. Mojave/10 series 4w trucks 23-24	(3)	**250**
	2. Mojave/6w trucks 25-33	(2)	**225**
	3. Apple green/apple green/red 29-33	(4)	**375**
419	**Combine** 23-33		
	1. Mojave/10 series 4w trucks 23-24	(2)	**250**
	2. Mojave/6w trucks 25-33	(3)	**275**
	3. Apple green/apple green/red 29-33	(4)	**325**
431	**Diner** 27-33		
	1. Mojave/6w trucks 27-33	(4)	**500**
	2. Mojave/6w trucks with hinged roof	(5)	**1000**
	3. Apple green/apple green/red 29-33	(4)	**500**
	4. Apple green/apple green/red with hinged roof	(5)	**800**
490	**Observation** 23-33		
	1. Mojave/10 series 4w trucks 23-24	(3)	**250**
	2. Mojave/6w trucks 25-33	(2)	**225**
	3. Apple green/apple green/red 29-33	(4)	**325**

BLUE COMET SERIES 30-40

420	**Pullman FAYE**		
	1. Medium blue/dark blue/brass	(3)	**1000**
	2. Light blue/dark blue/nickel and brass	(4)	**1200**
	3. Light blue/dark blue/all nickel	(5)	**1400**
421	**Pullman WESTPHAL**		
	1. Medium blue/dark blue/brass	(3)	**1000**
	2. Light blue/dark blue/nickel and brass	(4)	**1200**
	3. Light blue/dark blue/all nickel	(5)	**1400**
422	**Observation TEMPEL**		
	1. Medium blue/dark blue/brass	(3)	**1000**
	2. Light/blue/dark blue/nickel and brass	(4)	**1200**
	3. Light blue/dark blue/all nickel	(5)	**1400**

STEPHEN GIRARD SERIES Green/dark green/cream, 31-40

424	**Pullman LIBERTY BELL**		
	1. Brass trim	(4)	**500**
	2. Nickel trim	(4)	**750**
425	**Pullman STEPHEN GIRARD**		
	1. Brass trim	(4)	**500**
	2. Nickel trim	(4)	**750**
426	**Observation CORAL ISLE**		
	1. Brass trim	(4)	**500**
	2. Nickel trim	(4)	**750**

428, 429, 430 Series *Lionel Lines* markings, 26-30

427	**Diner** (made as 431)	**Never made**	
428	**Pullman**		
	1. Dark green/dark green/maroon	(2)	**425**
	2. Dark green/dark green/orange	(3)	**450**
	3. Orange/orange/SG green	(5)	**750**
429	**Combine**		
	1. Dark green/dark green/maroon	(2)	**425**
	2. Dark green/dark green/orange	(3)	**450**
	3. Orange/orange/SG green	(5)	**750**
430	**Observation**		
	1. Dark green/dark green/maroon	(2)	**400**
	2. Dark green/dark green/orange	(3)	**450**
	3. Orange/orange/SG green	(5)	**750**

Reminder: Passenger car prices are for EACH car.

Medium Classic Era Passenger Cars

309, 310, 312 Series New York Central, 26-40 or Lionel Lines markings. ***Price listed is for EACH car.***

309	**Pullman**		
	1. Mojave/mojave/maroon	(3)	**200**
	2. Pea green/pea green/orange	(1)	**150**
	3. Maroon/terra cotta/cream	(5)	**400▲**
	4. State brown/dark brown/cream	(3)	**200**
	5. Medium blue/dark blue/cream	(5)	**400▲**
	6. Stephen Girard green/dk green/cream	(4)	**350▲**
	7. Light blue/silver/silver	(2)	**150▲**
	8. Red-orange/aluminum/aluminum, U		**5P**
310	**Baggage**		
	1. Mojave/mojave/maroon	(3)	**200**
	2. Pea green/pea green/orange	(1)	**150**
	3. Maroon/terra cotta/cream	(5)	**400▲**
	4. State brown/dark brown/cream	(3)	**200**
	5. Medium blue/dark blue/cream	(5)	**400▲**
	6. Stephen Girard green/dk green/cream	(4)	**350▲**
	7. Light blue/silver/silver	(2)	**150▲**
	8. Red-orange/aluminum/aluminum, U		**5P**
312	**Observation**		
	1. Mojave/mojave/maroon	(3)	**200**
	2. Pea green/pea green/orange	(1)	**150**
	3. Maroon/terra cotta/cream	(5)	**400▲**
	4. State brown/dark brown/cream	(3)	**200**
	5. Medium blue/dark blue/cream	(5)	**400▲**
	6. Stephen Girard green/dk green/cream	(4)	**350▲**
	7. Light blue/silver/silver	(2)	**150▲**
	8. Red-orange/aluminum/aluminum, U		**5P**

319, 320, 322 Series Maroon/maroon/mojave only, 24-27

319	**Pullman**		
	1. *New York Central*	(2)	**125**
	2. *Illinois Central*	(4)	**400**
	3. *Lionel Lines*	(2)	**125**
320	**Baggage** 25-27		
	1. *New York Central*	(2)	**125**
	2. *Illinois Central*	(4)	**400**
	3. *Lionel Lines*	(3)	**175**
	4. *Lionel Electric Railroad*	(3)	**200**
322	**Observation**		
	1. *New York Central*	(2)	**125**
	2. *Illinois Central*	(4)	**400**
	3. *Lionel Lines*	(2)	**125**

1766, 1767, 1768 Series Lionel Lines 34-40

1766	**Pullman**		
	1. Terra cotta/maroon/cream/brass	(4)	**650**
	2. Vermilion/maroon/nickel	(5)	**750**
1767	**Baggage**		
	1. Terra cotta/maroon/cream/brass	(4)	**650**
	2. Vermilion/maroon/nickel	(5)	**750**
1768	**Observation**		
	1. Terra cotta/maroon/cream/brass	(4)	**650**
	2. Vermilion/maroon/nickel	(5)	**750**

Small Classic Era Passenger Cars

Price listed is for EACH car.

332	**Baggage** came in sets with 337,338 series, 26-33 and 339,341 series		
	1. Gray/maroon	(2)	**75**
	2. Peacock/orange/orange door	(2)	**75**
	3. Peacock/orange/red doors	(3)	**100**
	4. Olive green/red	(3)	**100**
	5. Red/cream	(3)	**150**
	6. Peacock/dark green/orange	(4)	**150**
	7. State brown/dark brown/cream, U	(5)	**300**
	8. Peacock/orange/red doors w/divider	(3)	**150**
	9. Olive/maroon doors	(5)	*

337, 338 Series 25-32

Note: Both 337,338 and 339,341 series came with Lionel Lines, New York Central, and llinois Central markings. NDV

337	**Pullman**		
	1. Mojave/maroon	(2)	**75**
	2. Olive green/maroon	(1)	**75**
	3. Olive green/red	(2)	**75**
	4. Pea green/cream Macy's, U	(4)	**300**
	5. Red/cream (also came in Macy's U set)	(3)	**150**
338	**Observation**		
	1. Mojave/maroon	(2)	**75**
	2. Olive green/maroon	(1)	**75**
	3. Olive green/red	(2)	**75**
	4. Pea green/cream Macy's U	(4)	**300**
	5. Red/cream	(3)	**150**
	6. Red/cream with Macy's sticker on drumhead	(4)	**300**

339, 341 Series 25-33

339	**Pullman**		
	1. Gray/maroon	(2)	**75**
	2. Peacock/orange	(1)	**75**
	3. Peacock/dark green/orange	(2)	**75**
	4. State brown/dark brown/cream U	(5)	**300**
	5. Ives 1694 gray/maroon/cream U	(4)	**150**
341	**Observation**		
	1. Gray/maroon	(2)	**75**
	2. Peacock/orange	(1)	**75**
	3. Peacock/dark green/orange	(2)	**75**
	4. State brown/dark brown/cream U	(5)	**300**
	5. Ives 1694 gray/maroon/cream U	(4)	**150**
341	**Observation** RS *THE IVES RAILWAY LINES* Peacock/dark green/orange	(4)	**150**

Rolling Stock

Note: Most desirable items in the Early Period are extremely rare. In some cases, less than 10 are known to exist. Therefore, rarity ratings indicate relative rarity and desirability to other items within the Early Period.

10 Series Freights

11	**Flatcar** RS *Pennsylvania RR* rare, 06-26		
	1. Orange DSS	(5)	**250***
	2. Red	(3)	**75**
	3. Brown	(2)	**75**
	4. Maroon handrails	(5)	**400**
	5. Maroon no handrails	(2)	**75**
	6. Gray DSS	(5)	**?***
	7. Dark olive green	(5)	**?***
12	**Gondola** RS *Lake Shore* or *Rock Island,* 06-26		
	1. Red	(4)	**75**
	2. Brown	(4)	**75**
	3. Gray	(4)	**75**
	4. Maroon	(4)	**75**

Note: Early versions have brake wheel outside and flat edges. Later versions have brake wheel inside and rolled edges. Add $200 for early versions.

13	**Cattle Car** various shades of green, 06-26		
	Early Five slats/smooth surface, two-piece roof, *Lionel Mfg.*	(5)	**400**
	Middle 6 slats/embossed surface, one-piece roof, *Lionel Corp*	(3)	**75**
	Late 6 slats, embossed surface, no brakewheel, *Lionel Corp*	(3)	**75**
14	**Boxcar** 06-26		
	1. Red/smooth sides	(5)	**600**
	2. Red/embossed sides	(4)	**450**
	3. Yellow-orange/embossed sides	(3)	**100**
	4. Orange/embossed sides	(2)	**75**
	5. Dk olive grn/embossed sides, DSS	(4)	**250**
14	**Harmony Creamery** Dark green, 21 only	(5+)	*
15	**Oil Tank** 06-26		
	1. Red/wood domes, ends/U-shaped wire step RS *416 Pennsylvania*	(5)	**700**
	2. Wine/three-piece step/metal ends	(4)	**200**
	3. Wine or brn/single step w/three holes/metal ends	(2)	**75**
16	**Ballast** 06-26		
	1. Gray	(5)	**400**
	2. Brown	(3)	**200**
	3. Red	(3)	**200**
	4. Dark green	(3)	**200**
	5. Wine	(2)	**150**
17	**Caboose** 06-26		
	Early Smooth sides/awnings over main windows, no cupola awnings, vertical striping, steps formed from platform		
	Middle Embossed sides, no awnings over main windows, awnings over cupola windows, steps formed from platform		
	Late Embossed sides, no awnings over cupola or main windows, soldered on 3-hole steps, rounded windows rather than square		
	1. Early maroon/black, smooth w/painted slats, awnings, 3-rivet trks	(5)	**650**
	2. Maroon/black Embossed/painted slats	(4)	**300**
	3. Brown/black (embossed, single rivet trks)	(3)	**150**
	4. Maroon/black	(2)	**75**
	5. Dk red/black	(3)	**200**

100 Series Freights

112	**Gondola** 10-26		
	Early (7-inches long) 10-12		
	1. Dk olive green/red RS *Lake Shore* or *NYNH&H*	(5)	**300**
	Middle (9 1/2-inches long) 13-26		
	2. Red/dark olive green trim	(4)	**150**
	3. Maroon	(3)	**75**
	4. Brown	(3)	**75**
	5. Dark gray	(2)	**50**
	6. Gray	(2)	**50**
	7. Orange	(5)	**200**
113	**Cattle Car** Grn/embossed sides/no lettering, 12-26	(3)	**50**
	Note: Early cars are darker green than later cars.		
114	**Boxcar** 12-26		
	1. Red	(4)	**300**
	2. Yellow-orange	(3)	**75**
	3. Orange	(2)	**50**
	4. Dark olive green DSS	(5)	**?***
116	**Ballast** 10-26		
	1. Dark olive green	(5)	**?***
	2. Maroon	(4)	**75**
	3. Brown	(2)	**60**
	4. Dark gray	(2)	**60**
	5. Gray	(2)	**60**
	6. Dark green	(3)	**75**

117	**Caboose** RS *NYC&HRRR* 4351, 12-26		
	1. Red/black roof	(5)	**75**
	2. Brown/black roof	(4)	**65**
	3. Maroon/black roof	(3)	**50**

200 Series Freights

211	**Flatcar** Black/RS *Lionel Lines*, 26-40 w/wood load	(2)	**150**
212	**Gondola** 26-40		
	Light green used on 812, 2812, 512, 212, crane booms etc 1936 and after is called 45N green (gateman base color). First year of this green, 1935, is a darker shade "1935 green"		
	1. Gray	(4)	**200▲**
	2. Maroon	(2)	**150▼**
	3. Green	(3)	**175**
	4. Medium green	(4)	**200**
	5. Mojave	(5)	**?***
	6. Dark green	(5)	**300**
213	**Cattle Car** 26-40		
	Roofs from 213 and 214 are interchangeable		
	1. Mojave/maroon	(4)	**400**
	2. Terra-cotta/pea green	(3)	**300**
	3. Cream/maroon	(5)	**1200***
214	**Boxcar** 26-40		
	Roofs from 213 and 214 are interchangeable		
	1. Terra-cotta/dark green	(3)	**500**
	2. Cream/orange	(2)	**250**
	3. Yellow/brown	(4)	**700**
214R	**Refrigerator** 29-40		
	1. Ivory/peacock	(4)	**1000**
	2. White/light blue/brass	(5)	**1200**
	3. White/light blue/nickel	(5)	**1200**
215	**Tank Car** 26-40		
	1. Pea green	(2)	**275▼**
	2. Pea green/Sunoco decal	(5)	**?***
	3. Ivory/Sunoco decal	(4)	**600**
	4. Ivory/no Sunoco decal	(3)	**400**
	5. Alum/Sunoco decal/brass	(4)	**550**
	6. Alum/Sunoco decal/nickel	(5)	**650**
216	**Hopper** Dark green, 26-38		
	1. Brass	(3)	**400**
	2. Nickel	(5)	**2000▲**
217	**Caboose** 26-40		
	1. Orange/maroon	(4)	**700▲**
	2. Light red/nickel	(4)	**475▲**
	3. Red/peacock/red cupola	(2)	**200**
	4. Red/peacock/peacock cupola	(4)	**475▼**
	5. Pea green/red/brass		**5P**
218	**Dump** 26-38		
	1. Mojave/2 brass knobs/brass ends	(3)	**375**
	2. Mojave/1 brass knob/brass ends	(2)	**325**
	3. Mojave/1 brass knob/mojave ends	(4)	**400**
	4. Green/red/brass ends 1926		**5P**
	5. Gray/brass ends		**5P**
	6. Pea green/maroon ends		**5P**
219	**Derrick** 26-40		
	1. Peacock/red boom	(2)	**275**
	2. Yellow/red/green or red boom NDV	(4)	**650**
	3. Ivory/red/green boom	(5)	**850**
	4. Early colors w/window in front of door	(5)	**900**
220	**Floodlight Car** 31-40		
	1. Terra-cotta/brass lights	(2)	**425▼**
	2. Green/nickel-plated lights	(3)	**450**

500 Series Freights

511	**Flatcar** 27-39		
	1. Dark green/gold RS lettering	(2)	**100**
	2. Medium green/silver RS lettering	(3)	**135▲**
	3. Medium green/gold RS lettering	(2)	**135▲**
	Note: Brakewheel placed differently through the years. NDV		
512	**Gondola** 27-39		
	1. Peacock	(2)	**50**
	2. Green	(3)	**100**
513	**Cattle Car** 27-38		
	1. Olive green/orange	(3)	**200**
	2. Orange/pea green	(2)	**125**
	3. Cream/maroon	(5)	**650▲**
514	**Boxcar** 29-40		
	1. Cream/orange	(2)	**150**
	2. Yellow/brown	(3)	**325**
514	**Refrigerator** Ivory/peacock, 27,28	(3)	**400**
514R	**Refrigerator** 29-40		
	1. Ivory/peacock	(3)	**350**
	2. White/light blue	(4)	**550▼**
	3. White/light blue/gray	(5)	**800**
515	**Tank Car** 27-40		
	1. Terra cotta/no decal	(2)	**125**
	2. Ivory/no Sunoco decal	(2)	**175▼**
	3. Ivory/Sunoco decal	(3)	**250▲**
	4. Alum/Sunoco decal	(3)	**250▼**
	5. Tan w&w/o Sunoco decal	(4)	**350**
	6. Shell orange/Shell decal	(5)	**2200***
	Note: Brakewheel on left side on early versions; right side on later versions. NDV		
516	**Hopper** Red, 28-40		
	1. No coal load/brass	(2)	**250▼**
	2. Coal load/brass	(3)	**300▼**
	3. Coal load/RS lettering	(4)	**425▼**
	4. Coal load/nickel	(5)	**450▼**
517	**Caboose** 27-40		
	1. Pea green/red/brass	(2)	**100**
	2. Pea green/red/orange	(2)	**100**
	3. Red/black/orange	(5)	**2000▲**
	4. Red/aluminum	(4)	**200**
	5. Red/alum/no number plates, number rubber-stamped on bottom	(5)	**?***
520	**Floodlight Car** 31-40		
	1. Terra-cotta/brass lights	(2)	**175▼**
	2. Green/nickel plated lights	(3)	**200▼**
	Early: brakewheel left. Late: right. NDV		
	Early: light green overpaint	(4)	**400**

Trolleys

Note: All 1, 2, 3, and 4 series trolleys and trailers had number plus Electric Rapid Transit on side, except as indicated.

1	**Trolley** 4-wheels 5 window, no reverse, 06 no headlight/smooth sides, *New Departure Motor* Orange/cream	(5)	**4000***
1	**Trailer** 5 window Blue/cream, 07	(5)	**3500***
1	**Trolley** 6 window Embossed sides/standard motor, 08		
	1. Blue/cream	(4)	**3500***
	2. Dark green/cream	(5)	**4000***
1	**Trailer** 6 windows blue/cream, 08	(3)	**3000***
1	**Trolley** 6 window, 10-14 used 1908/09 version of number 2 trolley body		
	1. Blue/cream	(4)	**3500***
	2. Blue/cream *Curtis Bay*	(5)	**4000***

2	**Trolley** 4-wheels headlight and reverse, 06-14		
	1. Cream/red/open ends 06	(5)	**3000***
	2. Blue/cream windows/open ends, 08	(4)	**3000***
	3. Red/cream windows closed offset ends, 10-12	(4)	**3000***
	4. Dark olive green/orange windows, 13-16 closed flush ends	(5)	**3200***
	5. Cream/red/closed flush ends	(4)	**2800***
2	**Trailer**		
200	1. Cream/red/matches no. 1 above	(5)	**2800***
	2. Red/cream/matches no. 3 above	(4)	**2500***
3	**Trolley** 8-wheels 06-13		
	1. Cream/dk olive grn/flat windows open ends, 1906	(5)	**4000***
	2. Cream/dk olive grn/inset windows open ends 1908	(5)	**4000***
	3. Cream/orange/open ends inset windows, 1908	(5)	**4000***
	4. Orange/cream/open ends inset windows, 1908	(5)	**4000***
	5. Dark olive green/cream/closed offset ends, 1910	(5)	**4000***
	6. Dark olive green/cream/closed flush ends, 1913	(5)	**4000***
	7. Same but lettered *Bay Shore*	(5)	**4000***
3	**Trailer** 08	(5)	**3800***
300	Matches nos. 2,3, and 4		
4	**Trolley** 8 wheels, Same body as 3, 06-13 but with 2 motors - early		
	1. Dark olive green/cream, open ends - late	(5)	**6000***
	2. Dark olive green/cream/flush ends	(5)	**6000***
8	**Trolley** *PAY AS YOU ENTER* 8-wheels, 09-15 single motor		
	1. Cream/orange/9 windows	(5)	**7000***
	2. Dark olive green/cream 11 windows	(5)	**7000***
9	**Trolley** *PAY AS YOU ENTER* 8-wheels, 09-12 double motor		
	1. Cream/orange/9 windows	(5)	**7000***
	2. Dark olive green/cream/11 windows	(5)	**7000***
10	**Interurban** 10-16	(5)	**5000***
1010	**Trailer** (powered and trailer units stamped 1010)		
	1. Maroon/gold/high knobs	(5)	**5000***
	2. Dk olive green/low knobs	(4)	**4000***
	3. Dk olive green/no knobs	(4)	**2500***
	4. Same but RS *WB&A,* both		*****
100	**Trolley** 5 windows Blue/cream, 10	(4)	**3000***
1000	**Trailer** Blue/cream, 10	(4)	**2500***
100	**Trolley** 5 windows, 13-14		
	1. Red/cream	(4)	**3000***
	2. Blue/cream	(4)	**3000***
	3. Blue/cream/*Linden Ave*	(5)	**5000***
1000	**Trailer** matches nos. 1 and 2 NDV, 13-14	(4)	**2500***
1000	**Trailer** *Linden Ave*13-14	(5)	**4500***
100	**Trolley** 6 windows, 14-16		
	1. Red/cream	(4)	**3000***
	2. Blue/cream	(4)	**3000***
1000	**Trailer** matches nos. 1 and 2 NDV, 14-16	(4)	**2500***
101	**Open Summer Trolley** four wheels, 10-13		
	1. Blue roof and ends	(4)	**3000***
	2. Same as 1 w/*101 Wilkins Ave*	(5)	**3500***
	3. Red roof and ends	(4)	**3000***
1100	**Trailer** matches 101		
202	**Open Summer Trolley** 4-wheels, 10-13 Red/cream/black	(5)	**4000***
2200	**Trailer** matches 202	(5)	**3500***
303	**Open Summer Trolley** 8-wheels, 10-13 Green/cream/maroon	(5)	**4000***
3300	**Trailer** matches 303	(5)	**3500***

2 7/8-Inch Gauge

Note: These were the first trains Joshua Lionel Cowen made. They are extremely rare. About 30 collectible variations exist. The largest known 2 7/8-inch gauge collection has nine pieces. Few items in this category are ever sold so the prices listed are estimates. All metal and iron cars have black frames, 4 wheels, and Lionel Manufacturing Company stamped on floor. Reproductions exist.

100	**Electric Locomotive** 01-05		
	1. Maroon/black roof	(5)	**6000***
	2. Apple green	(5)	**6000***
200	**Electric Express** 01-05		
	1. Electric Express/wooden car body no corner braces	(5)	**7000***
	2. Same with corner braces	(5)	**6000***
	3. Sheet-metal body/maroon	(5)	**6000***
	4. Sheet-metal body/apple green	(5)	**6000***
300	**Electric Trolley** 6 reversible seats, 01-05 Maroon/light green, lettered *City Hall Park* on one end and *Union Depot* on the other	(5)	**6000***
309	**Trolley Trailer** matches 300, 01-05		
400	**Express Trailer** matches 200, RS lettering		
	1. Gold *Lake Shore*	(5)	**4000***
	2. Green/gold *B&O*	(5)	**4000***
500	**Electric Derrick** Maroon/black, 03,04 Derrick made of cast iron, brass chain with tackle attached	(5)	**4000***
600	**Derrick Trailer** Same as 500 but w/o motor, 03,04	(5)	**4000***
800	**Electric Box** Maroon/maroon roof, 04,05 gold RS lettering *Metropolitan Express*	(5)	**4000***
900	**Electric Box Trailer** Matches 800, 04,05	(5)	**4000***
1000	**Electric Passenger** 05		
	1. Maroon/black roof/gold RS lettering *Metropolitan St. R.R. CO.*	(5)	**6000***
	2. Same as 1 but lettered *Maryland St. RY Co.*	(5)	**6000***
1050	**Passenger Trailer** Matches 1000, 04,05		
	1. Maroon/black roof/gold RS lettering *Metropolitan St. R.R. Co.*	(5)	**6000***
	2. Lettered *Maryland St. RY Co.*	(5)	**6000***
	3. Lettered *Philadelphia R.T. Co.*	(5)	**6000***

Postwar 1945-1969

Diesels

Alcos

Note: Later Alcos (1957 and beyond) often turn up with cracked pilots. Be sure to check pilots before buying.

202	**Union Pacific A** Orange/black 57	(3)	**75▼**
204	**Santa Fe AA** Blue/yellow 57	(4)	**225▼**
205	**Missouri Pacific AA** Blue/white 57,58		
	1. Blue/white	(2)	**130▼**
	2. Dark blue/white	(4)	**175▼**
208	**Santa Fe AA** Blue/yellow 58,59	(3)	**225▼**
209	**New Haven AA** Black/orange/white 58	(4)	**450▼**
210	**Texas Special AA** Red/white 58	(3)	**140▼**
211	**Texas Special AA** Red/white 62,63,65,66		
	1. Glossy Red	(3)	**125**
	2. Flat Red	(4)	**125**
212	**US Marine Corps A** Blue/white, 58,59		
	No coupler opening in front, fixed rear coupler only came w/Blue unpainted shell, Red shell painted blue, Black shell painted blue NDV		
	1. With Magnetraction/E unit	(3)	**225▼**
	2. No Magnetraction/E unit	(4)	**275▼**
	(no E Unit slot to be legitimate)		
212T	**US Marine Corps** Dummy Blue/white 58,59	(4)	**700▼**
	Made to match 212. Fixed couplers front and rear		
212	**Santa Fe AA** Silver/red 64-66		
	1. Gray shell	(3)	**150▼**
	2. Black shell	(4)	**225▼**
213	**Minneapolis & St. Louis** Red/white **AA** 64	(3)	**200▼**
215	**Santa Fe AA** Silver/red/black-yell stripes U64,65	(3)	**150▼**
	Power A **215**, Dummy A **212**		
216	**Burlington A** Silver/red 58	(4)	**400▼**
216	**Minneapolis & St. Louis A** Red/white U	(3)	**125▼**
217	**Boston & Maine AB** Black/blue/white 59	(3)	**200▼**
218	**Santa Fe AA** Silver/red 59-63		
	1. Front decal red, yellow and black	(3)	**160▼**
	2. Front decal yellow and black	(5)	**200▼**
218	**Santa Fe AB** Silver/red 61	(3)	**225▼**
219	**Missouri Pacific AA** Blue/white U59	(3)	**200▼**
220	**Santa Fe A** Silver/red 61	(2)	**180▼**
221	**Rio Grande A** Yellow/black 63,64	(2)	**75**
221	**USMC A** Olive drab/white U64	(4)	**350▼**
221	**Santa Fe A** Olive drab/white U64	(4)	**450▼**
222	**Rio Grande A** Yellow/black stripes 62	(2)	**75**
223,212	**Santa Fe AA** Silver/red U64		*
223,218C	**Santa Fe AB** Silver/red 63	(5)	**275▼**
224	**US Navy AB** Blue/white 60	(3+)	**300▼**
225	**Chesapeake & Ohio A** Dark blue/yellow 60	(3)	**150▼**
226	**Boston & Maine AB** Black/blue/white U59		
	1. Unpainted blue shell	(3)	**200▼**
	2. A unit w/painted gray shell	(5)	**450▼**
227	**Canadian National A** Green/yellow U59,60	(3)	**180▼**
228	**Canadian National A** Green/yellow U60,61	(4)	**200▼**
229	**Minneapolis & St. Louis A** Red/white 61	(3)	**150▼**
229	**Minneapolis & St. Louis AB** 62,63A		
	1. Red/white	(3)	**200▼**
	2. Olive drab uncataloged	(5)	**200▼***

Continued on page 89

Toy Train Revue

For Collectors and Operators · The Collectors Journal · Toy Trains Forever

Fall 2010

Madison Hardware Redux

by Tom McComas

Note: TM's 1991 Lionel Postwar Guide included an article about Dick Kughn's purchase of Madison Hardware and the subsequent move of Madison Hardware to Detroit. This is an update.

Lou Shur and Carl Shaw were brothers and the owners of the legendary Madison Hardware store located at 105 East 23rd Street in Manhattan. Madison Hardware opened in 1909 and was the oldest Lionel Service Station in the country. Both Lou and Carl were close friends with Lionel's founder, Joshua Lionel Cowan, whose corporate offices were only three blocks away.

Madison Hardware sold a lot of trains. At Christmas time, the store was so crowded the police were needed to help control the crowds. The shoppers would come in the front door, go through the store, find what they wanted, then go to the rear and pay Lou (in cash). Lou would be sitting on a stool behind a big, gray National cash register. After paying, the customers would go out the back door. Madison was known to have the largest inventory of Lionel trains and parts in the world.

There is a rumor that one summer day in the mid-thirties, Joshua Lionel Cowan drove a silver Rolls Royce over to Madison. He wanted to give the car to Lou for being such a good customer and friend. Lou looked at the car, thanked Josh, whom he affectionately called "Pop," but declined the offer. "Pop," he asked, "where would I park it?"

Lou and Carl (mostly Lou) continued to run Madison Hardware until July 12, 1989 when the brothers sold Madison Hardware to Dick Kughn, the owner of Lionel Trains.

From the TM Postwar Guide published in 1991:
Madison Hardware was the sort of a store that collectors for decades have made pilgrimages just to see, regardless of what they bought. And years from now they will still be saying they were there. Madison was tiny compared to its reputation. Quite narrow, it ran straight back about 100 feet or so from 23rd Street with a rear left-hand exit to Park Avenue South. It had a high ceiling with original tin tiling reaching one and one-half stories above the floor.

The Madison owners had always been rather secretive about the store, never showing anyone its deep, dark recesses. Through the years, there were rumors about a warehouse somewhere, perhaps even in Brooklyn, where the brothers would slip off to retrieve an esoteric item, but it turned out the rumors were false. The warehouse – and the brothers did refer to them as warehouses – were a series of storage rooms in various buildings in the neighborhood, as well as a storage area in a labyrinth of dark and dank passages in basement rooms that were dirty, often unlighted, and infested with bugs and rats.

Over the years, John La Lima, owner of East Coast Train Parts, purchased large quantities of mint Postwar items from Madison. "Starting in about 1986, I'd go there every Wednesday afternoon with a stack of one-hundred dollar bills," John recalls. "I'd take whatever Lou had at whatever price it was marked. I remember one time Lou had 230 6462 Gondolas, all mint and boxed, never opened. I had a little calculator. I'd multiply 230 times $18. Okay Lou, I owe you $4140. What else do you have?" John never quibbled about price. "If you tried to bargain or disagree with something Lou said, it was over. He'd throw you out and never talk to you again. It was all Lou's way or nothing.

"Then when Kughn bought Madison and moved everything to that warehouse in Detroit, I'd drive a big truck to Detroit every month and continue to buy whatever mint items they had. My first two purchases were $50,000 each. Then my purchasing dropped off because they didn't have that many mint trains left."

Madison Hardware had lots of trains, mint and otherwise. After Kughn made the deal with Lou and Carl, the move to Detroit required 16 semi-trailer trucks filled with 1500 boxes measuring 48X24X28. As the boxes were unloaded at the 18,000 square-foot warehouse in Detroit, the items were placed on shelves in bins. The ceiling was 13-feet six-inches high, and the bins were 10-feet high. There were 27 aisles, each with five shelves. The aisles were 50-feet long. Included in the deal were the front door, the cash register, and the famous neon sign which was secured to the front of the building, above the window. For years, that sign had been a beacon leading to the Promised Land for train collectors.

La Lima became friendly with Lou. "I loved his stories. One was about Frank Sinatra. When Sinatra was in town, he would call Lou and tell him he wanted to buy some trains. Usually it would be on a Saturday. Lou would close the door to the public and wait. Sinatra would come in and hand Lou $10,000 in cash. Then Lou let him go wherever he wanted, even to the storage areas upstairs – places where no customer was ever allowed. Sinatra would point to this and that and his guys would carry it out. Sometimes the stuff would total more than $10,000, sometimes less. Lou didn't care. It was Frank Sinatra."

Cars fabricated by Madison out of parts. Car on bottom shelf is a searchlight car with the searchlight missing.

Madison made three O gauge diners from their parts cache. Here are two of them. The third was made from a Flying Yankee coach (not pictured).

During the war, when no one had toy trains to sell, Madison Hardware had toy trains to sell. The ever-resourceful Lou assembled cars out of his enormous parts inventory, sprayed them black, and sold them. He also assembled three different diner accessories out of various parts. There was a time when there was a shortage of straight track. Plenty of curves but no straights. Lou bought a machine that turned curved track into straight track and Madison Hardware was the only Lionel dealer selling straight track. As Lou once told a vendor, "Being successful is easy. You just have to be smart, work hard, and get there first."

Madison Hardware's sales were all cash. "He had an old mechanical adding machine that must have been new when he opened," recalls La Lima. "Lou would punch the keys, pull the handle, then rip off the white tape and hand it to the customer. Then he'd reach out and take the cash. No Visa. No MasterCard. Cash."

After the sale of Madison, Lou and Carl decided to move to Ft. Lauderdale, Florida. They drove to Florida in a Cadillac with the trunk filled with one-hundred bills. No boxes. Just loose one hundred dollar bills stuck in every nook and cranny (the Caddy had a big trunk and they put the spare tire in the back seat). This was money Lou had accumulated over the years. The Kughn deal was in addition to the cash.

So the colorful brothers from Long Island who owned a little train store on 23rd Street in Manhattan retired to Florida in comfort. Carl was 96 when he died and Lou was 101. When Lou reached 100, he received personal congratulatory letters from ex-New York Mayor Rudy Giuliani, Governor Jeb Bush of Florida, and President George Bush.

Lou was the business brains, and Carl was the man-about-town who loved Manhattan's nightlife. They opened the store as partners, but Carl quickly grew bored with trains, and Lou bought him out. Carl wanted to pursue a career in show business. He came up with a tap dance routine where he told jokes and wore funny hats. In those early vaudeville days he palled around with Jack Benny, Bob Hope, and Jimmy Durante. There's a picture of Carl with Babe Ruth and one with Mayor Jimmy Walker. Carl was a fine jazz drummer and formed his own band, the Carl Shaw Orchestra (he changed his name after entering show business).

Carl, who also played a fine game of polo, was a handsome guy with a full head of wavy gray hair. He loved the ladies and the ladies loved him. He was still playing competitive polo at 94 years old. There was a pool-side bar in Ft. Lauderdale for ladies only. Some ladies went topless to get an all-over tan. Carl, always eager to help, volunteered to be the bartender at no salary. The girls let him because, at 94, they figured he was harmless. Not sure they figured correctly. Remember, he was still playing polo.

Lou was a shrewd businessman and elegant dresser. His usual work attire was a crewneck or cardigan sweater, shirt with top button buttoned, snappy tie, pressed slacks, and loafers, always perfectly polished. When having lunch with friends or customers, he always picked up the tab, but not without some comment like, "Hey, I didn't want to buy the joint. Just rent it for the day." In his early 80s, he still had an iron-grip of a handshake and loved to shake hands with unsuspecting younger guys. He'd grip their hand, squeeze hard, and say, "Not bad for an old guy, huh." Lou also carried a licensed gun which he liked to occasionally show off. Lou and Carl were quintessential New York guys, smart and aggressive. Both had a wry sense of humor, and they loved to play little tricks on their unsuspecting visitors.

Through the years, Carl would help out occasionally at the store. Lou kept him on salary and paid all his bills. Carl was a fun-loving guy who loved show business but never made much of a living from it.

A series of misfortunes led to Lou's decision to sell. Back in 1914, Lou had signed a 75-year lease for $100 a month. The lease ran out in 1989 and the rent was raised to $10,000 a month. At about that same time Lou's wife and beloved dog died. To add to Lou's grief, Joe, Lou's trusted employee for years, was killed in a car accident. The younger employees hired to replace Joe started making their own back door deals with collectors and keeping the money. "Lou was devastated and had had enough," says La Lima.

Word got out that Lou wanted to sell and some offers were made. No deal was consummated because nobody could get in all the rooms and little cubbyholes where the trains were stashed to take an inventory. The Kughn deal went through because Kughn was willing to make the deal based on his estimates and without taking an actual inventory.

Dick Kughn kept Madison Hardware open for more than 10 years. "We sold a lot, but I kept some items for my own collection," says Dick. He closed Madison Hardware on December 31, 2001. The remaining inventory was sold in a series of auctions between November 2001 and April 2005.

"Both Lou and Carl were fascinating gentlemen," remembers Kughn. "I thoroughly enjoyed negotiating and working with them. It was a magnificent experience to bring back to Detroit this icon of our hobby. It took 16 semi-trailer trucks to move the boxes and almost three years to open the boxes. Sometimes we'd be thrilled at what was inside and sometime we'd be disappointed. But all in all, it was a lot of fun and a good deal for me in every way."

The famous Madison Hardware sign sold at one of the auctions for $37,500.

Listen to Your Inner Lionel

by Ron Grossman, Chicago Tribune
(Marx collector and operator)

In retrospect, I can see that my life was divided into the same three parts as Western Civilization: a time of ancient glory, an era of present progress, and in between, the Dark Ages. Family and friends may have seen it differently. In that middle period, I studied Greek and Latin literature, got a Ph.D., taught at several universities, and became a newspaper reporter. I had six wonderful children.

Even so, I'd get an annual hint, a sixth sense, that something was lacking. As winter approached, I'd have a visit from a ghost of Christmas past, just as Scrooge had. Mine wasn't a former business partner, but a boyhood chum who'd gone to that Great Hobby Shop in the Sky. He was bound not in chains, but a garland of O-27 track. He beckoned to me with a dog-eared Lionel catalog, the words Magne-Traction barely visible.

He'd take me by the arm and lead me to living rooms covered with three-rail track and Lionels long gone. Off to the side are shreds of gift-wrapping from which anxious fingers had pulled a GG-1 or a smoke-belching Hudson. In my reverie it's Christmas Day plus 1. A group of school-yard buddies are gathered at one of our parents' homes to merge switches and signals. We're again exchanging oohs and ahs over newly acquired automated milk-can loaders, Hell Gate bridges, and illuminated observation cars.

Then it'd be over. I'd go back to another hum-drum year of interviewing Arthur Miller and Joan Rivers, Joseph Heller and Milton Berle. I visited with Big Bird on the set of "Sesame Street." I was a guest of First Lady Laura Bush at a White House shindig. But evidently scoops and celebrities do not a life make.

I should have recognized that. The symptoms were there. When the Museum of Science and Industry updated its model railroad layout, I elbowed other Chicago Tribune reporters out of the way to get the assignment.

Then one Sunday a few years ago, on a lark I went to the monthly Great Midwest Train Show in Wheaton, IL. I walked in the door, saw table after table of locos and boxcars, and the words of a saint came back to me. No, not St. Nicholas. St Augustine, the great theologian whose works I'd read in graduate school.

"When I became a man, I put away childish things," Augustine wrote, 16 Centuries ago. Maybe that worked for him. There weren't electric trains back then. But clearly, it wasn't working for me. Thinking of my long-lost train, I was never so lonely in my life.

I bought a much-used engine at the train show, went back the next month, and have scarcely missed one since.

My life is fulfilled. My basement is filled with trains and track. I take engines apart and search flea-markets for missing parts. Every day of my life is Christmas morning.

Once I could recite whole passages of the "Iliad." That ability is now lost. Maybe it was nature's way of cleaning out brain space to store other data--like the prices and part numbers and desirable variations described in this guide. Many now come to my mind as effortlessly as Cicero's words used to. They're the poetry with which I communicate with fellow train nuts. They resuscitate my youth.

Now, here's a bit of advice for those idly leafing through this book. Maybe you picked it up off a magazine rack by accident. Perhaps you were inspired by a flashback to the electric trains of your Christmases past.

Take heed from my wasted years. Act on impulse.

Listen to your inner Lionel.

Prewar Gallery

Number 6 4-4-0 Steamer with 8-wheel tender. Thick rims. Produced between 1912 and 1923. Runs great. We have it running in our new Lionel Christmas DVD pulling three trimmed-out-for-Christmas 10-series freight cars.

No.6 loco and tender was cataloged 1906 to 1923. This is a very early example with thin rim drivers, slide-on pedestal light, large bell and 2-piece split frame. Note solid-frame 3-rivet trucks on 6T tender. Couplers on early models should all be short or long straight hook.

"PLAY WAR!" was the insensitive proclamation in Lionel's 1917 and 1918 catalogs. Outfit #215 included the No. 203 Armored Motor Car, and 2 No. 702 supply cars shown in photo. A second outfit #214 included the 203 and pair of No. 900 ammunition box cars. Lionel's first military sets were cataloged 1917 to 1920. By 1920 the more appropriate slogan "I Jumped for Joy" was being used.

Transition 156 4-4-4 loco has pedestal headlight, gold vents and Manufacturing motor, characteristic of the earlier 703 loco, but later 156 number and die-cast pony wheels. Speculation indicates it would be made 1916-17, but Lionel was just making toys and was known to put together parts from different years to fulfill an order.

No. 701 early electric c. 1915 has gold vents, pedestal headlight, cast iron wheels and Lionel MFG emboss directly on copper pick-up, not on separate plate.

No 602 baggage and 603 Pullman in rare light orange, made for uncataloged sets c.1922. Same 7 inch car body as dark green 601, 602 cars.

Outfit No. 169 made 1922 to 1924, consisting of 0-4-0 156X loco, 610 and 612 in rare brown with dark green trim. It is believed that many 150 series locos in colors other than dark green are factory repaints. 2 examples of brown 156X locos examined by the author were mojave on the inside.

Very early No.14 boxcar. Characteristics include, solid-frame 3-rivet trucks, 2-piece roof, smooth sides with painted slats and primer yellow under and inside. Car dates to 1906-08.

No. 154 electric in light olive green. Loco has later type frame and brass strap headlight. Likely made during end of production in 1923.

No. 150 small electric in very scarce mojave. As side-note this loco was in Lou Redman's collection. Lou was one of the top experts in Early Lionel O-gauge.

Primer yellow underside and inside of early No. 13.

No. 13 early stock car has type II open-frame 3-rivet trucks, smooth non-embossed sides, 2-piece roof. Underside and inside of early cars is painted primer yellow.

No. 35 Pullman and 36 observation with ribbed sides, nickel rivet-type trucks. Note maroon door variation on 35 and long platform on 36. Cars are circa mid-teens.

Underside of early No. 6 with split frame

54 Electric *in brass with rounded roof cab, 1913-1924. Came with both single and double motor versions.* *p43*

5 Steamer *with thick rims, 1906-26* *p46*

No. 87 Rheostat *for Racing Auto Sets. Note that this item does not appear in any Lionel catalogs or books. Pictured here it is in its original box. It was made between 1912 and 1915.*

No. 601 Pullman and 602 baggage c. 1915-16 with type I half-moon cut-out trucks.

Set 291 1926 only. *Cataloged with both early (801 caboose and 800 box). And later cars (802 hopper and 907 tank). All with no journals. W/ box $1800-$2200.*

186 Accessory Set
Lithographed houses. Earlier sets came enameled. Yellow box series (usually deteriorate due to high acid content. (5) $2200-$2400

1049 Accessory Car Set
$250-$325 w/box

1060 Set of Passenger Cars
$375-$450 w/ box

***300 Early Hellgate Bridge with box and shipping carton**. Bridge has dropped to $750. With box and shipping carton, $1200/$1500*

241 Passenger Set
260 w/chugger, two 710 coaches and one 712 Obvs w/o box $1700-$2000. With box, $3400-$3800

***This 254 Olive Passenger Set** was uncataloged and assigned the designation "SPECIAL." No set number. One of the 5 rarest Prewar O gauge sets. W/box $3500-$4000.*

***226E w/ Irvington cars, 41** w/o box $1700-$1900. With box $2400-$2600*

194 Deluxe Accessory Set 27, 28

Set 194 contained accessories in boxes with Standard Gauge numbers, 78, 69,76, 80 and 77. Set 193 contained the same accessories but the boxes were marked with O gauge numbers (O78, O69, etc.). Each contained sections of special track to activate the accessories. (5) $2500-$3000 complete with all boxes. Empty set box alone sold at auction for $1800.

***Lionel Boats** hit hard by reproductions. The 44 used to be $1500 and the 43 around $900. Now both $600-$800 with box.*

290X Single Span O Gauge Bridge *"X" indicates Standard Gauge bridge modified to accommodate O and O27 track. (5) 400-500 w/ box. $250 w/o box.*

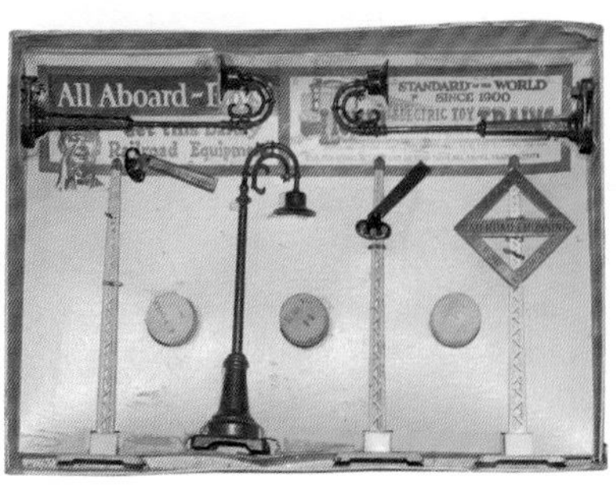

70 Accessory Set (modified)*. Originally came with two 62 semaphores, one 59 street lamp, one 68 Warning Signal, and two 14v globes. Dealer added two 58 Lamp Post and additional 14v globe. Modified set sold at auction for $5000. 5 rarity.*

Dealer Display for 43-73 Lamps *Lanterns for 46 and 47 Gates. Rare (5) $800-$1000*

127 Station *is common with Mojave base. Rare (5) with green base. W/box $500-$700.*

Set 295W Blue Streak *w/box $2200-$2700*

***The 278E Red Comet Set** was available in 1934 (picture) and 35 IN 35, it came with a waffle tender. The 34 version is harder-to-find. With box, $2200-$2800*

***Handcars** l to r 1100 Mickey Mouse, 1107 Donald Duck Rail Car, 1103 Chickmobile. 1107 w/box $800-$1200*

***129 Terrace Station Platform 28-33, 35-42** p13*

***114 Double-Window Station**, 31-34 Big drop. Used to be in the $1500-$1700 range. Now $800.*

***Uncataloged Sears Set, 41** 204 gray, 2689W tender, two 609s and one 611 Obvs. $1000-$1200*

***1927 Macy's DSS**, 27 Red 253 w/cream trim. Two 607 coaches and one 608 Obvs.$1200-$1500 w/ no box*

Sears Uncataloged Set 59-79P186WX 40,41
Black 238, 2225W tender, 2602, 2600, and 2601. Truck installed at end of cars. High coupler on all cars and tender. Similar set sold on eBay for $3800.

Classic Lionel – The 755W Hiawatha

124 Lionel City Station *20-30, 33-36*
Terra cotta/pea green p13

292 Set *This olive with orange trim version of the 248 was made in 1927 only. 248 came with combination couplers. It is the hardest-to-find 248. p28*

Clockwork Set 1547 36,37
1511 Commodore Vanderbilt streamline loco, 1516T , 1515 tank, 1514 Baby Ruth boxcar, 1514 Erie boxcar (add on, rare with black door), 1512 gondola (add on), 1517 caboose

840 Power Station 35-42 *Cream/orange/gray floor p17*

Lionel's largest Standard Gauge steamer, the 400E was first cataloged in 1930 and was available through 1939. This early version has brass and copper trim and unpainted brass bands.

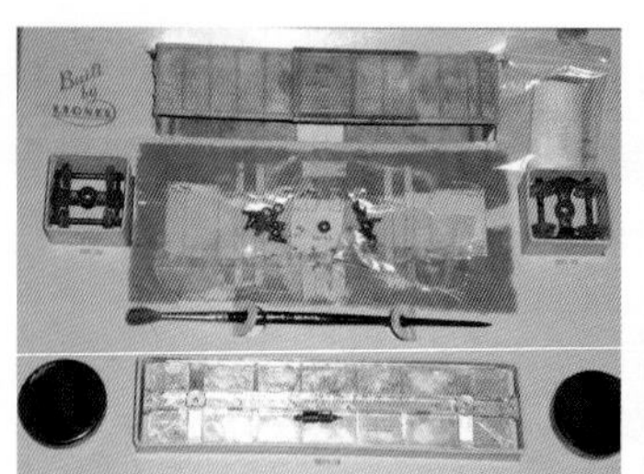

OO Boxcar kit in orignal box. Never assembled. p42

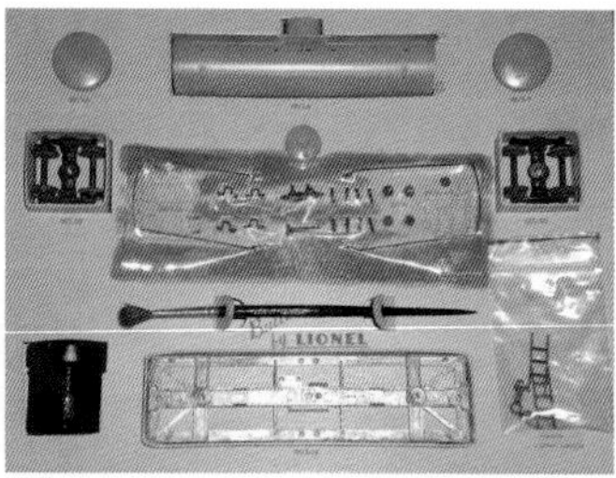

OO Tank kit in original box. Never assembled. p42

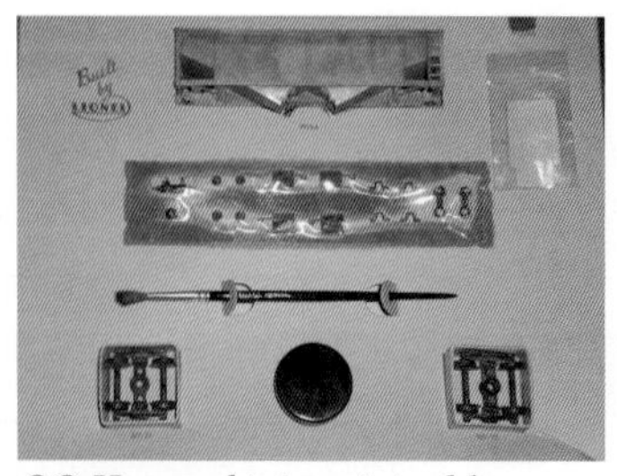

OO Hopper kit in original box. Never assembled. p42

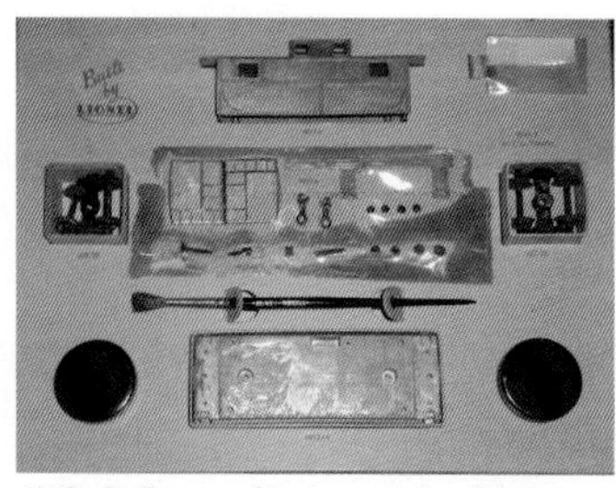

OO Caboose kit in original box. Never assembled. p42

First issue

Second issue

Lionel Standard Gauge Billboard Set (left) U32,33 (5) $400-$500. Second issue (5) $600-$700. Special "mail-in" promotion by Lionel. Billboards came in Lionel envelope. Second set harder to find. Reproductions available. Add $500 if you have correct envelope.

Set 240E Work Train, 33-35
260E w/ cream stripe, 260T, 811 flat, 812 gondola, 810 crane, 817 caboose. W/box $2200-$2500

The King of the Hill –709W The Rail Chief Set, 37-41

916 Tunnel, 33, 34
Some sold through Macy's and came in Macy's box. w/Macy's box $700-800

Set 299E, 26-28
254 Olive w/ maroon vents, 814 box w/ pea green door guides, 813 cattle, and 817 caboose (door guides may be changed)

Two of our favorite things – Lionel Hudsons
763 Hudson Gunmetal w/rare 2226WX coal tender 40 only p31
763 Hudson Black w/2226W coal 41,42 p31

Boxed 1054 Lionel Jr. Freight Set, 1934

Extremely rare 436 Power Station. "Edison" printed over door. Box has letter "E" rubber stamped above the word "Station" on box. p16

Set 764W, 1937. *Came with gray 763E and gray Vandy tender, 2814 box, 2815 tank, 2312 gondola, and 2817 caboose. With original box – $3500-$4000. Back in 1937 this set sold for $40, so in 73 years it has increased 100X in value. Seems about right.*

Early 810 Crane on the left and later 810 Crane on the right.
Both with their original boxes. p38

195 Illuminated Terrace, 27-30. *Came with 90 flag, 184 bungalow, two 56 lamp posts, 198 villa, and 191 villa. p15*

Boxed 1054 Lionel Jr. Freight Set, 1934

Postwar Gallery

Operating Generator Car
3530 Long stripe, number underlined. p121
3530 Short stripe – rivet in center of upper door guide
3530 Long stripe – divot in center of upper door guide
3530 Short stripe – rivet in center of upper door guide

Rare 2350 *White over orange, painted, rivet shows p92*
2350 Orange *over black, decal covers rivet p92*

2331 Gray shell painted blue/light yellow (4) p90
2322 Blue shell painted yellow/blue (3) p90

6464 Cars
6464-175 Rock Island black lettering (5) p104
6464-475 B&M Purplish (4) p105
6464-1 Western Pacific red lettering (5) p103
6464-0500 Timken "butternut" yellow (4) p106

3494-550 Monon w/overstamp p101
6464-325 Sentinel p105

6464-325 Sentinel p105
6468-1 B&O Automobile Car p106

Hoppers *p117*
6436-500 Girl's Train Hopper
643657 Maroon w/ number that appeared on Girl's Train hopper.

64361 No spreader bar
643625 No spreader bar

Rare 2338 Milwaukee Road *orange stripe through cab (5) p91*

Rare 2347 Sears C&O *(5) p91*

41 Army *painted (5) p93*

41 Army *unpainted (2) p93*

42 Picatinny Arsenal *p93*

57 AEC *p93*

Military & Space

3510 Satellite Launch red (3) p118
3413 Mercury Capsule Car p118
3470 Target Launcher light blue flat p118
3619 Helicopter 3413 (3) p119
6844 Missile car red (5) p120
3419 Rare with clear blades (normally black) p118

Cabooses

6417-50 Gray (2) p107
6417-50 Tuscan (5)
6047 Red (2) p108
6047 Tuscan (5)

Lionel Train-O-Ramas

Came in boxes of Nabisco Shredded Wheat. Three sheets with scenes to be punched out. 12 different. Both assembled and non-assembled very hard-to-find. Premium for mailing envelope.

***GG1s** p92*

2332 Black w/decals. Purchased from non-collector. Decals not right.
2340 Tuscan 5 stripe, 55
2340 Green, 55
2360 Solid Stripe, 61-62

6828 Black (4) p115
6414 (2), 55 p113
6501 Jet Boat w/ packet p114
6828 Red (5) p115
6414 with rare blue car, red and white cars still in original packaging p114
6410-25 Unlettered flat, 2 red autos (4)

Hoppers page 116

6456-25 Glossy red/yellow (4)
2456 3 lines of data (rare)
6176 Bright lemon yellow unlettered (rare)
6456-25 Glossy red/white (5)
2456 2 lines of data (common)
6176 Yellow

"Halloween" General with rare Plasticville 963-100 Log Cabin. Came only in set.

***2333 New York Central AA F3s** p89*
Top Chubby RS lettering, black decal, 49
Middle Same with red decal, 49
Bottom Heat-stamped, thin lettering, black decal

Tank Cars page 122
2855 Black, gas and oils, 46
6315 Burnt orange, 56
6315 Orange 65,66
6555 Silver, thick lettering, no gas and oils
2855 RS on bottom
6315 Painted orange, Hagerstown box

***Two 6418 Girder Bridge Cars** with four sets of four-wheel trucks. Bridge came in three colors, orange, black, and a pinkish orange (top shelf). The pinkish-orange version is probably the hardest to find but all are worth about the same. Current eBay "sold for" price is $60 with a box. We have them at $90. p111*

Set box for 9820 Sears Military Train Set, made in 1964, with paper.

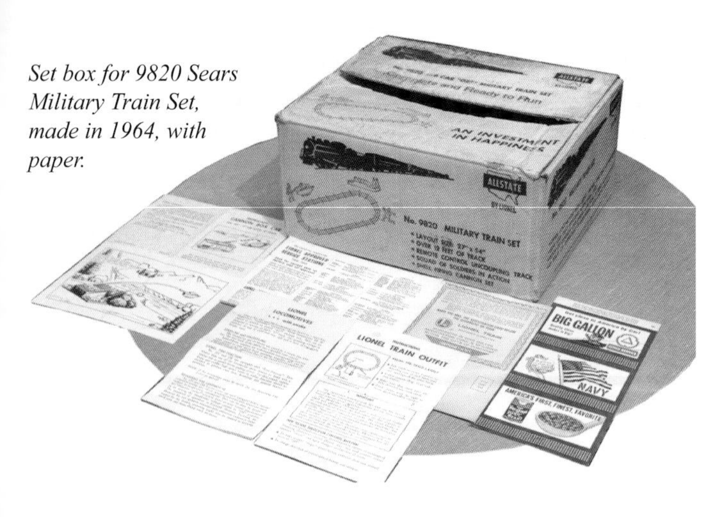

9820 Sears Military Train Set, 1964
240 with tender, 3666 with cannon (came only in this set), 6470 Exploding box car, Flat with tank, and 6814 with black frame.

This set also came with rare (5) 347 Cannon Firing Set (not pictured)

***4110WS Electronic Set, 49** p144*
671R Turbine, 4671W, 5459 Dump, 4454 box, 4452 gondola, 4357 caboose. Came in set box inside shipping carton along with track, switches, 97 coal loader, 151 semaphore, VW transformer, ECU1 Electronic Control Unit.

Switchers
6250 Seaboard w/ decal (3) p91
600 MKT gray frame, black railing p90
613 Union Pacific p91

6250 Seaboard RS lettering (4) p91
600 MKT gray frame, yellow railing, black steps p90
614 Alaska p91

***Searchlight Cars** p121*
6520 Maroon generator, crackle flat gray light, 49,50
3620 Orange generator, sans serif, gray painted light, 54
3650 Olive gray, 58

6520 Green generator, smooth light, 49 rare
3620 Maroon generator, glossy gray light, 49,50
6822, one operating coupler, 64

460 Piggy Back Transportation Set

470 Launching Platform with Exploding Target Car *Mint w/box*

462 Derrick Platform Set *Mint w/ box*

Box for smoke pellets

443 Missile Launching Platform with Exploding Ammunition Dump *Mint w/ box*

448 Missile Firing Range Set

671-75 Replacement lamps for 671 Turbine

Cataloged in 1957, the 2396W Canadian Pacific AA, four-car passenger set (three vista domes) is one of the most desirable of the entire Postwar era.

2379 Rio Grand F3 AB 57,58 p91

2348 Minneapolis & St. Louis GP-9 p91 and 2349 Northern Pacific GP-9 p92

The early Lionel Alcos were fine runners. The rare gray-nose yellow 2023 UP version is on the top, 2031 Rock Island in the middle, and the 2032 Erie AA is on the bottom shelf. p89

Three late Irvington cars *with original boxes. Silhouettes. 2625 Irvington, 2627 Madison, and 2628 Manhattan. Novice collectors refer to these cars as "Madison." p99*

2328 Burlington *with original box. p91*

746 N&W J with 746X tender and box. "X" designates long-stripe tender. One of the few Postwar items going up in this down market. p94

400 Budd car with box and liner. p89

FM Units
Two versions to the 2341 Jersey Central FM, dull and glossy. The glossy (top) is rarer and worth about $200 more. The Lackawanna FM came with maroon roof in 54 and a gray roof in 55 and 56. The maroon-roof version is a little harder to find and worth about $100 more. p90

2330 GG1 *complete with box, inner liner and paper, just like you opened it for the first time in 1950. First Lionel GG1 with two motors. p92*

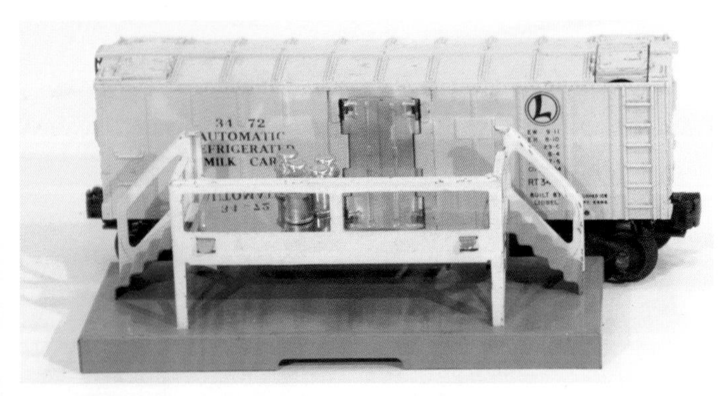

3472 Milk Car *Best-selling operating car Lionel ever produced. Early version with metal doors. p120*

230	**Chesapeake & Ohio A** Blue/yellow 61	(2)	**100▼**
231	**Rock Island A** Black 61-63		
	1. Red stripe and white stripe	(3)	**100▼**
	2. Red stripe/no white stripe	(3)	**125▼**
	3. White stripe/no red stripe	(4+)	**600***
232	**New Haven A** 62 Orange/black	(3)	**175▼**
1055	**Texas Special A** Red/white U59,60	(2)	**60▼**
1065	**Union Pacific A** Yellow/red U61	(2)	**100▼**
1066	**Union Pacific A** Yellow/red U64	(2)	**100▼**
2023	**Union Pacific AA** 50,51		
	1. Yellow/gray nose, roof & trucks 50	(5)	**3500▼***
	2. Yellow/gray roof & black trucks 50	(2)	**200▼**
	3. Silver/gray roof & black trucks 51	(4)	**200▼**
2024	**Chesapeake & Ohio A** Blue/yellow 69	(2)	**75▼**
2031	**Rock Island AA** Black/white 52-54	(4)	**300▼**
2032	**Erie AA** Black/yellow 52-54	(4)	**200▼**
2033	**Union Pacific AA** Silver/black 52-54	(3)	**200▼**
2041	**Rock Island AA** Black 69		
	1. White lettering/red stripe	(3)	**140▼**
	2. No lettering, no red stripe	(3)	**125▼**

Budd Cars

400	**Baltimore & Ohio** Silver/blue 56-58	(3)	**250▼**
404	**Baltimore & Ohio** Silver/blue 57,58	(3+)	**275▼**
2550	**Baltimore & Ohio** dummy 57,58	(4)	**325▼**
2559	**Baltimore & Ohio** dummy 57,58	(4)	**250▼**

F-3 Units

Note: Most reproductions have silk-screen lettering; however, some 2345 reproductions exist with heat-stamped lettering

2240	**Wabash AB** Gray/blue/white 56	(3)	**650▼**
2242	**New Haven AB** Silver/black/orange 58,59	(4)	**800▼**
2243	**Santa Fe AB** Silver/red 55-57	(3)	**350▼**
2243C	**Santa Fe B Unit** Silver/red 55-57	(3)	**225▼**
2245	**Texas Special AB** 54,55		
	1. Silver trucks/red pilot/portholes	(3)	**500▼**
	2. Black trucks/silver pilot/A w/portholes/B w/solid portholes late 55 only	(5)	**750▼***
	3. Same as 2 but A and B have solid portholes *Note: possible dealer replacement shells*	(5)	**1000▼***
2333	**Santa Fe AA** Silver/red 48,49		
	1. RS larger lettering	(3+)	**500▼**
	2. HS smaller lettering	(3)	**475▼**
2333	**Santa Fe** Clear bodies (Vol. 5, pg 65)		**5X**
2333	**New York Central AA** Dark gray/gray/white 48,49		
	1. RS larger "chubby" lettering	(4)	**550▼**
	2. HS smaller lettering *Note: Original NYC's had black or red decals and original Santa Fe's had red decals. Replacement decals are available and can be applied to either.*	(3)	**500▼**
2343	**Santa Fe AA** Silver/red 50-52	(2)	**500▼**
2343C	**Santa Fe B Unit** Silver/red 50-55		
	1. Screen roof vents matches 2343 50-52	(4)	**275▼**
	2. Louver vents matches 2353 53-55	(3)	**225▼**
2344	**New York Central AA** 50-52	(3)	**500▼**
2344C	**New York Central B Unit** 50-55		
	1. Screen roof vents matches 2344 50-52	(4)	**250▼**
	2. Louver vents matches 2354 53-55	(3)	**225▼**
2345	**Western Pacific AA** Silver/orange/black 52	(4)	**1000▼**

2353	**Santa Fe AA** Silver/red 53-55	(3)	**500**
2354	**New York Central AA** Dark gray/gray/white 53-55	(3+)	**575**
2355	**Western Pacific AA** Silver/orange/black 53	(4)	**1200▼**
Also reported no lettering on one side, NDV			
2356	**Southern AA** Green/gray/yellow 54-56	(4)	**750▼**
2356C	**Southern B Unit** Green/gray/yellow 54-56	(4)	**350**
2363	**Illinois Central AB** Brown/orange/yellow 55,56		
	1. Black lettering	(4)	**700▼**
	2. Brown lettering	(5)	**800▼**
2367	**Wabash AB** Gray/blue/white 55,56	(4)	**725▼**
2368	**Baltimore & Ohio AB** Blue/white/black 56	(4)	**1200▼**
2373	**Canadian Pacific AA** Gray/maroon/yellow 57	(4)	**1500▼**
2378	**Milwaukee Road AB** 56		
	1. No yellow stripe along roof	(4)	**1000▼**
	2. Yellow stripe along roof	(4)	**1100▼**
	3. A unit no stripe, B unit with stripe	(4)	**1100▼**
2379	**Rio Grande AB** Yellow/silver/black 57,58	(4)	**800▼**
2383	**Santa Fe AA** Silver/red 58-66	(3)	**475▼**

FM Units

Note: Watch for Jersey Central reproductions being sold as originals. The best way to tell an original is by checking the spacing between Jersey and Central. On the original, there is more space between the words on one side than there is on the other. On reproductions, the space between the words is the same on both sides.

2321	**Lackawanna** Gray body 54-56		
	1. Maroon roof 54	(3+)	**500**
	2. Gray roof 55,56	(3)	**400**
2322	**Virginian** Blue/yellow 65,66		
	1. Unpainted blue shell	(3+)	**700**
	2. Painted blue shell	(4)	**800**
2331	**Virginian** 55-58		
	Note: The yellow on the second version is much lighter than the yellow on the third version, which is almost gold.		
	1. Yellow/black both colors painted on gray mold	(4)	**875**
	2. Blue/light yellow/both colors painted on gray mold	(4+)	**1000***
	3. Blue/yellow - yellow only painted on blue plastic mold	(3+)	**600**
2341	**Jersey Central** Orange/blue/blue stripe 56		
	Note: Originals are heat-stamped; reproductions are silk-screened		
	1. Glossy finish	(5)	**2000▼**
	2. Dull finish	(4)	**1800▼**

GE 44-Ton Switchers

Note: Difficult to find in Like New condition. All have a tendency to flake and are usually found with broken screw holes.

625	**Lehigh Valley** Red/black/white 57,58	(3)	**100▼**
626	**Baltimore & Ohio** Blue/yellow 57	(4)	**300▼**
627	**Lehigh Valley** Red/white 56,57	(2)	**125▼**
628	**Northern Pacific** Black/yellow 56,57	(3)	**125▼**
629	**Burlington** Silver/red 56	(4)	**400▼**

GM Switchers

600	**MKT** Red/white 55		
	1. Black frame/black rails	(3)	**100▼**
	2. Gray frame/yellow rails	(3+)	**195**
	3. Gray frame/black rails	(4)	**275**
601	**Seaboard** Black/red/white 56		
	1. Red stripes/rounded ends	(3)	**175▼**
	2. Red stripes/squared ends	(4)	**200▼**

602	**Seaboard** Black/red/red 57,58	(3)	**175**
610	**Erie** 55 Black/yellow		
	1. Black frame	(3)	**165**
	2. Yellow frame	(4)	**355**
	3. Dealer replacement shell w/raised nameplate	(4)	**270**
611	**Jersey Central** Orange/blue 57,58	(3)	**185**
613	**Union Pacific** Yellow/gray/red 58	(4)	**275▼**
614	**Alaska** Blue/yellow with dynamic brake unit 59,60		
	1. *Built by Lionel* in blue raised letters	(3)	**245**
	2. *Built by Lionel* in yellow raised letters	(4)	**450**
616	**Santa Fe** Black/white/safety stripes 61,62		
	1. No dummy horn, bell, or E unit slot	(5)	**285**
	2. Has dummy horn, bell, & E unit slot	(4)	**200**
617	**Santa Fe** Black/white/safety stripes 63	(4)	**325**
621	**Jersey Central** Blue/orange 56,57	(3)	**185**
622	**Santa Fe** Black/white, operating bell 49,50		
	1. Large *GM* decal	(4+)	**400▼**
	2. Small *GM* decal	(3)	**165**
	3. Large *GM* decal and *Built by Lionel* in white	(4)	**225▼**
	4. Same as 3 plus small decal	(4+)	**350▼**
623	**Santa Fe** Black/white 52-54		
	1. 10 Handrail stanchions	(4)	**150**
	2. 3 Handrail stanchions	(3)	**125**
624	**Chesapeake & Ohio** Blue/yellow 52-54		
	1. 10 Handrail stanchions	(4)	**240**
	2. 3 Handrail stanchions	(3)	**210**
633	**Santa Fe** Blue/yellow 62		
	1. No safety stripes	(3)	**130**
	2. Safety stripes	(3+)	**165**
634	**Santa Fe** Blue/yellow 63,65,66		
	1. Safety Stripes	(2)	**125**
	2. No Safety Stripes	(3)	**145**
635	**Union Pacific** Yellow/red U65	(4)	**170**
645	**Union Pacific** Yellow/red 69	(3)	**140**
6220	**Santa Fe** Black/white, operating bell 49,50		
	1. Large *GM* decal, 1949	(4+)	**200▼**
	2. Small *GM* decal, 1950	(3)	**175▼**
6250	**Seaboard** Blue/orange/white-blue 54,55		
	Note: Fewer rubber-stamped versions produced but decal version with decal in excellent condition is more desirable.		
	1. Decal	(4)	**200▼**
	2. Rubber-stamped	(4)	**200▼**

GP-7s and GP-9s

Note: Originals have HS lettering. Reproductions have RS lettering or are silk-screened. Known reproductions include 2337, 2339, 2349, 2347, 2365.

2028	**Pennsylvania GP-7** Tuscan 55		
	1. Yellow RS lettering/gold frame	(4)	**240**
	2. Gold RS lettering/gold frame	(4+)	**300**
	3. Gold RS lettering/tan frame	(5)	**1000***
2328	**Burlington GP-7** Silver/black/red 55,56	(3)	**395**
2337	**Wabash GP-7** Blue/gray/white58	(4)	**275▼**
2338	**Milwaukee Road GP-7** 55,56		
	1. Orange stripe through cab	(5)	**1825***
	2. All-black cab	(3)	**225**
2339	**Wabash GP-7** Blue/gray/white 57	(3+)	**275▼**
2346	**Boston & Maine GP-9** 65,66	(3)	**250▼**
2347	**Chesapeake & Ohio GP-7** Blue/yellow *Sears*U65	(5)	**3000***
2348	**Minneapolis & St. Louis GP-9** 58,59		
	1. Red/white	(4)	**325▼**
	2. Red/yellow		**FAKE**

2349	**Northern Pacific GP-9** Black/gold/red 59,60	(4)	**500▼**
2359	**Boston & Maine GP-9** Blue/black/white 61,62	(3)	**250▼**
2365	**Chesapeake & Ohio GP-7** Dummy couplers 62,63		
	1. Blue/yellow	(3)	**200**
	2. Blue/white		**FAKE**

Electrics

520	**Box Cab** Red/white 56,57		
	1. Black plastic pantograph	(3)	**95**
	2. Copper plastic pantograph	(4)	**140**
2329	**Virginian EL-C** Rectifier Blue/yellow 58,59	(4)	**425▼**

EP-5s

Note: Difficult to find EP-5s in Like New condition due to flaking and fading. Beware of repaints, particularly Milwaukee Road because of no decal. 2352 price not commensurate with its rarity because of its drab color scheme.

2350	**New Haven EP-5** Black/white/orange 56-58		
	Note:The major variation of the New Haven has to do with the color of the N and H. The common version has a white N and orange H. The rare version has an orange N and black H. Both versions come with either the nose trim painted or a decal. Versions with the painted nose trim are far more sought after than the decal versions.		
	1. White *N* orange *H*/nose trim decal	(3)	**300▼**
	2. White *N* orange *H*/painted nose trim	(4)	**700**
	3. Orange *N* black *H*/nose trim decal	(4)	**1800***
	4. Orange *N* black *H*/painted nose trim	(5)	**2000***
2351	**Milwaukee Road EP-5** Yellow/black/red 57,58	(3)	**475**
2352	**Pennsylvania EP-5** Tuscan/gold 58,59	(3)	**475**
2358	**GN EP-5** Orange/green/yellow 59,60	(4)	**900▼**

GG-1s

2330	**GG-1** Dark green/5 gold stripes 50	(4)	**1150**
2330	**GG-1** Nickel-plate		**5P**
2332	**GG-1** single motor 47-49		
	Note: Only came with electric horn that soundslike the buzz of a doorbell. All other GG1's came with same horn as the Alcos.		
	1. Black/5 silver stripes	(5)	**2500***
	2. Black/5 gold stripes	(5)	**2500***
	3. Dark green/5 gold stripes decaled keystones	(3)	**750**
	4. Dark green/5 gold stripes RS keystones	(4)	**900▼***
	5. Dark green/5 silver stripes RS keystones	(4)	**900▼***
2340-1	**GG-1** Tuscan 5 gold stripes *Congressional Set* 55	(4)	**1200▼***
2340-25	**GG-1** Brunswick Green 5 gold stripes 55	(4)	**1200▼***
2360-1	**GG-1** Tuscan 56-58, 61-63		
	Note: Variations exist having to do with louvres, shape of headlights, and steps. NDV.		
	1. 1956/5 gold stripes/RS/small *PRR* keystone	(4)	**1200▼**
	2. Same as 1 but large *PRR* keystone usually found on solid-stripe versions	(5)	**1200▼**
	3. 1957,58 Solid stripe/RS/OB marked 2360-10/large *PRR* keystone	(3)	**1200▼**
	4. 1961-63 Solid stripe/painted/HS markings	(3)	**950▼**
	5. Late 1963 Solid stripe/painted/decaled markings	(3)	**950▼**
	6. Very glossy finish/5 gold stripes		**5P**
2360-25	**GG-1** Brunswick green 5 RS gold stripes 56-58	(4)	**1200▲**

Motorized Units

Note: High prices, restorations and reissues have lessened the demand. Beware of repaired window struts. Like New, 54, 55, and 3360 must be complete with track actuator.

No.	Item	Rarity	Price
41	**US Army** 55-57		
	1. Unpainted black plastic w/white lettering	(3)	**120**
	2. Yellow lettering		**FAKE**
	3. Painted	(5)	**?***
42	**Picatinny Arsenal** Olive drab/white 57	(4)	**300**
44	**US Army** Blue/white/gray 59-62	(3)	**225**
45	**US Marines** Olive drab/white/gray 60-62	(3+)	**250**
50	**Gang Car** Orange/blue 54-64		
	1. Gray bumpers (54 only). Men in reversed colors	(5)	**900▼***
	2. Same, blue bumpers	(3)	**90**
	3. Horn changed to solid type attached off-center. Blue bumpers	(1)	**60**
51	**Navy Yard** Blue/white 56,57	(2)	**200**
52	**Fire Car** Red/white 58-61	(3)	**200**
53	**Rio Grande Snowplow** Black/yellow 57-60		
	1. *a* printed backwards	(4)	**275**
	2. *a* printed correctly	(5)	**700**
54	**Ballast Tamper** Black/yellow 58-62,66,68,69	(3)	**175▼**
55	**Tie-Jector** Red/white 57-61 Some came with a horizontal opening behind man, some didn't. NDV	(4)	**175▼**
56	**Minneapolis & St. Louis** Red/white 58	(4+)	**600**
57	**AEC Switcher** White/red/white 59,60	(4)	**850**
58	**GN Rotary Snowplow** Green/white 59-61	(4)	**700**
59	**Minuteman** White/blue 62,63	(4)	**800**
60	**Lionelville Trolley** Yellow/red/blue 55-58 ***Note: Some cars with red lettering may actually be faded black cars since black pigment has red in it.***		
	1. Yellow/black lettering 55	(3+)	**150▼**
	2. Yellow/blue lettering	(3)	**125▼**
	3. Roof vents	(4)	**225**
	4. Yellow/red lettering	(5)	**5000*▲**
	5. The first versions off the production line had black silhouettes of motormen at each end of the trolley. They would appear and disappear according to which direction the car was traveling. However, the motormen silhouettes were rather indistinct and Lionel soon discontinued putting them on. The motormen remained available for separate sale and today trolleys exist with motormen, but most were put on by collectors.	(5)	**325**
65	**Handcar** 62-66	(4)	**300▼**
	1. First versions were made of light yellow plastic which had a tendency to melt and are almost impossible to find in Like New condition. This version came with two sizes of rectifiers: thick (extends through slot in chassis wall) and thin (clipped to chassis wall). The thick version (two rubber-tire wheels) is harder to find than the thin version (one rubber-tire wheel). NDV		
	2. Dark yellow	(4+)	**275▼**
68	**Executive Inspection Car** 58-61		
	1. Red/cream	(3+)	**250▼**
	2. Red throughout		**5P**
	3. Blue/cream stripe		**5P**
69	**Maintenance Car** Dark gray/black 60-62	(3)	**250▼**
3360	**Burro Crane** 56,57		
	1. Yellow	(3)	**200▼**
	2. Brown		**5P**

3927	**Track Cleaning Car** Complete w/2 bottles, 56-60 brush, and wiper		
	1. Orange/blue	(3)	**85**
	2. Orange/black	(4)	**85**

Steamers

Berkshires

726	2-8-4 2426W Turned stanchions, *Atomic Motor* 46 double worm drive, horizontal motor, Baldwin drivers	(4)	**600**
726	2-8-4 2426W Cotter pin stanchions, single 47-49 worm drive and slanted motor, Baldwin drivers	(3)	**425**
726	2-8-4 2046W Korean War issue Spoked drivers, 52 no Magnetraction		
	1. 726RR stamped on cab	(3)	**325**
	2. No RR	(4)	**325**
736	2-8-4 2671WX 12-wheels, Magnetraction, 50,51 smoke, diecast trailing trucks, RS cab number	(3)	**325▼**
736	2-8-4 2046W 8-wheels, diecast trailing trucks, 53-55 Magnetraction, smoke, heat-stamped cab number	(2)	**300▼**
736	2-8-4 2046W,736 MT, HS cab number 55-66 smoke, sheet-metal trucks w/plastic side frames	(2)	**275▼**
746	4-8-4 *Norfolk & Western* 746W 57-60		
	1. Short stripe tender	(4)	**1000▲**
	2. Long stripe tender	(4)	**1200▲**

The General

1862	4-4-0 1862T Gray/red, no smoke, no MT, 59-62 headlight *Note: Red or black headlight housings are interchangeable. NDV*	(3)	**225▼**
1872	4-4-0 1872T Gray/red, smoke, MT, 59-62 headlight, oper. couplers	(3+)	**250**
1882	4-4-0 1882T Black/orange MT, sold by *Sears* U60 no smoke *Note: See Set Section as Generals usually are sold in sets.*	(4)	**500**

Hudsons

646	4-6-4 2046W, S, MT 54-58		
	1. Plastic side frames on stamped trailing trucks, larger *646* RS in silver	(3)	**195▼**
	2. Same as 2 but *646* HS in white	(3)	**185▼**
665	4-6-4, S, MT Plastic side frames on TT, 54-59,66 Same as 685 but with feedwater heater and lower marker lights. Both HS and RS cab number. NDV.		
	1. 6026W *Lionel Lines*	(3+)	**175▼**
	2. 2046W *Lionel Lines*	(3+)	**225**
	3. 736W *Pennsylvania* 66	(3)	**200**
685	4-6-4 6026W Smoke, Magnetraction 53		
	1. *685* RS in silver below cab window	(4)	**200▼**
	2. *685* HS in white below cab window	(3)	**200▼**
773	4-6-4 50, S, MT 64-66		
	1. 1950/2426W tender, has slide valve guide, silver RS *773* on cab/white, HS *Lionel Line*s lettering on tender	(4)	**1400▲**
	2. 1964/736W tender, no slide valve guide/larger, thicker *773* RS in white on cab/HS *Pennsylvania* on tender	(4)	**1000**
	3. 1965,66, same as 65 version but with *New York Central* in SanSerif type on 773W tender	(4)	**1000**
	4. Same as 3 version but with *New York Central* in Serif type on 773W tender	(4)	**1050**

2046	4-6-4 2046W 50,53		
	1. Early 1950, *2046* RS in silver/metal TT	(3+)	**180▼**
	2. Later 1950, *2046* HS in white/metal TT	(3+)	**180▼**
	3. 1953/2046 HS in white/plastic TT	(3)	**175▼**
2055	4-6-4 2046W, 6026W, S, MT 53-56		
	1. 1953, *2055* RS in silver/6026W	(3)	**160▼**
	2. 1954-56, *2055* HS in white/2046W	(2)	**150**
2055	4-6-4 6026W Blue Boy's Train (Locomotive only)		*
2056	4-6-4 2046W S 52	(3)	**200▼**
	(*Lionel Lines* in larger lettering than 50-51 2046W)		
2065	4-6-4 2046W,6026W, S, MT 54-56		
	1. 1954, *2065* RS in silver, 2046W	(3+)	**185▼**
	2. 1955,56, *2065* HS in white, 6026W	(2)	**175▼**

2-6-2 & 2-6-4

Type (Prairie, K-4 or Streamlined) listed in entry.

221	2-6-4 221W,221T *New York Central* 46,47 Streamlined		
	1. Gray/aluminum-painted wheels/46	(5)	**300▼**
	2. Gray/black wheels/46	(3)	**175▼**
	3. Black/black drivers with nickel rims	(3)	**175▼**
224	2-6-2 Prairie, 2466W,2466T 45,46		
	1. Black handrails, 1945	(4)	**125▼**
	2. Stainless handrails, 1946	(3)	**100▼**
637	2-6-4 Prairie, 2046W MT, 2037 boiler casting 59-63 HS or RS numbers. NDV	(3+)	**125▼**
675	2-6-2 K-4 *Lionel Lines* 47-49		
	1. Early 47, *675* HS on boiler front, 2466WX, 2466T, Baldwin disc drivers,	(4)	**200▼**
	2. Late 47, red decal *5690* on boiler front RS on cab, 2466WX, 2466T	(3)	**150▼**
	3. 48, 2466WX/2466T	(3)	**125▼**
	4. 49, 6466WX	(3)	**125▼**
675	2-6-4 K-4, 2046W Sintered iron spoked drivers, 52 5690 decal	(3+)	**150▼**
1666	2-6-2 Prairie, 2466WX,2466T Number plates, 46 Nickel-rimmed drivers	(2+)	**90▼**
1666	2-6-2 Prairie, 2466WX, RS number U47	(3+)	**90▼**
2016	2-6-4 Prairie, 6026W no MT or smoke, 55,56 Same as 2037, HS or RS numbers. NDV	(3)	**125▼**
2018	2-6-4 Prairie, 6026W,6026T,1130T smoke, 56-59 no MT	(2)	**100▼**
2018	2-6-4 Prairie, 6026W Blue Boy's Train		**5P**
2025	2-6-2 K-4, 2466WX,6466WX, 47-49 Die-cast trailing truck, Baldwin disc drivers		
	1. Early 47, 2025 HS on boiler front, 2466WX	(3)	**150▼**
	2. Late 47, red *5690* decal, 2466WX 2025 RS on cab	(2)	**100▼**
	3. 48,49 6466WX	(2)	**100▼**
2025	2-6-4 K-4, 6466WX No MT, Spoked drivers, 52 5690 or 6200 on red decal	(2)	**90▼**
2026	2-6-2 Prairie, 6466WX Wire handrails, smoke 48,49		
	1. Visible smoke-unit wire, 1948	(3)	**110▼**
	2. Hidden smoke-unit wire, 1949	(3)	**110▼**
2026	2-6-4 Prairie, 6466W,6466T,6066T, 51-53 Cast handrails, smoke, no MT	(2)	**100▼**
2026X	2-6-2 K-4, 6466T Same as 2025 but no smoke U49	(5)	**350▼**
2029	2-6-4 Prairie, 1060T,243W 64-66	(2)	**150**
2029	2-6-4 Prairie, 243W *PRR* markings 68,69	(4)	**175▼**
2035	2-6-4 K-4, 6466W MT, Spoked drivers, 50,51 stamped four-wheel trailing truck	(3)	**125▼**
2036	2-6-4 Prairie, 6466W Magnetraction, no smoke 50	(2)	**125**

2037	2-6-4 Prairie, 6066T,6026T 53-64 6026W,243W 57-63		
	1. HS	(2)	**115**
	2. RS	(2)	**135**
2037-500	2-6-4 Prairie, 1130T-500 Pink Girl's Loco, 57,58 Either RS or HS numbers. NDV	(4+)	**800**

Scout and Scout Type

233	243W, 233W, S, HL, MT 61,62	(3)	**125**
234	Not known to exist but 234W does exist		
235	1130T, S, HL, MT U61	(4)	**175**
236	1130T, 1050T, S, HL, MT 61,62	(3)	**75**
237	1130T, S, HL 63-66		
	1. Narrow white stripe	(3)	**85**
	2. Thick white stripe	(4)	**85**
238	243W, 63,64	(3)	**100**
239	243W, 242T HS and RS numbers, 65,66 RS rarer but NDV	(2)	**100**
240	242T, 2P, S,HL, RT *Sears* 9820 U64	(4)	**275**
241	1130T Diecast, S, 1 RT *JC Penney* U65		
	1. Thick white stripe	(4)	**125**
	2. Narrow white stripe	(2)	**125**
242	1130T, 1062T, 1060T 62-66		
	1. Thin-sided walkway	(2)	**50**
	2. Thick-sided walkway	(2)	**50**
243	243W, HL, RT 60	(3)	**100**
244	244T, 1130T, S, HL 60,61	(2)	**60**
245	1130T Timken trucks, 2P U59	(4)	**225**
246	1130T, 244T, HL, MT 59-61,A62	(1)	**60**
247	247T, S, No MT Blue stripe *B&O* A60,A61 Also came with uncataloged whistle tender	(3)	**100**
248	1130T U58	(4)	**150**
249	250T Red stripe/*Pennsylvania* liquid smoke unit 58	(4)	**75**
250	250T Red stripe/*Pennsylvania* 57	(3)	**80**
251	1130T, 244T slope back, U66	(4+)	**400**
1001	1001T Only plastic Scout locomotive 48 Some diecast 1101s show up rubber-stamped *1001*		
	1. White HS *1001* on cab	(3)	**60**
	2. Silver RS *1001* on cab	(4)	**100**
	3. Diecast 1101 RS *1001*	(4)	**200**
1050	0-4-0 1050T U59	(4+)	**275**
1060	1060T A60,A61	(3)	**35**
1061	1061T, 1062T A63,A64,69		
	1. 0-4-0/no tire on drive wheel/1061T	(2)	**35**
	2. 0-4-0/1062-50/1061T, tire on drive wheel	(2)	**35**
	3. 2-4-2/tire on drive wheel/1062T	(4)	**35**
	4. 2-4-2/tire on drive wheel/ number printed on paper and glued to cab, one geared drive wheel instead of two	(4)	**110**
1062	1061T, 1062T 63,64		
	1. No tire on drive wheel/1061T	(2)	**35**
	2. Tire on drive wheel (1062-50)/1062T	(3)	**40**
1101	1001T Scout, diecast, 3P U48		
	1. Heat-stamped 1101	(2)	**60**
	2. RS 1001	(4+)	**200**
1110	1001T Scout, diecast 49,51,52		
	1. Wire handrails	(3)	**50**
	2. No wire handrails	(2)	**35**
	3. Same with hole in boiler front over light, silver reverse lever	(3)	**60**

1120	1001T Scout 50	(2)	**50**
1130	1130T, 6066T 53,54		
	1. Plastic boiler/3P/1130T or 6066T	(2)	**60**
	2. Die-cast boiler/3P/6066T	(4)	**300**
1654	1654T, 1654W, Diecast, 3P 46,47	(3)	**60**
1655	6654W, Diecast, 3P 48,49	(3)	**70**
2034	6066T,3P 52	(3)	**60**
6110	6001T, Diecast, 2P, MT, Smoke, no light 50	(3)	**40**

Switchers

1615	0-4-0 1615T No bell, back-up light, or handrails 55-57		
	1. Silver RS numbers, early 1955	(3+)	**200▼**
	2. White HS numbers, later 1955-57	(2)	**175**
1625	0-4-0 1625T dummy front coupler 58 No bell, back-up light, or handrails	(4)	**325***
1656	0-4-0 6403B Tender has handrails, back-up 48,49 light, and bell. Some come misnumbered 6043B.		
	1. Sans-serif numerals on cab & *Lionel Lines* lettering on tender condensed	(4)	**300▼**
	2. Serif numerals on cab and lettering on tender elongated	(4)	**350**
1665	0-4-0 2403B Similar to prewar 1662. Usually 46 found with red and green marker lights broken. Tender has handrails, back-up light, and bell. Number rubber-stamped in silver on cab/elongated heat-stamped lettering on tender	(5)	**550***

Turbines

671	6-8-6 671W 46-49		
	1. Dbl worm drive, horz motor, 671W 46	(3)	**200▼**
	2. Sgl worm drive, slanted motor 671W 47	(3)	**225▼**
	3. 2671W with back-up lights early 48	(5)	**450**
	4. 2671W no back-up lights later 48 and 49	(2)	**225▼**
671(671RR)	6-8-6 2046W-50 No Magnetraction S 52 This version came with or without RR (re-run) printed below 671. NDV	(4)	**275▼**
671R	6-8-6 4671W Engine and tender only. 46-48 White on black electronic control decals. 671R on box only. *Electronic Control Set*	(4)	**250**
681	6-8-6 50,51,53		
	1. 2671W, 12-wheel tender 50, 51	(3)	**275**
	2. 2046-50, 8-wheel tender 53	(3)	**250**
682	6-8-6 2046W-50 White stripe and oiler linkage 54,55	(4)	**425**
2020	6-8-6 2020W, 2466WX 027 gauge version 46 of 671 Double worm drive/horizontal motor	(3)	**225**
2020	6-8-6 2020W,6020W Single worm drive 47-49 and slanted motor	(3)	**200**
4681	6-8-6 4681W 50		**Not known to exist**

Passenger Cars

The General Cars

1865	**Western & Atlantic** Yellow/brown 59-62	(2)	**50**
1866	**Western & Atlantic** Yellow/brown 59-62	(2)	**50**
1875	**Western & Atlantic** Yellow/Tuscan 59,60	(4+)	**350**
1875W	**Western & Atlantic** Yellow/Tuscan, whistle 59-62	(4)	**200**
1876	**Western & Atlantic** Yellow/brown 59-62	(2)	**95**
1885	**Western & Atlantic** *Sears,* Blue/black/white U60	(4)	**325**

Sheet-Metal Cars

Note: Sets consist of 2 Pullmans and 1 Observation. Cars came with both silver and white lettering. Silver is rarer. Prices are for white lettering. Add 20% if silver lettering.

2430	Pullman Blue/silver 46,47	(3)	**85▼**
2431	Observation Blue/silver 46,47	(3)	**85▼**
2440	Pullman Green/cream 46,47	(3)	**70▼**
2441	Observation Green/cream 46,47	(3)	**70▼**
2442	Pullman Brown/gray 46-48	(3)	**80▼**
2443	Observation Brown/gray 46-48	(3)	**80▼**
6440	Pullman Green/cream 48,49	(3)	**70▼**
6441	Observation Green/cream 48,49	(3)	**70▼**
6442	Pullman Brown/gray 49	(3)	**80▼**
6443	Observation Brown/gray 49	(3)	**80▼**

Streamline Passenger Cars (Small)

Green/yellow 48,49			
2400	**Maplewood** Pullman	(4)	**100▼**
2401	**Hillside** Observation	(4)	**100▼**
2402	**Chatham** Pullman	(4)	**100▼**
Aluminum/blue (no lights) 64,65			
2404	**Santa Fe** Vista Dome	(3)	**75**
2405	**Santa Fe** Pullman	(3)	**75**
2406	**Santa Fe** Observation	(3)	**65**
Aluminum/blue 66			
2408	**Santa Fe** Vista Dome	(3)	**85**
2409	**Santa Fe** Pullman	(3)	**85**
2410	**Santa Fe** Observation	(3)	**85**
Aluminum/blue/blue stripe 59-63			
2412	**Santa Fe** Vista Dome	(3)	**90**
2414	**Santa Fe** Pullman	(4)	**100**
2416	**Santa Fe** Observation	(3)	**90**
Aluminum/black 52,53			
2421	**Maplewood** Pullman	(3)	**100**
2422	**Chatham** Pullman	(3)	**100**
2423	**Hillside** Observation	(3)	**100**
2429	**Livingston** Pullman 52,53 only	(4)	**120**
Aluminum/black/black stripe gray roof 50,51			
2421	**Maplewood** Pullman	(4)	**100**
2422	**Chatham** Pullman	(4)	**100**
2423	**Hillside** Observation	(4)	**100**
Aluminum/red 54-58			
2432	**Clifton** Vista Dome	(3)	**90**
2434	**Newark** Pullman	(3)	**90**
2435	**Elizabeth** Pullman	(4)	**125**
2436	**Summit** Observation	(3)	**90**
2436	**Mooseheart** Observation 57,58 only	(4)	**100**
Aluminum/red/red stripe 56			
2442	**Clifton** Vista Dome	(4)	**125**
2444	**Newark** Pullman	(4)	**125**
2445	**Elizabeth** Pullman (sold separately) 56	(5)	**250▼**
	Elizabeth Pullman (with box) 56	(5)	**350**
2446	**Summit** Observation	(4)	**125**
Yellow/red 50			
2481	**Plainfield** Pullman	(5)	**300▼**
2482	**Westfield** Pullman	(5)	**300▼**
2483	**Livingston** Observation	(5)	**300▼**

Streamline Passenger Cars (Large)

Presidential 62-66

2521	**McKinley** Observation	(4)	**175**
2522	**Harrison** Vista Dome	(4)	**175**
2523	**Garfield** Pullman	(4)	**175**
2530	**Railway Express Agency** Baggage Car 54-60		
	1. Small doors	(3)	**200**
	2. Large doors	(5)	**700**

Super Speedliner 52-60

Note: Some plates have dots, others don't. Different wiring methods are used to connect the lights to the pick-up assemblies. These minor variations don't affect the price. Some plates are glued on, some are secured by rivets; others by hex nuts. If hex nuts add $50. per car. The other important variation has to do with the channel along the side of the car. Most are ribbed. A few are smooth. If smooth, add 20% to the prices listed.

2531	**Silver Dawn** Observation	(3)	**100▼**
2532	**Silver Range** Vista Dome	(3)	**100▼**
2533	**Silver Cloud** Pullman	(3)	**100▼**
2534	**Silver Bluff** Pullman	(4)	**125▼**

Congressional 55,56

2541	**Alexander Hamilton** Observation	(4)	**200▼**
2542	**Betsy Ross** Vista Dome	(4)	**200▼**
2543	**William Penn** Pullman	(4)	**200▼**
2544	**Molly Pitcher** Pullman	(4)	**200▼**

Canadian Pacific 57

2551	**Banff Park** Observation	(4)	**250▼**
2552	**Skyline 500** Vista Dome	(4)	**250▼**
2553	**Blair Manor** (separate sale only)	(5)	**400▼**
2554	**Craig Manor** (separate sale only)	(5)	**400▼**

Super Chief 59-61

2561	**Vista Valley** Observation	(4)	**225▼**
2562	**Regal Pass** Vista Dome	(4)	**225▼**
2563	**Indian Falls** Pullman	(4)	**225▼**

Irvington Cars 46-50

Note: Prices for cars with plain window inserts. Add $75 -$125 for Like New with all boxes and components, including inserts with people in silhouette but beware of reproductions. The original Irvington cars had heat-stamped lettering, and it has dulled with age. Reproductions have silk-screened lettering, which is bright, and the rivets around the area of the lettering have been removed to accommodate the silk screen. Watch for broken steps.

2625	**Irvington**	(4)	**225▼**
2625	**Manhattan** 47 only	(4+)	**250▼**
2625	**Madison** 47 only	(4+)	**250▼**
2627	**Madison**	(4)	**225▼**
2628	**Manhattan**	(4)	**225▼**

Rolling Stock

Action and Animated Cars

Note: See also Military and Space. Operating cars are in there normal sections.

3357	**Cop and Hobo Car** Also known as Hydraulic 62-64 Platform Maintenance Car. Comes with cop, hobo, and platform. First reissued in 1982 as 7901		
	1. Blue/white	(3)	**90**
	2. Aqua/white	(4)	**100▲**
	3. Prototype (Vol. 5)		**5P**
3370	**Sheriff and Outlaw** 61-64		
	1. Green/yellow	(3)	**75**
	2. Decal version (Vol. 5)		**5P**
	3. Arch-bar trucks/blue car/no lettering		**5P**
	4. Same but green car/no lettering		**5P**
3376	**Operating Giraffe Car** 60-64, 69		
	1. Blue car/white lettering	(2)	**60**
	2. Green car/yellow lettering	(3)	**125**
	3. Blue car/yellow lettering	(4)	**300**
	4. Blue car/no lettering	(3)	**175**
	5. Mock-up (Vol. 5)		**5+**
	6. Decal version mock-up		**5+**
	Note: Giraffe comes two ways: yellow with brown spots and solid yellow. NDV.		
3386	**Operating Giraffe Car** U66		
	1. Blue, white lettering	(3)	**75▼***
	2. Bongo and Bobo (Vol. 4)		**5P**
3424	**Wabash** Two tell-tale poles 56-58		
	1. Blue/white/blue man	(3)	**85▼**
	2. Same but white man	(4)	**100▼**
3434	**Operating Chicken Car** Brown/white 59,60 64-68 (Poultry Dispatch Car)		
	1. Blue sweeper man	(4)	**200**
	2. Gray sweeper man	(3)	**125**
3435	**Aquarium Car** Green 59-62 (reissued in 1981 as 9308)		
	1. Yellow lettering, no circle around L, no tank designation	(3)	**250**
	2. Same as 1 but gold lettering	(3+)	**275**
	3. Gold lettering, circle around L, *Tank No. 1* and *Tank No. 2*	(5)	**1200***
	4. Same as 3 but no circle around L	(5)	**800***
	5. White lettering		**FAKE**
3444	**Erie Animated Gondola** Red/white 57-59 (reissued in 1980 as 9307)	(2)	**75**
6473	**Horse Transport Rodeo Car** 62-66, 69 with red and brown lettering		
	1. Light yellow	(3)	**30**
	2. Dark yellow	(3)	**30**

Boxcars

638-2361	**Van Camps Pork & Beans** Scout-Type, U62,63 Bank slot		
	1. Light red/white-yellow	(4)	**35**
	2. Dark red/white-yellow	(3+)	**30**
1004	**Baby Ruth** Scout-Type Orange/blue 48,49,51,52		
	1. Blue outlined *Baby Ruth*	(1)	**10**
	2. Solid blue *Baby Ruth*	(1)	**10**
X2454	**Pennsylvania** 9 1/4", Orange/black, Early-Style 46		
	1. Orange door	(4+)	**225**
	2. Brown door	(3+)	**200**
X2454	**Baby Ruth** Orange/blk, brn door, Early-Style 46,47	(2+)	**45**
X2458	**Pennsylvania** Auto box Dark brown/white 45-48	(3+)	**75**

2758	**Pennsylvania** Auto box U45,46	(3)	**65**
	Note: Cataloged as 2458. Lionel had left-over 2758 bodies so they were fitted with a postwar frame and trucks and sold as a 2458.		
3428	**United States Mail** Type 3, Operating, 59,60,65,66	(3)	**100▼**
	Red/white/blue w/gray man or blue man. NDV		
3454	**PRR Merchandise Car** 46,47		
	Note: Baby Ruth on original cartons, not on reproductions.		
	1. Silver/blue	(3)	**150**
	2. Silver/red	(5)	**1000***
3464	**AT&SF** Early-Style Operating 49-52		
	1. Orange/black, brown painted door 1949 Information requested		
	2. Orange/black, blackened metal door 1949	(3)	**30**
	3. Unpainted orange plastic/black plastic doors	(4)	**50**
	4. *NYC* Tan/White	(5)	**900***
X3464	**New York Central** Early-Style Operating 50-52	(3)	**35**
3474	**Western Pacific** Silver/black Early-Style 52,53	(4)	**100▲**
	Operating		
3484	**Pennsylvania** Type 1 Tuscan/wht Operating 53,U54		
	1. Non-painted man 53	(2)	**70**
	2. Flesh tones painted on	(3)	**70**
3484-25	**AT&SF** Orange Operating 54,56		
	1. HS black/Type 1 2A 2B	(5)	**1200***
	2. RS white/Type 1	(3)	**125**
	3. HS white/Type 1 2A 2B	(4)	**150**
3494-1	**NYC Pacemaker** Type 2A Gray/red/white 55	(4)	**140**
	Operating		
3494-150	**Missouri Pacific** Type 2B Blue/gray/yell door 56	(4)	**140**
	Operating		
3494-275	**State of Maine** Type 2B Operating 56-58		
	1. Line above and below B.A.R. and 3494275	(3)	**150**
	2. No line above or below B.A.R. 56 only and 3494275 omitted	(4)	**200**
3494-550	**Monon** Type 2B Maroon/white Operating 57,58		
	1. Built Date	(4)	**375▼**
	2. No built date	(4+)	**450**
	3. With over stamp	(5)	**?***
3494-625	**Soo** Type 2B Tuscan/white Operating 57,58	(4)	**550**
3854	**Pennsylvania Merchandise Car** 11" long 46,47		
	Dark brown/white		
	1. Brown door 46 only	(4+)	**650**
	2. Black door 46,47	(4)	**550**
4454	**Baby Ruth** Orange/black, Early-Style 46-48	(4)	**225**
	brown-painted doors, *Electronic Set*		
	Note: Black doors questionable		
6004	**Baby Ruth** Orange/blue Scout-Type 50	(3)	**10**
	Blue outlined only		
6014	**Airex** Red/yellow-white Scout-Type SM59, A60		
	1. Regular style lettering	(3)	**50**
	2. Bold style lettering	(4)	**70**
X6014	**Baby Ruth** *PRR* Scout-Type 51,52,54-56		
	1. White/black 51,52	(2)	**10**
	2. Red/white 54-56	(2)	**10**
6014	**Bosco** Scout-Type 58		
	1. White/black	(4)	**45▼**
	2. Red/white	(2)	**10**
	3. Orange/black	(3)	**10**
6014	**Campbell Soup** Red/white Scout-Type U69		*
6014	**Chun King** Red/white Scout-Type U56	(4)	**150**
6014	**Frisco** White/black 57,58		
	1. White/black	(1)	**10**
	2. Red/white	(2)	**10**
	3. Orange/black	(4)	**40**

6014	**Wix** White/red Scout-Type U59	(4)	**200**
6014-85	**Frisco** Scout-Type 69		
	1. Orange/bright blue	(2)	**20**
	2. Orange/dark blue	(2)	**20**
	3. In Hagerstown box	(4)	**50**
6014-335	**Frisco** White/black Scout-Type 63-66,68		
	1.With coin slot	(4)	**100▼**
	2.Without coin slot	(1)	**15**
6024	**Nabisco Shredded Wheat** Scout-Type 57 Orange/black		
	1. No bank slot	(2)	**25**
	2. Bank slot		**5P**
	3. Orange/brn, no bank slot	(4)	**70**
6024-60	**RCA Whirlpool** Red/wht Scout-Type U57,58	(4)	**75**
6034	**Baby Ruth** *PRR* Scout-Type 53,54		
	1. Orange/dark blue	(2)	**10**
	2. Orange/blue	(1)	**10**
6044	**Airex** Scout-Type U A59,A60		
	1. Blue/yellow-white	(1)	**25**
	2. Dark blue/yellow-white	(5)	**300**
	3. Teal blue	(4)	**125**
6044-1X	Scout-Type Blue Plastic/No lettering, McCall/Nestle's *decal* *Note: Reproduction decals available*	(5)	**825***
6050	**Libby's Tomato Juice** Scout-Type 63,63		
	1. With green stems	(2)	**35**
	2. Without green stems	(4)	**200**
	3. Without white lines between tomatoes	(3)	**90**
6050	**Lionel Savings Bank** White/green Scout-Type 61		
	1. *Built by Lionel* spelled out	(4)	**100**
	2. *Blt by Lionel*	(3)	**35**
6050	**Swift** Red/white Scout-Type 62,63		
	1. Bank slot	(2)	**25**
	2. No bank slot		**5X**
	3. Minus two rows of rivets left of door	(3)	**30**
6352-1	**Pacific Fruit Express** Type 2B Operating 55-57		
	1. Lettering with *CU. FT.*	(3)	**100**
	2. No *CU. FT.*	(4)	**150**
	3. As replacement accessory (must have box), came with 352 Ice Depot and 5 cubes of ice. Original cubes have bubbles, reproductions don't.	(5)	**2000▼***
6428	**US Mail** Red-white-blue/HS black-white 60,61,65,66		
	1. Lettering on both sides	(3)	**50**
	2. Lettering on one side	(4)	**60**
6454	**Baby Ruth** Early-Style 48 Dark orange/black/brown doors	(4+)	**240**
6454	**New York Central** Early-Style 48,49		
	1. Brown/white/brown door	(2)	**60**
	2. Bright orange/black, brown door	(4)	**150**
	3. Burnt orange/white, brown door	(2)	**60**
6454	**Santa Fe** Orange/blk, brn doors Early-Style U48,49	(2)	**50**
6454	**Southern Pacific** Early-Style 50,51 Also made in 49,52 and 53 but not cataloged		
	1. Brown/white/large circular herald with 1/16" break in outside circle between *R* and *N* 1949	(4)	**65**
	2. Same with small herald 1950 no break in outside circle	(3)	**45**
	3. Reddish brown/white/small herald/no break 51-52	(3)	**45**
X6454	**Erie** Brown/white, brn doors Early-Style U49,50-53	(3)	**55**
X6454	**Pennsylvania** Tuscan/white Early-Style U49-53		
	1. Tuscan doors	(4)	**75**
	2. Black plastic doors	(4+)	**100**

6464 Boxcars

The 6464 boxcars are the most popular category of Lionel's postwar rolling stock. Their splashy graphics make them some of the best-looking cars Lionel ever made in the postwar era. There are so many variations – both major and minor – that they present an endless challenge to collectors. The category also contains some of the rarest and most valuable items of the postwar era.

To understand the variations, the collector must be familiar with the different body and door types that were used. The identification and labeling of the different body types, which has become the accepted standard of the hobby, was first published by Charles Weber of Norristown, Pennsylvania.

Doors used in 1953, 1954, and early 1955 had a single, large block in the middle. Those used in 1955 through 1969 had three additional blocks. The first door is called the 1953 single block (SB) door and the second is called the 1955 multiple block (MB) door.

Body Type 1, SB Door

In 1953, the first body type had four rows of rivets to the left of the door (rows 1 through 4) and four rows of rivets to the right of the door (rows 5 through 8). The rows to the right of the door were not interrupted but three of the rows to the left of the door were interrupted by smooth areas. The rivets were removed because they interfered with the heat-stamping process used in applying graphics. Row 4 was the only row on the left side that was not interrupted.

The Type 1 body type comes with the SB door only.

Body Type 2A, SB Door

In 1954, the increase in the size of graphics necessitated more changes in the rivet detail. The middle portion of row 2 and all of row 7 were removed.

Most Type 2As come with the SB door but some 2As were still being used in 1955 after the MB door was introduced so Type 2A exists with both SB and MB doors. The most common examples of Type 2A with MB doors are the 6464-125 NYC, 6464-150 Missouri Pacific and the 6464-275 State of Maine.

Body Type 2B, MB Door

In 1955, the only change on the body had to do with the roof. The Pacific Fruit Express car was introduced and it used the same mold as the 6464 boxcars. To make the PFE, Lionel altered the die to make an opening for the ice hatch. When the die was used again to make 6464 boxcars, a plug was inserted in the die to cover the opening but a thin plastic ridge was discernible on the roof. This third body type is called 2B.

It was a transition year for doors. Lionel started using the multiple-block doors about mid-way through the year. So Type 2B exists with both MB and SB doors.

Body Type 3, MB Door

A new mold was introduced in 1958. The result was a boxcar made of lighter weight plastic with ribs on the underside of the roof. The thin line from the ice hatch was gone and the rivet detail changed slightly, for no apparent reason. The change had to do with row 7. Two rivets were added to the top and two rivets were added to the bottom.

Body Type 4

In 1960, the number of rivets changed in row 3. They were almost all removed.

As with other categories, we recommend the collector concern himself with only major variations, i.e. those that can be readily seen on the exterior of the car and those generally accepted by the majority of experienced collectors.

6464-1	**Western Pacific** Type 1 53,54		
	1. Silver/blue	(3)	**100**
	2. Silver/blue inside roof ribs	(4+)	**350**
	3. Silver/red	(5)	**1500▼***
	4. Silver/black		**5P**
	5. Orange/white		**5P**
	6. Orange/silver		**5P**
	7. Powder blue/black		**5P**
	8. Dark blue/white		**5P**
	9. Orange/black		**5P**
	10. Silver/light blue feather RS both sides		*
6464-25	**Great Northern** Type 1 53,54		
	1. Orange/white	(2)	**95**
	2. Tuscan/white		**5P**
	3. Same, red/green decals	(5)	**600***
	To be legitimate, decal must be applied over smooth surface. If traces of heat-stamping can be detected under decal, it was applied outside the Lionel factory.		

6464-50 Minneapolis & St. Louis Type 1 53-56

1. Tuscan/white (2) **80**
2. Dark green/gold **5P**
3. Tuscan/yellow **5P**
4. Light bluish green/black **5P**
5. Copper primer/Tuscan and white (5) **500***

6464-75 Rock Island Dark green/gold 53,54,69

1. Type 1 53,54 (3) **95**
2. Type 4 69 (2) **95**

6464-100 Western Pacific 54,55

1. Orange/white/blue feather *1954* Type 1 (5+) **6000***
2. Same but no *1954* Type 1 (5) **2000***
3. Silver/black/yellow feather Type 1 54 (4) **175**
4. Silver/black/yellow feather Type 2A 54,55 (3) **135**
   Long feather or short feather NDV
5. Orange/white or gray/blue feather Type 2A 54,55 (4) **800***

6464-125 New York Central 54-56

1. Gray-red/HS white, gray top row of rivets, 54 (4) **140**
   SB no cedilia Type 2A
2. Gray-red/RS white red top row of rivets, 55,56 (3) **115**
   SB, cedilia, Type 2A
3. Same as 2 but no cedilia (4) **175**
4. Same as 2 but MB (3) **100**
5. Lilac/red Type 2B **5X**
6. Pink/red Type 2B **5X**

6464-150 Missouri Pacific 54,55,57

Note: The 6464-150 has more variations than any other boxcar. The seven listed below represent a reasonable number to collect. The number is limited to keep the collector (and the authors) from going crazy. The variations listed are in chronological order. Many more variations – all worth about $150 – were made by Lionel by interchanging the various kinds of doors, using grooves, not using grooves, changing the sizes of the Eagle and using different shades of blue paint and plastic.

1. Blue-gray/RS black, gray stripe on SB door, no *XME*, 3/4-inch *Eagle* and *New 3-54* to right, 6464-150 to left, no grooves, no *Built by Lionel,* blue plastic/painted gray stripe, Type 2A, early 54 first run (3) **130**
2. *New 3/54* moves to the left, *BLT by Lionel* and *XME* are added to the right, late 54 second run (3) **150**
3. White shell painted blue-gray, grooves, 5/8-inch *Eagle, BLT by Lionel* and *XME* to right, *BLT 3/54* and *6464-150* to left, gray stripe on SB door, early 55 (4) **275**
4. Same as 3 but blue plastic shell early 55 (3) **125**
5. Blue-gray, RS black solid yellow SB door, *XME,* 5/8 inch *Eagle* to right, *New 3-54* and *6464-150* to left, grooves, *Built by Lionel,* MP seal in first panel to left of door, blue plastic, painted gray stripe, Type 2A, 55 (5) **1800***
6. Same as 4 but white plastic SB door painted yellow, last run 1955 (4) **150**
7. Blue-gray, RS black/solid yellow MB door, *XME,* (2)

125

1/2 inch *Eagle* and *New 3-54* to left, *6464-150* to right, no grooves, *Built by Lionel,* gray plastic painted blue, Type 2B, 57

6464-175 Rock Island 54,55

1. Silver/blue (3) **130**
2. Silver/black (5) **1500***

6464-200 Pennsylvania Tuscan/white 54,55,69

1. Type 1 (4) **160**
2. Type 2A (4) **160**
3. Type 4 (3) **125**

6464-225	**Southern Pacific** Black/white 54-56		
	1. Red/yellow herald Type 2A	(3+)	**160**
	2. Red/yellow herald Type 1	(5)	**1350***
	3. White herald Type 2A	(5)	**1800***
6464-250	**Western Pacific** Orange/white 66		
	1. Type 4	(4)	**300**
	2. Type 3	(5)	**1000**
6464-275	**State of Maine** 55,57-59		
	Note: 2A is HS, 2B both HS and RS. NDV		
	1. Red-white-blue/white-black Type 2A, 2B	(3)	**100**
	2. White body, painted red and blue stripes, solid red door Type 2A	(4)	**250**
	3. Red-white-blue, no 6464-275, same shell used on 3494-275 Type 2B	(4+)	**250**
	4. Red-white-blue Type 3	(3)	**100**
6464-300	**Rutland** 55,56		
	Note: Fakes have devalued #5 and #6		
	1. Green-yellow/RS green-yellow, yellow plastic door Type 2A	(3)	**175**
	2. Same, white plastic door painted yellow	(3)	**175**
	3. Irregular spacing HS MB Type 2B 56	(4)	**175**
	4. Gray body painted green/yellow	(4)	*****
	5. Yellow body and door models, RS yellow-green, yellow and green SB door, Type 2A	(5)	**1000***
	6. Yellow body painted glossy green solid yellow plastic SB door, solid shield herald, Type 2A	(5)	**2500***
6464-325	**Sentinel** Type 2B 56		
	1. Normal production	(4)	**700**
	2. Decaled one side only		**5P**
6464-350	**Katy** Type 2B 56		
	1. Maroon/white	(4)	**300**
	2. Pink/black		**5X**
6464-375	**Central of Georgia** 56,57,66		
	Note: Types 2B and 4 come with both maroon and red lettering. NDV		
	1. Maroon plastic, painted silver oval & roof, red-white lettering 3-56 built date Type 2B 56,57	(3)	**125**
	2. No built date Type 4, 66	(2)	**125**
	3. Gray plastic painted red, painted silver oval and roof, red/white lettering, 3-56 built date Type 4, 66	(5)	**2500***
	4. Red decal lettering, silver oval Type 2B		**5P**
6464-400	**B&O Time-Saver** 56,57,69		
	1. Blue-silver-orange/blue-wht, Built 5-54 Type 2B	(3+)	**150**
	2. Same, built 2-56 Type 2B	(4)	**175**
	3. Two different built dates: 5-54 on one side and 2-56 on the other Type 2B	(5)	**1500▼***
	4. Blue-silver-orange/blue-white Type 4	(3)	**125**
	5. *B&O* markings Timken colors Type 4	(5)	**1200***
	6. Solid green/white Type 4	(5)	**1200*▲**
6464-425	**New Haven** Black/white56-58		
	1. Half-serif N Type 2B 56,57	(3)	**120**
	2. Full-serif N Type 2B 57,58	(3)	**75**
	3. Type 3, 58	(2)	**50**
6464-450	**Great Northern** Olive-orange/yell stripe 56,57,66		
	1. Type 2B	(3+)	**125**
	2. Type 3	(5)	**1500***
	3. Type 4	(3)	**125**
	4. White lettering, white stripe Type 4		**FAKE**
	5. White lettering, yellow stripe Type 4		**FAKE**
6464-475	**Boston & Maine** 57-60,65,66,68		
	Note: This car comes in many different shades of blue w/ and w/o built dates (harder to find). NDV		
	1. Blue/black-white Type 2B	(2)	**75**
	2. Same but Type 3,4	(3)	**150**
	3. Purplish/black-white, gray mold, 66	(4)	**300▼**
	4. Same as 3 but blue mold	(4)	**325▼**

No.	Description	Rarity	Price
6464-500	**Timken** 57,58,69		
	1. Yellow/blue-gray Type 2B	(3+)	**150**
	2. Decal markings Type 2B		**5P**
	3. Yellow/black Type 4	(4)	**150**
	4. Same as 3 but Type 3	(4)	**200**
	5. Yellow/red Type 4		**5X**
	6. Green/white Type 4		**5X**
	7. Green/red Type 4		**5X**
	8. Green/gold Type 4		**5X**
	9. Beige/black Type 3	(4+)	**340**
6464-510	**NYC Pacemaker** Girl's Train, Type 2B 57,58		
	1. Bluish green/black	(4)	**1100▲**
	2. Sky blue/black	(5)	**1100***
	3. Yellow/black		**5X**
6464-515	**Katy** Girl's Train, Type 2B 57,58		
	1. Yellow/black	(4)	**1100▲**
	2. White/black	(5+)	
	3. Beige/black		**5P**
	4. Blue/black		**5X**
6464-525	**Minneapolis & St. Louis** 57,58,54-66		
	1. Red/white Type 2B Gray mold	(2)	**75**
	2. Red/white Type 2B Black mold	(2)	**150**
	3. Red/white Type 3	(3)	**125**
	4. Red/white Type 4	(2)	**75**
	5. Red/yellow Type 2B		**5X**
	6. Red/yellow Type 4		**5X**
	7. Bright-pink purple/white Type 4		**5X**
	8. Raspberry-gray/white Type 4		**5X**
6464-650	**Rio Grande** Yellow-silver 57,58,66		
	Note: The rare painted yellow-roof version is on a gray Type 4 body mold. Type 2s with a yellow roof (unpainted) are created by removing the silver paint.		
	1. Black/roof painted silver/built date/Type 2B	(3)	**160**
	2. No built date Type 4	(3)	**160**
	3. Yellow-painted roof, built date Type 4	(5)	**2200▲**
6464-700	**Santa Fe** Red/white 61,66		
	1. Type 4	(3)	**175**
	2. Type 3	(5)	**2200▲***
6464-725	**New Haven** 62-66,68,69		
	1. Orange/black Type 4 62-66, 68	(2)	**125**
	2. Black/white Type 4 69	(4)	**250**
6464-825	**Alaska** 59,60		
	Note: Types 3 and 4 came in both blue and gray body molds. NDV		
	1. Blue/yellow, yellow stripe, Type 3,4	(4)	**500**
	2. Blue/yellow, yellow stripe, yellow door Type 4	(5)	**400***
	3. Blue/white, white stripe, Type 3,4		**FAKE**
	4. Blue/white, yellow stripe, Type 3,4		**FAKE**
	5. Blue/white, white stripe, white door		**FAKE**
6464-900	**New York Central** 60-63,65,66		
	1. Jade green/black-red-white Type 4	(3)	**150**
	2. Same as #1 but w/black doors	(3)	**200**
	3. Same as #1 but Type 3	(5)	**1200***
	4. No red lettering or black trim, *NYC* Type 4		**5X**
	5. No red lettering or white date Type 4		**5X**
	6. Yellow/black-red-white Type 4		**5X**
6468-1	**Baltimore & Ohio** Auto box Blue/white 53-55	(3)	**85**
6468X	**Baltimore & Ohio** Auto box Tuscan/white, 55 027 *Santa Fe* Freight Set	(4+)	**475**
6468-25	**New Haven** Auto box 56-58		
	1. Black N with full serif, H in white, black doors	(2)	**90**
	2. Same, darker orange and Tuscan doors	(3)	**100**
	3. Black N with half serif, H in white	(2)	**90**
	4. White N with half serif, H in black	(4)	**350***
6530	**Fire Safety Training Car** 60, 61		
	1. Red/white	(3)	**125▼**
	2. Black/white	(5)	**3000***

Cabooses

Bay Window

6517	**Lionel Lines** Red/white 55-59		
	1. *Lionel* underscored	(4)	**100**
	2. *Lionel* not underscored	(3)	**80**
6517-75	**Erie** Red/white 66	(5)	**350**
6517-1966	**Train Collectors Association** Orange/white U66	(4)	**275**

Early Cupola Type

2457	**Pennsylvania** Red/white 45-47		
	1. Tool box, generator, steps and 2 couplers, *Eastern Div.* lettering	(3)	**50**
	2. Same, no steps	(2)	**45**
	3. Brown/white left-over inventory from the prewar 2757 caboose.	(4)	**85**
2472	**Pennsylvania** Red/white, one coupler,45-47 sintered iron wheels		
	1. Late 1945 trucks *Eastern Div.* lettering	(2)	**35**
	2. Late 1945 trucks without *Eastern Div.* lettering	(3)	**35**
	3. 1947 trucks without *Eastern Div.* lettering	(1)	**35**
4457	**Pennsylvania** Red/white, *Electronic Set* 46,47	(4)	**145**

N5c Pennsy Type

6417	**Pennsylvania** Tuscan/white 53-57		
	1. *New York Zone*	(2)	**45**
	2. No *New York Zone*	(4)	**225**
6417-25	**Lionel Lines** Tuscan/white 54	(2)	**35**
6417-50	**Lehigh Valley** 54		
	1. Gray/red	(3)	**150**
	2. Tuscan/white	(5)	**1000▼***
6427	**Lionel Lines** Tuscan/white 54-60	(2+)	**45**
6427-60	**Virginian** 58		
	Note: Reproduction Virginian cabooses exist. Originals are heat-stamped with rivet detail. Reproductions are silk-screened with rivet detail removed.		
	1. Blue/yellow	(4)	**250**
	2. Dark blue/white		**FAKE**
6427-500	**Pennsylvania** Sky blue/white, *Girl's Train* 57,58	(4)	**450**
6437	**Pennsylvania** Tuscan/white 61-68	(3)	**40**
6447	**Pennsylvania** Tuscan/white 63	(5)	**400**

Southern-Pacific Type

1007	**Lionel Lines** Red/white 48-52	(1)	**10**
2257	**SP** No light, 1 coupler, brake wheels U47,48		
	1. Bright red/white	(2)	**40**
	2. Brown/white	(5)	**700▲**
2357	**SP** U47,48		
	Note: Though not in the 47 catalog, both the 2257 and 2357 were available in 1947.		
	1. Bright Red with red stack	(5)	**700▲***
	2. Brown with brown stack	(2)	**50**
	3. Dark Red no stack	(2)	**135***
4357	**SP** Brown/white Electronic Set 48	(4)	**200▲**
6007	**Lionel Lines** Red/white 50	(2)	**10**
	Note: 6007 and 6017 were the cheapest cabooses Lionel made other than Scout cabooses. Similar to the 6257 but without brakewheels. Usually unpainted plastic w/no trim.		

6017	**Lionel Lines** Common, inexpensive caboose 51-61 made in many colors and shades. Major colors:		
	1. Red/white metal trucks	(1)	**10**
	2. Tuscan/white metal trucks	(2)	**10**
	3. Tuscan/white Timken trucks	(1)	**10**
	4. Light Tuscan/white Timken trucks	(1)	**10**
	5. Brown/white Timken trucks	(1)	**10**
	6. Olive drab/U	(5)	**375**
6017-50	**US Marine Corps** Blue/white, 58 Box marked 6017-60	(3)	**70**
6017-85	**Lionel Lines** Gray/black	(3)	**50**
6017-100	**Boston & Maine** 59,62,65,66		
	1. Dark blue/white 59	(5)	*
	2. Blue/white (blue can be light to medium and flat or shiny)	(2)	**50**
6017-185	**AT&SF** Gray/red 59,60	(3)	**40**
6017-200	**US Navy** Blue/white 60	(4)	**125▲**
6017-225	**AT&SF** Red/white U60	(3)	**60**
6017-235	**AT&SF** Red/wht 6017-235 stamped on box only, 62	(4)	**60**
6027	**Alaska** Dark blue/yellow 59	(3)	**100**
6037	**Lionel Lines** 52-54		
	1. Brown/white	(1)	**10**
	2. Light brown/white	(1)	**10**
	3. Tuscan/white	(2)	**25**
	4. Red/white	(2)	**30**
6047	**Lionel Lines** 62		
	1. Various shades of red/wht	(1)	**10**
	2. Unpainted Tuscan plastic	(5)	**75**
6057	**Lionel Lines** 59-62		
	1. Red/white	(1)	**10**
	2. Brown/white	(3)	**100**
	3. Orange-red/white	(1)	**10**
6057-50	**Lionel Lines** Orange/black 62,69		
	1. Regular production	(3)	**30**
	2. TTOS 1969 convention 69	(3)	*
6058	**Chesapeake & Ohio** Yellow/black many 61 shades of yellow NDV		
	1. Painted black frame, rails	(3)	**60**
	2. Unpainted frame, no rails	(3)	**60**
6059	**Minneapolis & St. Louis** 61,62,65-67,69		
	1. Painted dark red plastic/white	(1)	**30**
	2. Unpainted red plastic/white	(1)	**15**
	3. Unpainted brown plastic/white	(1)	**10**
6059-50	**Minneapolis & St. Louis** 63,64		
	1. Painted dark red/white	(3)	**65**
	2. Unpainted red plastic/white	(2)	**25**
6067	Not known to exist. Parts list shows this car but number for body is 6257		
6157-125	No Lettering		
	1. Red	(1)	**10**
	2. Light red	(1)	**10**
	3. Brown	(1)	**10**
6167	**Lionel Lines** 63		
	1. Red/white	(1)	**10**
	2. Red/no lettering in Hagerstown box	(3)	**50**
6167-25	No Lettering Red 64	(1)	**10**
6167-50	No Lettering Yellow 63	(2)	**10**
6167-85	**Union Pacific** Yellow/black 64-69	(3)	**20**
6167-100	No Lettering Red 64	(1)	**10**
6167-125	No Lettering 64		
	1. Brown	(1)	**10**
	2. Red	(1)	**10**

6167-150	No Lettering Yellow	(1)	**20**
6257	**Southern Pacific** or **Lionel** markings 48-56 ***Note: Previously 2257. Very common. Made in many colors & variations***	(1)	**10**
6257X	Same as 6257 but with 2 couplers 48,49		
	1. Bright red/white	(4)	**30**
	2. Dull red/white, in 1425B set w/1656 switcher	(4)	**30**
6257-100	**Lionel Lines** 56-63	(1)	**10**
6357	**SP** or **Lionel** markings 1 coupler, light, 48-61 inserts, 2 brakewheels		
	1. SP Dull red/white, 2357 on side, 6357, RS on base	(5)	**25**
	2. Same, 6357 on side	(2)	**25**
	3. SP Bright red/white	(2)	**20**
	4. *Lionel* Maroon/white	(2)	**25**
6357-50	**AT&SF** Red/white Came in rare 2555W set, 60 called both the *Over and Under* and the *Father and Son* set.	(5)	**1500▲**
6457	**Lionel** (previously 2357) 2 couplers, 49-52 light, inserts, ladders, tool boxes, smokestack		
	1. Brown/white 49	(3)	**35**
	2. Semi-gloss brown/white 50	(3)	**40**
	3. Reddish brown/white 52	(4)	**45**
6557	**Lionel** Tuscan/white smoking caboose 58,59	(4)	**250**
6657	**Rio Grande** Yellow/silver/black 57,58 (not made w/smoke unit by Lionel)	(4)	**200**

Work Cabooses

Note: Cabs, tool boxes easily switched

2419	**DL&W** Light gray/black 46,47	(2)	**75**
2420	**DL&W** 46-48		
	1. Dark gray/black HS serif *Lionel Lines* ***Note: Variations exist having to do with style of lettering, couplers, frame color, and shade of gray. NDV***	(3)	**100**
	2. Black/RS sans-serif *Lionel Lines* factory repaint	(4)	**175**
6119	**DL&W** 55,56		
	1. Red cab and tray, white HS serif *Lionel,* black painted frame	(1)	**25**
	2. Same as 1 but gray tray	(2)	**35**
	3. Same as 1 but sans-serif *Lionel*	(2)	**35**
6119-25	**DL&W** Orange cab and tray, painted frame, 57 black HS *Lionel*		
	1. Glossy orange frame	(4)	**60**
	2. Flat orange frame	(2)	**50**
6119-50	**DL&W** Brown cab and tray, white HS *Lionel* 56 brown painted frame	(3)	**65**
6119-75	**DL&W** Gray cab and tray, black HS 57 sans-serif *Lionel* on glossy or flat gray painted frame	(3)	**40**
6119-100	**DL&W** White or gray lettering, serif 63-66 and sans-serif. NDV		
	1. Red cab, gray tray, white RS serif *Lionel* black painted frame	(1)	**25**
	2. Same but no *Lionel* on blue metal frame, *Built by Lionel* HS on cab	(4)	**35**
6119-125	No Lettering Information requested 60		
6120	No Lettering U61,62		
	1. Yellow cab and tray, black painted frame, no stack but hole for one	(1)	**25**
	2. Same but without hole for stack	(2)	**30**
6130	**AT&SF** 65-68		
	1. Painted red cab and tray, white RS serif, *Lionel* black painted frame	(1)	**25**
	2. Same but unpainted gray tray, blue frame	(5)	**50**
	3. Unpainted red cab and tray, gold metal frame	(3)	**200▼***

6219	**Chesapeake & Ohio** Blue/yellow 60	(4)	**70**
6419	**DL&W** 48-50 52-57		
	Note: Numerous minor variations. NDV		
	1. Painted gray cab, tool boxes and frame, black HS serif *Lionel*	(2)	**40**
	2. Same but black RS sans-serif *Lionel Lines* (factory repaint)	(5)	**45**
	3. Same as 1 but unpainted gray cab, tool boxes and frame	(2)	**40**
6419-25	**DL&W** Gray/black 55	(3)	**40**
6419-50	**DL&W** Gray/black 56,57	(3)	**50**
6419-75	**DL&W** Gray/black 56,57	(3)	**45**
6419-100	**Norfolk & Western 576419** on cab, 57,58 Unpainted gray plastic cab, molded tool boxes and frame, black HS serif *Lionel Lines*	(4)	**200▲**
6420	**DL&W** Dark gray/black, searchlight 49,50	(4)	**135**
6429	**DL&W** Gray/black 63	(4)	**325**
6814	**First Aid Medical Car** White/red, man, 59-61 2 stretchers, oxygen tank unit		
	1. Black RS serif *Lionel,*/gray frame	(3)	**120**
6824-50	2. White HS serif *Lionel,* black frame, no tray U64 insert, no man, stretchers or oxygen unit/*Sears*	(4)	**275**
6824	**USMC First Aid Medical Car** 60		
	1. Olive drab and gray tray, white RS *USMC*, olive drab painted frame, tray insert, white HS 6824 on tray. Came in *Land, Sea, and Air Gift Pack 1805*	(4)	**170**
6119-125	2. Same except white RS serif *Lionel* on black painted frame, no tray insert, no "6824"on tray. Came in *19334 JC Penney* set	(4)	**250**

Coal Dump Cars

3359-55	**Lionel Lines Twin Dump** Black/red frame 55-58 two gray bins	(3+)	**50**
3459	**Lionel Lines** 46-48		
	1. Black/white	(2)	**45**
	2. Unpainted aluminum bin, blue lettering	(4)	**400**
	3. Same but blank on one side/FM	(4)	**350***
	4. Painted green bin, white lettering	(3)	**100**
	5. Painted yellow, black lettering	(5)	**8000***
	6. Red/white	(5)	*
3469	**Lionel Lines** Black/white 49-55	(2)	**40**
3559	**Coal Dump** Black/red 46-48	(2)	**45**
5459	**Electronic Set** Black/white/decal 46-48	(4)	**275▲**

Crane Cars

2460	**Bucyrus Erie** 6-wheel trucks 46-50		
	1. Glossy gray cab/black lettering 46	(4)	**375**
	2. Black cab/white lettering 46-50	(3)	**95**
2560	**Lionel Lines** 46,47		
	1. Green, brown or black Bakelite boom 46	(2)	**125**
	2. Black plastic boom 47	(2)	**125**
4460	**Bucyrus Erie** 6-wheel trucks 50		**NM**
6460	**Bucyrus Erie** 52-54		
	1. Black cab/white lettering 52-54	(2)	**60**
	2. Red cab/white lettering (6460-25 on box) 54	(4)	**125**

6560	**Bucyrus Erie** 55-64,66,68,69		
	1. Gray cab/black lettering Lionel used a screw to attach the trucks(not a horseshoe clip) on the first run. A number of different frames and cabs were used on these early versions. They were molded plastic in either:	(2)	**75**
	a. orange/red	(4)	**175**
	b. black	(5)	**175**
	Note: A few had no printing at all on the frames or printing without the 6560 number		
	2. Red cab/white lettering	(1)	**45**
	a. In Hagerstown Box	(3)	**95**
6560-25	**Bucyrus Erie** Red/white 56	(3)	**55**

Depressed Center Flatcars

2461	**Transformer Car** 47-48		
	1. Lt gray/black/red transformer/2462 RS on frame	(3)	**125▼**
	2. Same but no lettering *2461* RS on bottom	(4)	**150▼**
	3. Same as 1 but black transformer	(3)	**85**
6418	**Girder Bridge Car** Gray Four 4-wheel trucks 55-57 O gauge only. Will not negotiate 027 switches		
	1. Orange girders/*Lionel* in raised letters	(3)	**90▼**
	2. Pinkish-orange girders/black *US Steel*	(2)	**90▼**
	3. Black girders/raised lettering *US Steel*	(3)	**90▼**
6461	**Transformer Car** Gray/black Insulators usually 49 broken. Originals are brittle and yellowed with age, Repros are flexible. Applies to 2461 also	(3)	**100**
6518	**Transformer Car** Gray/white, black trans.56-58 former, four 4-wheel trucks, O gauge only. Will not negotiate 027 switches	(3)	**100▼**
6561	**Cable Car** Gray/black lettering w/two plastic 53-56 reels of aluminum wire		
	1. Orange reels	(2)	**60**
	2. Gray reels	(2)	**50**
	3. Dark gray reels	(3)	**70**

Flatcars

1877	**Fence and Horses** 59-62		
	1. Brown/yellow, 2 each white, black and brown horses, plastic arch-bar trucks, 2 operating couplers	(3)	**75**
	2. Same, Timken trucks	(3)	**75**
1887	**Fence and Horses** *Sears* Brown/yellow, same U60 as 1877, plastic arch-bar trucks, 2 operating couplers	(4)	**165**
2411	**Big Inch Flatcar** Lt gray/black, same frame 46-48 as 2419 Work Caboose		
	1. 46 only came with metal pipes. Original pipes have ridge inside. Reproductions are smooth inside	(4)	**75▼**
	2. In 47 and 48 w/3 stained or unstained wood logs	(2)	**40**
3361-55	**Log Dump** Gray/black 55-59 Variations: different shades of gray, different types of lettering. NDV This car is a 6362 rail car w/dumping mechanism added.	(2)	**50**
3362	**Helium Tank Unloading** Dark green/white, 61-63 3 silver-painted wood tanks		
	1. White lettering	(3)	**40**
	2. No lettering in Hagerstown box (3362/3364 Unloader Car) came as Helium Tank car only w/2 tanks *Note: RS lettering is easy to remove and leave no trace*	(3)	**50**
3364	**Operating Log Dump** Dark green/white 65-69 *with 3 dark stained logs* ***Note: Same car as 3362 but with logs. Catalog showed picture of 3362 but listed 3364. In 1969, box stamped 3362/3364; no number on car. NDV***	(2)	**45**

3451	**Log Dump** Black/white 5 unstained logs 46-48		
	1. Rubber-stamped	(3)	**50**
	2. Heat-stamped	(2)	**40**
3460	**Flatcar** w/Trailers Unpainted red/white, 55-57	(2)	**60**
	2 dark green *Lionel Trains* vans. Original vans have *Fruehauf* labels in back on a silver background		
3461	**Log Dump** 49-55		
	Note: Logs stained dark for the first time in 54		
	1. Black/wht RS & HS 49-54	(2)	**40**
	2. Green/white/dark logs 54,55	(3)	**65**
3512	**Operating Fireman and Ladder Car** 59-61		
	Unpainted red/white. Repro ladders available, same ladders used on 494 Beacon Tower		
	1. Black ladder	(2)	**125**
	2. Silver ladder	(4)	**250**
3545	**TV Car** Black/white Two men, yellow TV 61,62 camera, blue base	(3)	**200**
3545	Mock-up		**5X**
6111/6121	**Flatcar with Logs or Pipes** Steel-stamped car 55-58		
	made in a number of colors. HS lettering is either serif or non-serif, the latter being harder to find. Add $5. Some boxes stamped with different suffixes. NDV		
	1. Red/white	(1)	**15**
	2. Yellow/black	(1)	**30▲**
	3. Lt and medium gray/white	(3)	**30**
	4. Dark gray/white	(4)	**60**
6151	**Range Patrol Truck** White/black 58		
	plastic *Range Patrol* truck		
	1. Orange/black	(2)	**125**
	2. Light lemon yellow/black	(2)	**150**
	3. Dark yellow/black	(2)	**125**
	4. Cream/black	(4)	**100▼**
6262	**Wheel Car** (8 pairs of wheels with axles) 56,57		
	1. Black/white, metal trucks	(2)	**70**
	2. Red/white, metal trucks	(5)	**700▲**
6264	**Fork-Lift Car** Red/white, w/264 Operating 57-60		
	Fork Lift. Hard to find in original box.		
	1. Plastic trucks	(2)	**75**
	2. Metal trucks	(2)	**175**
	3. As replacement accessory (must have box)	(4)	**700▲***
6311	**Pipe Car** Reddish brown/white 55	(3)	**80▲**
6343	**Barrel Ramp Car** Red/white 6 stained 61,62 barrels, came in set 11222,	(2)	**40**
6361	**Timber Transport Car** Gold 60,61, 64-69		
	or black chains NDV		
	1. Green/white	(3)	**70**
	2. Green/no lettering in Hagerstown box	(4)	**125**
	Note: Gold chain version believed to come from Madison Hardware		
6362-55	**Railway Truck Car** Orange/black, 55, 56 w/3 trucks, no couplers, small & large lettering NDV	(2)	**50**
6401-1	**Flatcar** Gray no lettering 64		
	1. No box	(1)	**10**
	2. With separate sale box	(4)	**125***
	Note: 6401-1 through 6406 are General-type flat cars which came with a number of different loads. All were unnumbered except 6404 and 6405.		
6402	**Flatcar with Reels or Boat** Gray plastic, 64,65,69		
	Timken trucks, 1 operating and 1 non-operating coupler. Came with the following loads		
	1. Blue and white boat	(3)	**50**
	2. 2 Dark orange cable reels	(3)	**40**
	3. 2 Light orange cable reels, 2 operating couplers	(3)	**40**
6402-25	**Flatcar** Gray no lettering 64	(2)	**10**

6404	**Auto** Black/white/one auto, general-type flat car A60		
	1. Red auto/gray bumpers	(2)	**60**
	2. Yellow auto	(3)	**90**
	3. Green auto	(4)	**325***
	4. Brown auto/gray bumpers	(4)	**325***
6405	**Flatcar with Trailer** Maroon/yellow 61		
	1. Yellow van/no markings	(3)	**50**
	2. Gray van/no markings	(4)	**50**
6406	**Auto** Tuscan or Gray Flat/no markings		
	1. Dark yellow auto/gray bumpers A61	(5)	*
	2. Medium yellow auto/gray bumpers A61	(4)	**100**
	3. Brown auto/gray bumpers U61-63	(4+)	**300**
	4. Green auto/gray bumpers U61-63	(4+)	**300**
6407	*See Military and Space Chapter*		
6408	**Flatcar with Pipes** 63	(3)	**40**
6409-25	**Flatcar with Pipes** no number, Red/white 63	(2)	**40**
6411	**Flatcar** Logs 48-50		
	1. Flat light gray/black	(2)	**35**
	2. Glossy medium gray/black	(5)	**500▲***
6414	**Autoloader** Flatcar (6511-2 mold) Red/white, 55-66 with black superstructure added. Came with premium cars and cheapened cars. The premium cars had bumpers, windshields, axles and rubber tires. The cheapened versions had no bumpers, windshields, axles or tires.		
	1. Metal trucks, 6414 to right of *Lionel.* Red, white, blue and yellow premium cars.	(2)	**100**
	2. Timken trucks, 6414 to left of *Lionel*	(2)	**100**
	3. Same w/4 red premium cars, gray plastic bumpers	(4)	**175**
	4. Same w/4 yell premium cars, gray plastic bumpers	(4)	**450**
	5. Same w/4 grn premium cars, gray plastic bumpers	(5)	**900**
	6. Same w/4 brn premium cars, gray plastic bumpers	(5)	**1100**
	7. 6414-85, 4 cheapened cars, 2 red and 2 yellow, 6414 on left	(4)	**600**
	8. Decal on superstructure. 6414 on decal, not on flatcar. 4 red premium cars, gray plastic bumpers. Reproduction decals available.	(4)	**425**
	9. Black/white		**FAKE**
6416	**Boatloader** Red/white/black 61-63	(4)	**225**
	Note: Timken or Arch-bar trucks. NDV. Car originally came with 4 boats. The boats were made by Athearn and had a white hull, blue top, and brown interior. Athearn made the boat in a number of different colors but only the blue/white boat came with this car originally. In 1958, the same boat (in red/white) was cataloged on the HO gauge 0801 flatcar.		
6424	**2 Autos** Two premium autos in many of 56-59 the common colors. NDV		
	1. Black/white, plastic trucks	(2)	**60**
	2. Black/white, metal trucks	(2)	**60**
	3. Same as 2 on 6805 mold w/1 cream auto and 1 red auto w/chrome bumpers	(5)	**250***
	4. Red/white	(5)	**500***
6430	**Piggy-Back Car** Red/white, metal trucks, 56-58		
	1. 2 green 4-wheel vans, *Lionel Trains* plates	(3)	**70**
	2. 2 gray vans, *Cooper Jarrett* plates w/aluminum background	(2)	**70**
	3. 2 white vans, black background on plates	(2)	**75**
	4. Timken trucks, 2 gray vans, *Cooper Jarrett* plates w/Aluminum background and *Fruehauf* labels	(5)	**80**
6431	**Piggy-Back Car** Red/white *w/Midge* Toy Tractor 66 and two white unmarked vans. Some of the vans had holes on the sides for a sign. Most didn't have holes.		
	1. White vans with holes for name plates	(4+)	**225**
	2. Yellow vans without holes	(5)	**400**
	Note: Midge Toy Tractor has been re-issued by the Midge Toy Company		

6440	**Piggy-Back Van Car** Red/white 60-63		
	2 gray 2-wheel vans, no plates		
	1. w/2 operating couplers	(2)	**85**
	2. w/1 operating coupler 1 non-operating coupler	(4)	**100**
	3. Sears vans (Vol. 5)		**5P**
6467	**Miscellaneous Car** Red/white black bulkheads 56 stakes, metal trucks	(2)	**60**
6469	**Liquified Gas Car** Red/white 63	(4)	**175▼**
6477	**Miscellaneous Car** Red/white, black 57,58 bulkheads, 5 plastic pipes w/plastic or metal trucks	(2)	**70**
6500	**Bonanza Airplane Car** Black/white 62,63		
	1. Airplane w/red top/white bottom/red wings	(4)	**400**
	2. White top/red bottom/white wings	(4)	**500**
	Note: Airplane reproductions exist. Originals have Lionel Corp. in raised lettering.		
6501	**Jet Boat Car** Red/white w/white/brown boat 62,63	(3)	**135**
6502	**Girder Car** Black/white, no number/light 62 orange *Lionel* girder	(3)	**45**
6502-50	**Girder Car** Blue/white, no lettering/dark A62 orange *Lionel* girder	(2)	**40**
6502-75	**Girder Car** Aqua/white, no lettering, 64 light orange *Lionel* girder	(2)	**40**
6511	**Pipe Car** 5 aluminum-colored plastic pipes 53-56		
	1. Painted Red/white lettering	(2)	**35**
	2. Unpainted Brown/white lettering	(3)	**45**
	3. Same as 1 w/die-cast plates securing trucks	(4)	**100***
6512	See Military and Space		
6519	**Allis Chalmers Condenser Car** 58-61		
	Must have both brake wheels		
	1. Light orange/blue/gray condenser	(2)	**75**
	2. Dark orange/blue/gray condenser	(3)	**100**
	3. Medium orange/blue/gray condenser	(3)	**75**
6660	**Boom Car** Red/wht, yell boom, blk metal base 58	(3)	**75**
6670	**Derrick Car** 59,60		
	1. *6670* to left of *Lionel*	(3)	**70**
	2. *6670* to right of *Lionel*	(4)	**250***
6800	**Airplane Car** Red/white 57-60		
	1. Airplane/black top/yellow bottom, plastic trucks	(4)	**150**
	2. Airplane/yellow top/black bottom, metal trucks	(4+)	**175**
	Came in light and dark yellow. Repro planes available		
6801	**Boat Car** Red/white 57-60		
	Note: Reproduction boats available		
	1. Boat – white hull/brown deck/6801	(3)	**75▼**
	2. Boat – yellow hull/wht deck/6801-50	(4)	**95▼**
	3. Boat – blue hull/white deck/6801-75 (early box)	(2)	**75▼**
	4. Boat – aqua hull/cream deck 6801-75 (late box)	(3)	**125▲**
6802	**US Steel Girder** Red/white, black *US Steel* 58,59 girders come with and without 6418. NDV	(2)	**40**
6810	**Piggy-Back Car** Red/white, one white van, 58 *Cooper Jarrett* plates (black background)	(3)	**100**
6812	**Track Maintenance Car** Red/white bases 59-61 and tops are interchangeable		
	Note: Repro men available.		
	1. Dark yellow base and top	(3)	**125**
	2. Black base, gray top	(2)	**100**
	3. Gray base, black top	(2)	**100**
	4. Cream base and top	(4)	**200**
	5. Light yellow base and top	(2)	**100**
6816	**Allis Chalmers Bulldozer Car** 59,60		
	1. Red/white, light orange bulldozer, *Allis Chalmers* in black	(4)	**500**
	2. Red/white, dark-orange bulldozer, *Allis Chalmers* in white	(4)	**450**
	3. Black/white, light orange bulldozer	(5)	**900***

6817	**Allis Chalmers Scraper Car** 59,60		
	1. Red/white, light orange scraper	(4)	**500**
	2. Red/white, dark orange scraper, wire windshield, white *Allis Chalmers*	(4)	**800***
	3. Black/white	(5)	**1200***
6818	**Transformer Car** Red/white, black transformer 58	(2)	**60**
6821	**Crate Car** Red/white, tan crates 59,60	(2)	**40**
6825	**Trestle Bridge Car** Red/white, black trestle 59-62	(3)	**40**
	Note: the same trestle also came in gray		
6826	**Christmas Tree Car** Red/wht w/original trees 59,60	(4)	**150**
6827	**P&H Steam Shovel** (kit) Black/white 60-63		
	1. Dark yellow steam shovel	(4)	**200**
	2. Light yellow steam shovel	(4)	**150**
6828	**P&H Crane** (kit) 60-63, 66		
	1. Black/white flatcar, lt yellow crane	(4)	**225**
	2. Black/white flatcar, dk yellow crane	(4)	**275**
	3. Red/white flatcar	(5)	**700***
	Note: 6827 and 6828 came with booklet depicting the history of P&H. Among the many fascinating tidbits is thederivation of P&H. The P is for Alonzo Pawling and the H is for Henry Harnischfeger.		

Gondolas

1002	**Lionel Scout** 48-52		
	1. Blue/white, Scout couplers	(2)	**15**
	2. Black/white, Scout couplers	(1)	**10**
	3. Yellow/black, knuckle couplers	(4)	**450***
	4. Silver/black, knuckle couplers	(4)	**450***
	5. Red/white, knuckle couplers	(4)	**450***
	6. Black/white, knuckle couplers		*
2452	**Pennsylvania** Black/white, brakewheels, 45-47 some came with barrels		
	1. Regular wheels	(1)	**15**
	2. Whirly wheels	(4)	**25**
	3. Dished-out wheels	(4)	**25**
	4. Stamped 6462 not 2452	(4)	**250***
2452X	**Pennsylvania** Black/white, 46,47 2452X stamped on frame	(1)	**20**
3562	**AT&SF** Barrel Car Operating 54-58		
	1. 3562-1 Black/white/black trough 54	(3)	**225**
	2. 3562-1 Black/white/yellow trough 54	(3)	**175**
	3. 3562-25 Gray/red 54	(4)	**350**
	4. 3562-1 Gray/red 54	(5)	**800**
	5. 3562-25 Gray/blue 55	(2)	**75**
	6. 3562-50 Painted yellow/black	(4)	**150**
	7. 3562-50 Unpainted yellow plastic/black 55,56	(2)	**75**
	8. 3562-75 Unpainted orange plastic/black 57,58	(3)	**110**
	9. White/black	**Not Known To Exist**	
4452	**Pennsylvania** *Electronic Set* 46-48	(4)	**200▲**
6002	**Gondola** Black/white 50	(3)	**15**
6012	**Lionel** Black/white 51-56	(1)	**10**
6032	**Lionel** 52,53	(1)	**10**
6042	**Lionel** U59-61		
	1. Black unpainted/white	(3)	**15**
	2. Blue painted/white	(1)	**10**
6062	**New York Central** Black/white 59-64		
	1. Unpainted black plastic	(3)	**30▲**
	2. Painted	(4)	**40**
6062-50	**New York Central** Black/white 69	(3)	**35▲**
6112	**Lionel** Black/white 4 red canisters 56-58		
	1. Black/white	(1)	**10**
	2. Blue unpainted/white	(1)	**10**
	3. White/black	(4)	**30**

6142	**Lionel** Black/white 61-66	(2)	**20**
6162	**NYC** Blue/white 61-63	(2)	**10**
6162-60	**Alaska** 59		
	1. Yellow/blue	(3)	**90▲**
	2. Tan/blue		**FAKE**
6162-110	**NYC** w/2 red canisters 64-69		
	1. Blue/white	(2)	**15**
	2. Aqua blue/white	(3)	**75**
	3. Red /white	(4)	**150**
6342	**New York Central** Red/white 56-58, 64-69		
	1. Metal trucks	(3)	**40**
	2. Plastic trucks	(4)	**50**
	3. In separate sale box (overstamped).	(5)	**1200***
6452	**Pennsylvania** Black/white 48 only (cataloged in 1949 but not available)		
	1. 6462 on side, 6452 stamped on base	(3)	**30**
	2. 6452 on side and base	(2)	**20**
6462	**New York Central** 49-56		
	Note: Also came in - Painted orange, Painted gold, Gray/black Gray/white, Gray/red, Glossy green/white and Blue/black. All are 5X, NDV.		
	1. Black/white	(1)	**15**
	2. Red/white	(1)	**15**
	3. Green/white	(2)	**35**
6462-500	**New York Central** Pink/blue Girl's Train	(4)	**200**
6562	**New York Central** 56-58		
	1. Gray/maroon **6562-1**	(2)	**50**
	2. Gray/red **6562-1**	(3)	**55**
	3. Red/white **6562-25**	(2)	**50**
	4. Black/white **6562-50**	(3)	**70**

Hoppers

2456	**Lehigh Valley** 48		
	1. Matte black/white/2 lines of data	(3)	**40**
	2. Same with/3 lines of data	(5)	**?***
	3. Glossy black/white (information requested)	(5)	**?***
2856/2956	**B&O** Black/white 46,47	(4)	**300***
	Note: This was the prewar 2956 which was cataloged in 46 and 47 in gray with postwar trucks and the number 2856. 2856 was never made but some black 2956 hoppers turn up with postwar trucks. Whether Lionel or a service station or a customer put the trucks on, no one knows. But it's a nice car anyway.		
3456	**N&W** Black/white Operating bottom hatches 50-55		
	1. Corner braces	(2)	**50**
	2. No corner braces	(3)	**60**
6076	**Lehigh Valley** U63		
	1. Gray/black	(1)	**15**
	2. Black/white	(1)	**15**
	3. Red/white	(1)	**15**
	4. Yellow/black	(3)	**20**
6076	**AT&SF** Gray/black U63		
	1. Regular production	(1)	**10**
	2. **TTOS Convention Car** (overstamped)	(4)	**50**
6176	**Lehigh Valley** 64-66, 69		
	1. Different shades of yellow w/blk or blue lettering	(1)	**10**
	2. Lemon yellow	(4)	**?***
	3. Gray/black	(1)	**10**
	4. Black/white	(1)	**10**
	5. Black/gray	(2)	**10**
6176-100	Unpainted Olive drab/no lettering	(5)	**175▲**
6176-1967	**TTOS Convention Car** 67	(4)	**65**

6346-56	**Alcoa** Silver/blue Quad/hatch covers, 56 no center brace hole		
	1. Silver/blue HS	(3)	**100**
	2. Silver/red HS		**FAKE**
	3. Silver/blue decal		**5P**
6436-1	**Lehigh Valley** Black/white 55		
	1. No spreader bar holes	(3)	**75**
	2. Spreader bar and holes	(2)	**45**
6436-25	**Lehigh Valley** Maroon/white, 55-57 no covers/spreader bar	(3)	**55**
6436-110	**Lehigh Valley** Red/white 63-66,68		
	1. *Built Date 3/5/63*	(4)	**90**
	2. No built date 63,64-66,68	(2)	**40**
6436-500	**Lehigh Valley** Girl's Set Lilac/maroon/w or 57,58 w/o spreader bar holes	(4)	**400**
6436-1969	**TCA Convention Car** Red/white, U69 spreader bar/no cover	(4)	**125**
6446-1	**N&W Hopper** Gray/black covered 54,55,57,63		
	1. 546446 on car, 54	(2)	**75**
	2. 6446-25 on car, 55,57	(3)	**75**
	3. 6446-25 on car, plastic AAR trucks, 63 spreader bar,	(4)	**135**
6446-25	**N&W** Black/white covered		
	1. 54-6446 on car	(2)	**55**
	2. 6446-25 on car	(2)	**55**
6446-25	**Norfolk & Western** specials made for *N&W RR* 55-57		
	1. Gold/white		**5P**
	2. Pink/black		**5P**
	3. Light blue/white		**5P**
	4. Silver/white		**5P**
6446-60	**Lehigh Valley** Red/white, covered 63	(4)	**275**
6456	**Lehigh Valley** 48-55		
	1. Black/white 49-51	(1)	**20**
	2. Maroon/white 51	(2)	**25**
	3. Gray/maroon 54	(3)	**60**
	4. Glossy red/yellow 55	(4)	**175**
	5. Glossy red/white 55	(5)	**650***
	6. Gray/white		*****
6476	**Lehigh Valley** Unpainted 57-69		
	Note: Made through 1969 in many different colors, some with road names and some without, cataloged and uncataloged. None are worth more than $20.		
	1. Red plastic/white 57	(1)	**10**
	2. Black plastic/white 57	(2)	**10**
	3. Gray plastic/black 57	(3)	**15**
6476-1	**TTOS 69 Convention Car**	(4)	**65**
6476-125	**Lehigh Valley** Yellow/black (6176 on car) 64	(2)	**15**
6476-135	**Lehigh Valley** 68,69 Unpainted mustard yellow plastic/red	(2)	**10**
6536	**Minneapolis & St. Louis** 58,59,63		
	1. Red/white 58,59	(3)	**55**
	2. Shinier Red/white 63	(4)	**60**
6636	**Alaska** Black/yellow 59,60	(4)	**110**
6736	**Detroit & Mackinac** 60-62		
	1. Red/white	(3)	**50**
	2. Red/white, *Mackinac Mac's* face filled in due to flaw in die	(4)	**120**

Military and Space

943	**Exploding Ammo Dump** 59,60	(3)	**45**
3309	**Turbo Missile Launching Car** one missile, 63,64 arch-bar trucks, two fixed couplers, no missile holder	(2)	**50**
	1. Light red/white	(2)	**55**
	2. Cherry red/white	(3)	**65**
3330	**Flat Car with Operating Submarine Kit** 60,61		
	1. Submarine assembled	(3)	**100▼**
	2. Submarine unassembled	(5)	**175**
3330-100	**Operating Submarine Kit** <u>**(must have box)**</u>	(5)	**500***
3349	**Turbo Missile Launching Car** Missile 62-65 holder/Timken trucks/no number or lettering on car		
	1. Light red/white/2 operating couplers	(2)	**65**
	2. Dark red/white/2 operating couplers	(2)	**75**
	3. Olive drab/1 operating coupler and 1 fixed coupler	(4)	**600▲***
3409	**Helicopter Launching Car** Blue/white 61,62 ***Note: Manually cocked and released. Gray Navy helicopter with one propeller, yellow tail assembly. Flatcars are available and so are reproduction helicopters.***	(3)	**135**
3410	**Helicopter Launching Car** 61,62		
	1. Blue/white w/yellow unmarked helicopter/ one propeller	(4)	**200▲**
	2. Blue/white w/Navy helecopter	(2)	**100**
	3. Aqua/white w/yellow unmarked helicopter/ one propeller	(5)	**500▲***
3413	**Mercury Capsule Car** Red/white, Gray base, 62-64 red launcher, parachute inside of white/red rocket with gray nose		
	1. Light gray base	(4)	**175**
	2. Dark gray base	(4)	**175**
3419	**Helicopter Launching Car** 59-65 *Note: Two props more desirable than one prop*		
	1. Light blue/gray *US Navy* copter with 2 props/ large winding mechanism	(3)	**150**
	2. Same as 1 but dark blue	(2)	**125**
	3. Same as 2 but small winding mechanism	(2)	**100**
	4. Light blue/small winding mechanism	(3)	**100**
	5. Light blue/small winding mechanism, yellow copter/one propeller	(3)	**200***
	6. Same as 4 but dark blue	(3)	**100**
	7. Copter w/clear blades	(5)	**?***
3429	**USMC Helicopter Launching Car,** Olive drab 60 same mechanism as 3419/gray, one prop gray helicopter with *USMC* markings. Included in *1805 Land, Sea, and Air Gift Pack.*	(4)	**500**
3470	**Target Launcher** 62-64 *Note: Blower nozzle may be switched.*		
	a. Red Nozzle add $25.	(3)	
	b. Yellow Nozzle add $1700.	(5)	
	1. Dark blue flat w/clear or gray nozzle	(2)	**100**
	2. Light blue flat w/clear or gray nozzle	(4)	**400▲**
3509	**Satellite Car** Green/wht/black/silver satellite, 61,62 gray superstructure/yellow microwave disc	(3)	**90**
3510	**Satellite Car** Red/white, *Lionel* only on side, A62 no number plastic Timken trucks, fixed couplers, black & silver satellite, gray superstructure/yellow microwave dish.	(3)	**120**
3519	**Satellite Car** Green/wht, gray superstructure, 61-64 yellow dish, operated by remote control	(2)	**65**
3535	**AEC Security** Red/white, gray plastic roof, 60,61 gun usually missing, gray rotating searchlight, similar cab to 520 electric	(3)	**120**
3540	**Operating Radar Car** Red/white, gray base, 59,60 yellow dish, black & silver radar	(3)	**130**

3619 **Helicopter Recon Car** 62-64
1. OperatingYellow/red-black, black roof, same body & roof as 3665 and 3666/red copter (3) **125**
2. Same w/darker yellow body (4) **225▲**

3665 **Minuteman** White/blue with rocket 61-64
1. Dark blue roof (3) **100**
2. Light blue roof, (3619 mold)1964 (4) **350▲**

3666 **Cannon Boxcar** White/blue, lt blue roof U64 (5) **500***
Operating cannon fires silver painted wooden shells. Sears Set 3-9820,
Note: Reproduction roofs available

3820 **Operating Submarine** Olive/white 60 (4) **225▲**
USMC markings on car/*US Navy*markings on gray sub/part of 1805 *Land, Sea, and Air Gift Pack*

3830 **Operating Submarine** Blue/white, 60-63 (3+) **125**
gray sub/*US Navy* markings

6175 **Flatcar with Rocket** (same gray cradle used 58-61 with 6801 Boat Car) *US Navy* rocket/red/white/blue lettering, same rocket as 175 launcher
1. Red/white 58 (3) **80**
2. Black/white 59-61 (2) **90**

6402-Type Flat Car (mold 1877-3) w/green tank *Sears* U64 (4) **150**

6407 **Flatcar with Large Missile** Red/white 63 (5) **500**
(gray cradle is same used on 6501) holds large white-red rocket with removable blue nose with and without pencil sharpener. Repro sharpeners available

6413 **Mercury Capsule Carrying Car** Blue/white, 62,63
2 gray unlettered Mercury capsules secured by bands, same chassis as 6519
Note: Brakewheels may be added, reproduction capsules available
1. Blue/white (4) **100**
2. Aqua/white (4+) **400▲***

6448 **Target Car** 61-64
Note: Solid white can be made by combining 1 and 2
1. Red sides/white lettering (2) **60**
2. White sides/red lettering (3) **60**

6463 **Rocket Fuel** White/red 62,63 (3) **45**

6470 **Exploding Boxcar** Red/white, spring-loaded59-63 (2) **40**

6480 **Exploding Boxcar** Red/white 61 (4) **60**

6512 **Cherry Picker** Black/white, gray base holds 62,63 (3) **100**
black metal ladder, original vestibule orange, repros exist in both orange & black

6544 **Missile Launching Car** Blue/white, gray 60-64
launching mechanism usually found with brake-wheels broken, used 6519 chassis and 44 launching base, same firing mechanism as 448 range set
1. White lettered console (2) **125**
2. Black lettered console (4) **500▲**

6630 **Missile Launcher** Black/white, blue base,U60-64 (3) **100**
Black missile firing ramp, *Sears*

6640 **USMC Missile Launcher** 60
1. Olive/white (6511-3 mold) (3) **225**
2. No lettering (6424-11 mold) (4) **400▲***

6650 **Lionel Missile Launcher** Red/white, Blue 59-63
launcher (same as 6630) Black launching pad, white/red missile with blue nose
1. 6511-3 mold (3) **60**
2. 6424-11 mold (3) **100▲**

6651 **USMC Cannon** Olive/white U65 (4) **150**
Came in *JC Penney* set headed by 221 *USMC* Alco

6803 **USMC Tank & Microwave Truck** Gray 58,59 (4) **175▼**
microwave truck and tank

6804	**USMC Trucks** Red/white gray microwave 58,59 truck and truck w/2 guns	(4)	**225▼**
6805	**Radioactive Waste** Red/white/black plastic 58,59 containers painted gray ***Note: Reissued 9234 in 1980. Reissued containers are gray plastic. Sometimes found with 4 different shades of painted tan containers made for 462 derrick platform. NDV***	(2)	**160**
6806	**USMC Radar & Navy Hospital Trucks** 58,59 Red/white/1 gray USMC radar dish truck and 1 *US Navy* hospital truck	(4)	**175▼**
6807	**Flatcar with USMC Boat** Red/white, 58,59 large gray amphibious boat	(4)	**125**
6808	**Flatcar with USMC Truck & Tank** Red/wht 58,59 Gray searchlight truck & two-gun tank	(4)	**225▼**
6809	**Flatcar with 2 USMC Trucks** Red/white 58,59 Gray cannon truck & *Navy* hospital truck	(4)	**175▼**
6814	**First Aid Medical Car** White/red, man, 59-61, U64 2 stretchers, oxygen tank unit		
	1. Black RS serif *Lionel*/gray frame	(3)	**120**
	2. White HS serif *Lionel*/black frame, no tray insert, no man or stretchers or oxygen unit, *Sears* U64	(4)	**250**
6819	**Helicopter** Red/white Gray *Navy* one-prop 59,60 helicopter with prop end weights, reproduction helicopters available	(3)	**100**
6820	**Navy Helicopter** Gray *Navy* one-prop copter 60,61 with 2 missiles. Reproduction helicopters available		
	1. Light blue/white	(4)	**200**
	2. Dark blue/white	(3)	**150**
6823	**ICBM Missiles** Red/white, 2 red/white 59,60 ICBM-type missiles. Same missiles as on 6650 *Note: Missile and rocket parts interchangeable; therefore all color combinations are possible.*	(3)	**70**
6830	**US Navy Submarine** Gray non-operating 60,61 submarine with black lettering		
	1. Painted flat blue	(3)	**125**
	2. Painted gloss blue	(5)	**400***
6844	**Missile Carrying Car** 6 white missiles, 59,60 gray missile holder base. Reproductions of graybase available in gray and black		
	1. Black/white	(2)	**50**
	2. Red/white	(5)	**700***

Mint Car

6445	**Fort Knox Gold Reserve** Silver/black 61-63	(3)	**160**

Refrigerator Cars

3462	**Milk Car** Unpainted alum doors operating 47,48		
	1. Glossy white/brass-base mechanism	(4)	**80**
	2. Dull white/later mechanism	(2)	**50**
3472	**Milk Car** operating 49-53		
	1. Metal doors 49 only	(3)	**50**
	2. Plastic doors	(2)	**45**
3482	**Milk Car** operating 54,55		
	1. 3472 lower right/early production	(3)	**125**
	2. 3482 lower right	(2)	**55**
3662-1	**Milk Car** White/brown operating 55-60, 64-66		
	1. Built date/55-60	(3)	**80**
	2. No built date/64-66	(3+)	**100**
3672	**Bosco** Yellow/Tuscan operating 59,60		
	1. Painted yellow	(4)	**350***
	2. Yellow plastic	(3)	**225**
6472	**Milk Car** Dull white 50-53	(2)	**35**

6482	**Milk Car** White 57	(4)	**75**
6572	**Railway Express** 58,59,U64		
	1. Dark green/metal Timken trucks 58.59	(4)	**125**
	2. Light green *Madison Hardware* 4WPT U64	(2)	**90**
6672	**Santa Fe** White/brown non-operating 54-56		
	1. Black lettering/L in circle	(3+)	**75**
	2. Same but no L in circle	(3+)	**75**
	3. Blue lettering/L in circle	(3)	**60**
	4. Blue/3 lines of data right of door	(5)	**325***
	Note: Roof is either reddish brn or chocolate brn. NDV		

Searchlight Cars

3520	**Lionel Lines** Gray/black, orange generator, 52,53 gray searchlight on-off switch, serif and non-serif lettering. NDV	(2)	**60**
3530	**Operating Generator Car** w/searchlight, 56-58		
	1. Orange generator, short stripe	(3+)	**150**
	2. Orange generator, long stripe	(4)	**250**
	3. Gray generator	(5)	**?***
	4. Long stripe, numbed underlined	(5)	**?***
	Note: The base of pole came in black (common), blue (hard to find) and yellow (rare). Some fuel tanks are black and some are blue. On some cars the white stripe goes through the ladder (long stripe) and on others it does not (short stripe).		
3620	**Lionel Lines** Gray/black 54-56		
	1. Searchlight gray plastic	(2)	**50**
	2. Searchlight orange plastic painted gray	(4)	**150▲**
	3. Searchlight orange plastic		**FAKE**
	Note: Shown in 54 catalog, p. 20. Beware of painted gray version with the paint removed.		
3650	**Lionel Lines** Extension Searchlight 56-59		
	1. Gray frame/black	(3)	**75**
	2. Dark gray frame/black	(4)	**150**
	3. Olive gray frame/black	(4)	**200**
6520	**Lionel Lines** w/searchlight		
	Gray/black/gray housing 49-51		
	Same die-cast depressed-center frame as 2461		
	1. Green generator 49	(4)	**300**
	2. Orange generator	(2)	**65**
	3. Unpainted gray generator		*****
	4. Unpainted maroon generator	(3)	**70**
	5. Tan generator	(5)	**700***
	Note: Some cars have faded orange generators and black housings. NDV		
6822	**Lionel** Red/white 61-69		
	1. Gray searchlight housing	(2)	**60**
	2. Black searchlight housing	(3)	**75**

Stock Cars

3356	**Operating Horse Car & Corral** 56-60, 64-66	(3)	**150**
	Green/yellow, plastic & metal trucks		
	Car only, no box	(2)	**75**
	Separate sale car w/box	(5)	**450**
3366	**Circus and 3356-150 Corral** White/red, 59-62	(4)	**325**
	Car only	(3)	**125**
3656	**Armour** Orange w/cattle and corral 49-55		
	1. Black lettering/*Armour* sticker 49	(4)	**250**
	2. White lettering/*Armour* 49,50	(3)	**90**
	3. White lettering/no *Armour* 50-55	(2)	**75**
6356-1	**NYC** Yellow/black 54,55	(2)	**50**
6376	**Lionel Lines Circus Car** White/red 56,57	(2+)	**75**
6434	**Poultry** Red/white/gray doors 58,59	(3)	**65**
6473	See Action Cars		

6556	**Katy** Red/white *Set 2513W* 58	(4)	**325▲**
6646	**Lionel Lines** Orange/black 57	(3)	**75**
6656	**Lionel Lines** Yellow/black 50-55		
	1. *Armour* sticker 50	(4)	**75**
	2. No *Armour* sticker 50-55	(2+)	**25**

Tank Cars

1005	**Sunoco** Gray tank Scout Type 48-50 1d	(1)	**10**
2465	**Sunoco** Silver 46-48 2d		
	1. Black lettering/decal in center 46	(4)	**350**
	2. Same but decal off to one side 46	(1)	**15**
	3. Blue lettering 47	(2)	**25**
	4. Silk screening 48	(2)	**25**
2555	**Sunoco** Aluminum, same as 2755, 46-48 1d	(3)	**100**
2755	**Sunoco** Aluminum Prewar tank car 45 1d with postwar trucks	(4)	**175**
2855	**Sunoco** Black 46,47 1d		
	1. Gas-Oil in decal 46	(4)	**175**
	2. No Gas-Oil 47	(4)	**225**
2855	**Sunoco** Gray No Gas-Oil in decal 47 1d	(4)	**275**
6015	**Sunoco** Scout Type 54,55 1d		
	1. Yellow plastic	(2)	**40**
	2. Painted yellow	(5)	**?***
6025	**Gulf** Scout Type 56,57 1d	(2)	**45**
6035	**Sunoco** Scout Type 52,53 1d	(1)	**10**
6045	**Lionel Lines** 58-63 2d	(1)	**50**
6045	**Cities Service** Green/white, U60 2d non-operating couplers	(2)	**150**
6315	**Gulf** 56-59,66-69 1d		
	1. Glossy orange/black tank	(3)	**85**
	2. Flat orange/black tank	(3)	**65**
	3. Solid orange tank	(2)	**80**
	4. Same as 3 with *6315 Chemical Tank Car* on ends	(2)	**80**
6315	**Lionel Lines** Orange/black, plastic trucks 63-65 1d	(2)	**40**
6315-60	**Lionel Lines** 63,64 1d		
	1. Unpainted orange plastic no built date	(3)	**30**
	2. Same as 1 with built date	(4)	**40**
	3. Painted orange	(4)	**200▲**
6415	**Sunoco** Silver/black 53-55 3d	(1)	**40**
6425	**Gulf** Silver/blue 56-58 3d	(2)	**80**
6463	**Rocket Fuel** White/red 62,63 2d	(3)	**45**
6465	**Sunoco** 48-56 2d		
	Note: Common car with lots of variations, only one of which (so far) is worth more than $20		
	1. Silver/Sunoco decal normal production	(1)	**20**
	2. Painted black/Sunoco decal (Rare version owned by Nick Vernola)	(5)	*****
6465	**Gulf** 58 2d		
	1. Unpainted blk plastic tank	(3)	**50**
	2. Painted black plastic tank	(3)	**50**
	3. Painted gray plastic tank	(3)	**60**
6465	**Lionel Lines** Gray, orange or black. NDV 58,59 2d	(1)	**25**
6465	**Cities Service** Grn/wht, operating couplers 60-62 2d	(3)	**50**
6465-60	**Gulf** Gray/blue/black 58 2d	(2)	**60**
6555	**Sunoco** Silver/black 49,50 1d	(3)	**90**

TCA Convention Cars 1965-1967

Note: Special 6464 cars with brass and aluminum doors made for the Train Collecters Association. Fakes have turned up. Check the doors. The inside of the doors on originals is aluminum, outside is brass. On fakes, the doors are all brass. No reported sales for boxed/mint condition.

6464-250	**Western Pacific** (159 made) 67	(5)	**325**
6464-375	**Central of Georgia** (100 made) 67	(5)	**325**
6464-475	**Boston & Maine** Decal version 67		**5P**
6464-475	**Boston & Maine** (3 made) 67		**5X**
6464-525	**Minneapolis & St. Louis** (7 made) 67		**5X**
6464-650	**Denver & Rio Grande Western** (137 made) 67	(5)	**325**
6464-700	**A.T. & S.F.** (92 made) 67	(5)	**325**
6464-735	**New Haven** (3 made) 67		**5X**
6464-900	**New York Central** (2 made) 67		**5X**
6464-1965	**TCA Pittsburgh** 65	(5)	**275**
6464-1965X	**Pittsburgh** 65	(5)	**325**
6517-1966	**TCA** Bay Window Caboose 66	(4)	**250**

Vat Cars

6475	**Libby's Crushed Pineapple** 4 vats U63 w/silver labels/red & blue lettering		
	1. Blue/white	(2)	**150**
	2. Aqua blue/white	(4)	**500▲***
6475	**Pickle Car** Tan/brown/green 60-62		
	1. Slats on pickle vats	(2)	**50**
	2. No slats on pickle vats	(4)	**225**
	3. Blank vats	(3)	**150**
6475	**Heinz 57 Pickle Car** Tan/brown/green		*

Accessories

Note: Accessories still packaged in blister pack command a premium over those packed in boxes.

30	**Water Tower** 47-50		
	1. Brown roof, black superstructure/doubled-walled tank, fill hole in roof, 30 RS in black on base	(4)	**225**
	2. Red roof, brown superstructure/singled-walled tank, fill hole in roof, 30 RS in black on base	(4)	**100**
	3. Same as 2, gray roof brown superstructure	(3)	**100**
	4. Gray roof, brown superstructure, single-walled tank, no fill hole, no RS number	(3)	**100**
35	**Boulevard Lamp** 45-49		
	1. Aluminum	(2)	**50**
	2. Gray	(3)	**60**
38	**Water Tower** Clear, plastic funnel w/packet 46,47 of water coloring tablets		
	1. Red roof/tan base	(4)	**325**
	2. Brown roof/tan base	(4+)	**350**
45	**Gateman** White/red/green base 46-49	(2)	**50**
45N	**Gateman** White/red/green base 45	(2)	**65**
56	**Lamp Post** two shades of green NDV 46-49	(3)	**75**
58	**Goose Neck Lamp Post** Ivory, diecast 46-50	(3)	**50**
64	**Highway Lamp Post** L452W bulb, 45-49 Green, diecast	(3)	**60**
70	**Yard Lamp** Black, swivel light, round, 49,50 Bakelite base. Came with early 397 coal loader	(4)	**60**
71	**Lamp Post** Silver, diecast, bayonet bulb 49-59	(2)	**20**
75	**Goose Neck Lamps** Black, (2/box) 61-69 Price is for two.	(2)	**65**
76	**Boulevard Street Lamps** 2-pin bulb, 55-66,68,69 Dark green unpainted plastic, (3/box). Price for 3.	(2)	**30**

No.	Description	Rarity	Value
89	**Flagpole** White pole, tan base w/Lionel 56-58 pennant and American flag		
	1. Dark blue pennant	(5)	**125**
	2. Purple pennant	(4)	**75**
93	**Water Tower** "Lionel Lines" Aluminum/ 46-49 red base/black spout	(3)	**85**
97	**Coal Elevator** Yellow bunker with red roof, 46-50 black Bakelite base, 97C controller.	(3)	**250**
110	**Trestle Set** Package of 22 or 24 trestles 55-69		
	1. Gray trestles	(2)	**30**
	2. Black trestles	(4)	**35**
111	**Trestle Set** Pkg of 10 Trestles 56-69	(2)	**20**
114	**Newsstand with Horn** Yellow building, 57-59 silver roof, brown base control	(3)	**125**
115	**Lionel City Station** Prewar carry over 46-49 Cream/red/red base w/auto train stop	(4)	**500**
118	**Newsstand with Whistle** Yellow/silver/brn base 58	(3)	**100**
125	**Whistle Shack** White sides, red roof 50-55 Similar to 145 Automatic Gateman with whistle		
	1. Light gray base	(2)	**40**
	2. Dark gray base	(3)	**75**
	3. Apple green base	(4)	**100**
128	**Animated Newsstand** came with newspaper 57-60 inserted in boy's hand reissued by *Fundimensions* in 1982 as 2308.		
	1. Dark green stand	(3)	**150▼**
	2. Apple green stand	(4)	**200**
132	**Passenger Station** illuminated White, 49-55 green roof, maroon base, auto train stop, maroon chimney, green chimney, NDV.	(3)	**75**
133	**Passenger Station** White/green roof 57,61,62,66 and chimney, maroon base, no automatic train stop, illuminated	(2)	**65**
138	**Water Tower** Brown tank and frame, 53-57 gray base, black operating spout		
	1. Gray roof, 53 only	(4)	**150**
	2. Orange roof, 54-57	(3)	**125**
140	**Automatic Banjo Signal** Black 54-66 with operating arm	(2)	**40**
145	**Automatic Gateman** White shack/green base, 50-66 plastic crossbuck, red-gold *Lionelville* sticker above door, blue plastic man or painted with flesh- colored hands & face NDV		
	1. Maroon roof	(2)	**40**
	2. Red roof	(4)	**75**
148	**Dwarf Trackside Light** Tan/black 57-60 w/148C switch. Can also use 153C.	(4)	**50**
150	**Telegraph Pole Set** Brn, set of 6 w/track clips 47-50	(4)	**100**
151	**Semaphore** Operating plastic blade/painted 47-69 yellow tip w/red/green translucent plastic inserts.		
	1. Black base/painted aluminum pole	(1)	**40**
	2. Black base/unpainted aluminum pole	(3)	**75**
	3. Green base/painted aluminum pole	(4)	**85**
	4. Same as 1 but packaged in blister pack	(5)	*
152	**Automatic Crossing Gate** Red, diecast base 45-49 with pedestrian gate. Deduct $10-$20 if gate missing	(3)	**40**
153	**Automatic Block Control** Green base 45-69		
	1. Painted aluminum pole	(2)	**45**
	2. Unpainted aluminum pole	(3)	**50**
154	**Automatic Highway Signal** Black base, silver post 45-59		
	1. Diecast sign, screw-type bulbs	(3)	**65**
	2. Plastic sign, bayonet-type bulbs	(3)	**35**

155	**Ringing Highway Signal** Black/white 55-57 plastic base w/bell, same lights as 154		
	1. No feet, no rubber grommet 55	(3)	**60**
	2. With feet and rubber grommet 56,57	(3)	**75**
156	**Station Platform** illuminated Green base, 46-49 red roo, diecast posts, picket fence with signs, also prewar 39-42	(3)	**90**
157	**Station Platform** illuminated Green roof, 58,59 black metal posts/signs		
	1. Maroon base	(3)	**50**
	2. Molded, red base	(4)	**100**
161	**Mail Pick-Up Set** Tan base, red bag holder 61-63 arm, gray painted bag with magnet plus second magnet to be glued to car.	(4)	**75**
163	**Single Target Block Signal** 61-69 unpainted tan base	(2)	**40**
164	**Log Loader** Green/yellow/red, 46-50 w/97c controller	(3)	**250**
175	**Rocket Launcher** Price assumes complete 58-60 with original 175-50 rocket, control panel, tower and crane. Repro rockets available	(4)	**300**
182	**Magnet Crane** With 165C controller, 46-49 black base aluminum painted frame, same cab as 2460 crane car w/added stack	(4)	**350**
192	**Operating Control Tower** Yellow tower, 59,60 green frame, gray base, beware of heat damage to roof, broken railings, usually found with top piece missing	(4)	**225**
193	**Industrial Water Tower** Green shed, 53-55 gray base, silver top with red flashing light		
	1. Red superstructure	(2)	**100**
	2. Black superstructure	(5)	**225**
195	**Floodlight Tower** Tan base/silver tower, 57-66,69 eight two-pin bulbs		
	1. Without 95 stamped on base	(2)	**75**
	2. With 95 stamped on base in red	(5)	**100**
197	**Rotating Radar Antenna** Black plastic 58,59 gridwork with *Lionel* in orange letters		
	1. Gray platform	(3)	**85**
	2. Orange platform	(4)	**110**
199	**Microwave Relay Tower** Gray tower, 58,59 white antenna, gray or tan base (interchangeable with 195 Floodlight Tower)	(4)	**125**
213	**Lift Bridge**		**5P**
214	**Girder Plate Bridge** 53-69		
	1. *LIONEL* on sides	(2)	**25**
	2. US Steel girders (from 6418)	(2)	**40**
252	**Automatic Crossing Gate** Black base, 50-62,63 black and white gate, two red lanterns	(2)	**25**
253	**Block Control Signal** Tan base, white pole 56-59		
	1. Black control box	(2)	**40**
	2. Tan control box	(3)	**50**
256	**Freight Station** Maroon/white/green, 50-53 picket fence w/billboards	(2)	**55**
257	**Freight Station** Diesel horn, same as 56,57 256 w/battery-powered horn and control button		
	1. Maroon base	(2)	**75**
	2. Brown base	(4)	**125**
262	**Highway Crossing Gate** 62-66,69		
	1. Black/white gate	(2)	**50**
	2. Red/white gate	(4)	**75**
264	**Operating Fork Lift Platform** Black base, 57-60 brown deck area, orange lift truck with blue man, white crane, red 6264 with lumber	(4)	**300▼**

282	**Gantry Crane** Gray frame, white lettering, 54,55 black superstructure, 3 lever controller 282C, comes with both gray glued-on smokestack and black smokestack molded in plastic. NDV		
	1. Black magnet 54	(3)	**200▼**
	2. Nickel plated magnet, 55	(4)	**225▼**
282R	**Gantry Crane** 282 with modified motor 56,57 and platform "R" means redesigned. Cab is one piece molded plastic including stack, 282 secured with screws to base. 282R snapped on base	(3)	**250**
299	**Code Transmitter Beacon Set** 61-63	(4)	**175**
308	**Railroad Sign Set** Five die-cast signs 45-49	(3)	**65**
309	**Yard Sign Set** 12 plastic signs w/diecast bases 50-59	(2)	**30**
310	**Billboard Set** with 3 different billboards 50-68		
	1. Dark green frame	(3)	**45**
	2. Light green frame	(4)	*
	3. Yellow frame	(5)	*
	4. Red frame	(5)	*
313	**Bascule Bridge** Grn base, yellow/red shack, 46-49 black alignment frame, alum bridge. Reissued in 97	(4)	**375**
314	**Plate Girder Bridge** Gray sheet metal 45-48,50 base, diecast sides	(3)	**35**
315	**Trestle Bridge** Aluminum, Illuminated 46,47	(3)	**175**
316	**Trestle Bridge** same as 315 but painted gray, 49 and no light	(3)	**55**
317	**Trestle Bridge** Gray, same as 316, 50-56	(2)	**30**
321	**Trestle Bridge** Aluminum Sheet metal base, 58-64 gray plastic sides	(2)	**75**
332	**Arch Under Bridge** Black metal span, 59-66 gray plastic sides	(3)	**60**
334	**Operating Dispatching Board** Green board, 57-60 tan base, blue man	(4)	**300**
342	**Culvert Loader** Black metal base, red/gray 56-58 building operates with 345 and 6342 culvert car	(3)	**275**
345	**Culvert Unloading Station** Black metal base, 57-59 gray ramp, red-gray tower, operates w/342 and 6342	(4)	**350**
346	**Culvert Unloader** *Sears* Manual identical U64,65 to 348/9836 set with 2347 C&O GP-7, hand operated with crank	(4+)	**225**
347	**Cannon Firing Range Set** Olive drab, U64 4 cannons, 4 silver shells, *9820 Sears Military Set*	(5)	**800***
348	**Culvert Unloader** Manual 348s are 66-69 346s with a piece of tape, 348 rubber-stamped on it placed over the 346 number on the box	(4)	**240**
350	**Engine Transfer Table** Black metal base, 57-60 yell building, red light on top w/350-89 rail brackets	(4)	**300**
350-50	**Transfer Table Extension** Black metal base, 57-60 with 350-89 rail brackets	(4)	**200**
352	**Ice Depot** White shed, red roof, blue man 55-57 with orange arms and paddle, with 6352-1 car		
	1. Brown base	(4)	**350**
	2. Red base	(3)	**275**
353	**Trackside Control Signal** Tan base, 60,61 white pole with 2 target lamp cover	(2)	**40**
356	**Operating Freight Station** Maroon/white, 52-57 picket fence with signs two blue baggage men with carts, green, orange, or red carts (known to exist), some baggage loads lithographed		
	1. Dark green roof	(2)	**100**
	2. Light green roof	(5)	**300**

362	**Barrel Loader** Gray base/yellow ramp 52-57 brown plastic fence, cream or blue man. NDV		
	1. Gray molded plastic base	(3)	**125**
	2. Painted gray base	(3+)	**150**
364	**Conveyor Lumber Loader** 48-54		
	1. Painted gray, smooth finish	(3)	**100**
	2. Painted darker gray, crackle finish	(4)	**120**
365	**Dispatch Station** gray base, red control room, 59 gray roof, yell microwave tower, 2 yellow speakers	(3)	**175**
375	**Turntable** Battery operated 62-64	(4)	**150▼**
394	**Rotary Beacon** Beware of repro beacons. 49-53		
	1. Tower, base, top painted red	(2)	**35**
	2. Tower, base, top painted green	(4)	**90**
	3. Tower, base, top unpainted aluminum	(3)	**70**
	4. Tower, base, top painted aluminum	(3)	**50**
	5. Tower, top unpainted aluminum painted red base	(4)	**100**
	6. Tower unpainted aluminum/red base and top	(5)	*
395	**Floodlight Tower** 49,50,52-56		
	1. Tower, base, top painted yellow	(5)	**150**
	2. Tower, base, top painted silver	(3)	**50**
	3. Tower, base, top painted red	(4)	**75**
	4. Tower, base, top unpainted aluminum	(3)	**50**
	5. Tower, base, top painted green	(3)	**100**
397	**Diesel Operating Coal Loader** Gray metal 48-57 base, red tray		
	1. Yellow motor cover, yard light	(5)	**450**
	2. Blue motor cover, no yard light	(3)	**125**
410	**Billboard Blinker** Blk, goes w/310 billboard 56-58	(4)	**60**
415	**Diesel Fueling Station** White/red, gray base, 55-67 blue/white tank	(4)	**135**
419	**Heliport Control Tower** Red tower, gray roof, 62 spring mechanism, yellow dish/yellow-black copter, one-piece prop	(5)	**450**
443	**Missile Launching Platform** Blue launcher, 60-62 tan base, with exploding ammo dump	(3)	**110**
445	**Switch Tower** Two blue men white tower, 52-57 green roof, maroon base	(2)	**85**
448	**Missile Firing Range Set** Gray launcher, 61-63 tan base, 6448 Target car	(4)	**160**
450	**Signal Bridge** Spans 2 tracks Gray base, 52-58 black metal gridwork, two lights	(3)	**60**
452	**Gantry Signal** Gray base, black metal 61-63 gridwork, one signal light	(4)	**110**
455	**Oil Derrick** Red base, green tower, 50-54 metal Sunoco sign.		
	1. Green tower, red top	(4)	**325**
	2. Green tower, green top	(3)	**180**
	3. Light green tower, red top	(5)	**400***
	4. Light green tower, green top	(5)	*
456	**Coal Ramp** w/3456 *N&W* Operating Hopper 50-55 designed to operate with 397 Coal Loader, red light, 456C controller, red tray		
	1. Dark gray ramp	(3)	**325**
	2. Light gray ramp	(2)	**200**
460	**Piggyback Transportation** 55-57 Came with 2 versions of lift trucks ***Note: Must have lift truck driver***		
	1. White heat-stamped lettering	(3)	**125**
	2. Black stick-on label, white lettering	(3)	**125**
460P	**Piggyback Platform** 460P on box 55-57 (must have box)	(5)	**100**
461	**Platform with Truck & Midge** Gray base, U66 white *Midge Toy* trailer	(4)	**200**

462	**Derrick Platform Set** 61,62 Tan base/yellow crane, 3 black cranks	(5)	**500**
464	**Lumber Mill** Gray base, red roof 56-60 Reissued as 2301 in 1980, original has 464 in window	(3)	**195**
465	**Sound Dispatching Station** Tan base, 56,57 red room, gray roof yellow dish with gray microphone and internal speaker	(3)	**125**
470	**Missile Launching Platform** Tan base, 59-62 blue launcher, with 6470 Target car	(4)	**125**
494	**Rotary Beacon** 54-66		
	1. Tower, base, platform painted red	(3)	**50**
	2. Tower, base, platform unpainted alum	(3)	**50**
	3. Tower, base, platform painted alum	(3)	**50**
497	**Coaling Station** 53-58		
	1. Dk green roof/metal brace	(4)	**325**
	2. Dark green roof/no brace	(3)	**175**
	3. Light green roof/no brace	(3)	**175**
902	**Lionel Elevated Trestle Set** Packaged in paper U59 bag. Parts punched out of heavy cardboard sheets.	(5)	**375**
908	**Cardboard Railroad Station** U59-62 Came with uncataloged sets X810NA, 19394, 19395.	(5)	**1500▲***
910	**Cardboard Submarine Base** U61 Included in uncataloged set X-625 w/228 CN Alco X-714 w USMC.	(5)	**5000▲***
920	**Scenic Display Set** 57,58	(4)	**300▲**
920-2	**Tunnel Portals** "Hillside" 57	(4)	**75**
943	**Exploding Ammo Dump** Gray base, 59,60 olive drab body, mousetrap mechanism	(4)	**60**
970	**Ticket Booth** Cardboard, 46"h x 23w x 11deep 58-60	(4)	**250▲**
1045	**Operating Watchman** Requires 1045C, 46-50 Red base, blue man w/flesh-colored hands & face, aluminum pole, nickel or brass RR warning sign. NDV	(3)	**60**
1047	**Operating Switchman** Green metal base, 59-61 blue switchman with red flag, blue or black fuel tank on base. NDV	(4)	**150**

Replacement Accessories

Note: These were the smaller items, such as the cans for the operating milk car, that were often lost or broken. Lionel sold replacements, usually in a group, which came in their own boxes or other packages. Each box had its own catalog number. Most items are extremely hard to find. Values and rarity ratings are based on the items being in their original packaging.
Prices are for Excellent with the box with any additional packaging.

B909	Same as 909 but in blister pack 66		*
L363	**Miniature Lamps**	(3)	**15**
L461	**Miniature Lamps**	(3)	**15**
SP	**Smoke Pellets** (box of 12) 48-69	(4)	**500**
28	**Lamp "r"**		*
35-30	**Telephone Pole** for Generator Car	(3)	**250***
39-3	**12-Volt Lamp**		*
40	**Dealer display box** wire on eight plastic cables	(5)	**500***
40-25	**4-conductor Wire** on cable (envelope)	(4)	**50**
40-40	Same as 40-25 but 3-conductor wire	(4)	**75**
44-80	**Four Missiles** (envelope) 59-60	(2)	**40**
47-73	**12-Volt Red Lamps** (box of 12)	(4)	**25**
55-150	**24 Ties for Tie-Jector** (envelope) 59,60	(3)	**50**
64-15	**12-Volt Opal Lamps** (box of 12)	(4)	**25**
111-50	**Trestle Set** (Father-Son Set)	(5)	**500**
111-100	**Two Trestle Tiers** (envelope) 60	(3)	**50**

122	**Lamp Assortment Kit**	(4)	**85**
123	**Lamp Assortment**	(4)	**300**
123-60	**Lamp Assortment Kit**	(5)	**125**
152-33	**12-Volt Red Lamps** (box of 12)	(4)	**75**
153-23	**6-8-Volt Red Lamps** (box of 12)	(4)	**75**
160	**Unloading bin** w/separate sale box		
	1. Multicolored	(4+)	**60**
	2. Black	(4)	**100**
	3. Tuscan	(4+)	**60**
	4. Sheet-metal (no box)	(5)	**200***
164-64	**Five Logs** 52-58	(3)	**50**
165-53	**18-Volt Red Lamps** (box of 12)	(4)	**25**
175-50	**Rocket** (zip-lock plastic bag) 58-60	(4)	**175**
182-22	**Metal punch-outs** in cloth bag w/drawstring, for use with magnetic cranes	(5)	**150***
195-75	**Eight Bulb Floodlight Head**		
	1. In early box	(4)	**250**
	2. In late box	(5)	**350**
196	**Smoke Pellets,** in clear plastic "lunchbox" 46,47 containers (12 pack)	(5)	**200▲***
197-75	**Radar Screen** for 197		
	1. Silver screen	(5)	**500***
	2. Chrome screen	(5)	**500***
206	**Bag of Artificial Coal**, 46-59	(3)	**35**
207	**Bag of Artificial Coal** smaller than 206, usually included with operating coal cars and accessories	(5)	**75***
0209	**Six Small Barrels**	(3)	**50**
216	**Miniature Lamps**	(3)	**25**
264-150	**12 Boards for Forklift Platform** (envelope) 57-59	(4)	**60**
352-55	**7 Ice Cubes for Icing Station** (envelope) 55-57	(4)	**65**
356-35	**Two Baggage Trucks** 52-56		
	1. No load	(3)	**65**
	2. With load	(4)	**150**
362-78	**Six Barrels** 52-58	(2)	**35**
394-37	**Rotating Beacon Latern**, 54-60	(3)	**25**
450L	**Signal Light Head** 52-58	(4)	**150**
460-150	**Two Piggyback Vans** w/either 2 white 55-57 or 2 green vans	(5)	**450***
464-150	**6 Boards for Lumber Mill** (envelope) 56-58	(3)	**45**
479 and 479-1	**Trucks** for 6362 Railway Truck Car (envelope)	(2)	**35***
480-25	**Conversion Coupler** 50-60	(2)	**20***
480-32	**Conversion Coupler** 61-69	(2)	**20***
671S	**Conversion Kit** 47-49	(4)	**300▲***
671-75	**Smoke Lamps**	(4)	**50**
703-10	**Smoke Lamp**	(4)	**50**
726S	**Conversion Kit** 47-49	(5)	**400▲***
909	**Smoke Fluid** (box of 4) 58-69	(4)	**150**
919	**Artificial Grass** 46-64	(2)	**25**
920-3	**Green Grass** (Scenic Display Set) 57,58	(3)	**35**
920-4	**Yellow Grass** (Scenic Display Set) 57,58	(3)	**35**
920-5	**Artificial Rock** (Scenic Display Set) 57,58	(4)	**50**
920-8	**Lichen** (Scenic Display Set) 57,58	(4)	**50**
925	**Lubricant** 2-oz 46-69 (with box)	(2)	**35**
926	**Lubricant** 1/2-oz (same as above)		
927	**Lubricant and Maintenance Kit** 1-track cleaner, 1-lubricant, 1-oil, 1-wooden tamper, 1-brush, 2-pointed sticks, 6-emery boards	(4)	**65**

928	**Lubricant & Maintenance Kit** 60-63 oiler, eraser rail cleaner, grease, track cleaner	(5)	**200***
1640-100	**1960 Presidential Special Kit** 60	(5)	**500***
3330-100	**Operating Submarine Kit** 60	(5)	**750***
3356-2	**Operating Horse Car** in separate sale box	(4)	**750***
3356-100	**Nine Horses** 56-59	(4)	**75**
3356-150	**Horse Corral** 56,57	(4)	**600**
3357-27	**Components for Cop & Hobo Car**	(4)	**150***
3366-100	**Nine White Horses** 59,60	(3)	**200**
3424-50	**One Tell-Tale Pole**	(5)	**500***
3424-100	**Two Tell-Tale Poles** 56-58	(4)	**75***
3454-51	**Baby Ruth Packing Cases**	(5)	**150***
3462P	**Milk Car Platform** 52-55	(3)	**2000***
3462-70	**Seven Magnetic Milk Cans** 52-59	(3)	**40**
3530-50	**Telephone Pole** searchlight 56,57	(4)	**125**
3656-34	**Nine Cattle** 52-58	(3)	**75**
3656-150	**Cattle Corral** 52-55	(4)	**1100***
3662-79	**Seven Milk Cans** (envelope) 55-57,59	(5)	**40***
3672P	**Bosco Platform**	(5)	**5000***
3672-79	**Seven Bosco Milk Cans** 59,60	(5)	**125***
3927-50	**Cotton Track Cleaning Patches** (qty 25) 57-60	(2)	**35**
3927-75	**Track Cleaner** 56-69	(4)	**35**
5159	**Lubricant & Maintenance Kit** for slotcars, 65,65	(3)	**75**
6112-25	**Four Canisters** either 1 red & 1-white, 56-58 or 2 of either color		
	1.White lettering	(3)	**50**
	2. Black lettering	(3)	**600***
6352-25	**Box for Ice Car**	(5)	**2000***
6414-25	**Four Automobiles** 55-57	(4)	**750**
6454	**Replacement Car Bodies**	(4)	**50***
6511-24	**Five Pipes** 55-58	(3)	**100**
6650-80	**Missile** 59,60	(3)	**75**
6800-60	**Airplane** 57,58	(4)	**400***
6801-60	**Boat** 57,58	(4)	**200**
6816-100	**Bulldozer** 59,60	(4)	**1000***
6817-100	**Earth Scraper** 59,60	(4)	**1500***
6827-100	**Power Shovel** 60	(4)	**200***
6828-100	**Truck Crane** 60	(4)	**200***

Track

OC	**Curved Track** O gauge, 45-61	(1)	**10**
OCS	**Insulated Curved Track** O gauge, 50		*
OS	**Straight Track** O gauge, 45-61	(1)	**10**
OSS	**Insulated Straight Track** O gauge 46,50		*
OTC	**Lockon** 55-59	(1)	**3**
RCS	**Remote Control Track** O gauge 46-48 with RCS-20 two-button controller	(3)	**20**
UCS	**Remote Control Track** O gauge 49-66, 68,69	(3)	**25**
TOC	**Same as OC**		
TOS	**Same as OS**		
TO20	**90 Degree Crossing** O gauge 62-66,69	(3)	**20**
UCS	**Remote Control Track** O gauge		
1/2 OC	**1/2 Curve Track** O gauge		**25***
1/2OS	**1/2 Straight Track** O gauge		*
5/C	**Test Set**	(4)	**2800**

5/F	**Test Set**	(4)	**5000**
O20X	**45 Degree Crossover** 46-59	(1)	**20**
O20	**90 Degree Crossover** 45-61	(1)	**20**
O22	**Remote Control Switches** (price per pair) 45-61	(1)	**125**
O22A	**Remote Control Switch** 47U	(4)	**100**
O22LH	**Remote Control Switch** 45-61	(2)	**75**
O22RH	**Remote Control Switch** 45-61	(2)	**75**
O25	**Bumper** Black, O gauge 46,47	(3)	**30**
O26	**Bumper** 48-50		
	1. Gray, 48 only	(4)	**125**
	2. Red	(1)	**40**
O42	**Manual Switches** (pair) 47-59	(3)	**75**
31	**Curved Track** Super O 57-66	(3)	**3**
32	**Straight Track** Super O 57-66	(3)	**3**
33	**1/2 Curved Track** Super O 57-66	(3)	**2**
34	**1/2 Straight Track** Super O 57-66	(3)	**2**
36	**Remote Control Set** Super O includes 57-66 90 controller and wires	(3)	**20**
37	**Uncoupling Track Set** Super O includes 57-66 90 controller and wires	(3)	**20**
38	**Adapter Track** Super O Adapts other track 57-61 to Super O (pair of straight sections)	(3)	**20**
43	**Power Track** Super O 59-66	(3)	**10**
48	**Straight Track** Super O insulated 57-66	(3)	**10**
49	**Curved Track** Super O insulated, 57-66	(3)	**10**
112	**Super O Switches** (pair)	(4)	**125**
112-125 & 112LH	**Super O Switch** Left Hand 57-60	(4)	**60**
112-150 & 112RH	**Super O Switch** Right Hand 57-60	(4)	**60**
120	**Super O 90 Degree Crossing** 57-66	(3)	**12**
130	**Super O 60 Degree Crossing** 57-66	(4)	**40**
142	**Super O Manual Switches** (price per pair) 57-66	(3)	**60**
142-125	**Super O LH Manual Switch** 57-60	(3)	**40**
142-150	**Super O RH Manual Switch** 57-60	(3)	**40**
260	**Bumper** 51-69		
	1. Red diecast for regular O	(2)	**30**
	2. Black plastic for Super O	(5)	**150**
760	**O72 Track Package 16 Sections** 50, 54-57 (72" circle)	(4)	**60**
1008	**O27 Uncoupling Clip** 57-62	(3)	**10**
1008-50	**O27 Track** w/uncoupling clip	(3)	**10**
1009	**Manumatic Track Section** 48-52 Used with Scout Sets	(3)	**10**
1013	**O27 Curved Track** 45-66, 68,69	(1)	**1**
1018	**O27 Straight Track** 45-66, 68,69	(1)	**1**
1019	**Remote Control 0-27 Track** w/RCS 20, 46-48	(2)	**15**
1020	**O27 90 Degree Crossing** 55-66, 68,69	(2)	**10**
1022	**O27 Manual Switches** (price per pair) 53-66, 69,69	(2)	**25**
1023	**O27 45 Degree Crossing** 56-66, 68,69	(2)	**5**
1024	**0-27 Manual Switches** (price per pair) 46-52	(2)	**30**
1025	**O27 Bumper** Black w/lamp, 46,47	(2)	**15**
1121	**O27 Remote Control Switches** (pair) 46-51	(3)	**30**
1122	**O27 Remote Control Switches** (pair) 52	(2)	**50**
1122E	**O27 Remote Control Switches** (pair) 53-66, 68,69	(3)	**30**
1122LH	**O27 LH Remote Control Switch** 55-66,68,69	(3)	**15**
1122RH	**O27 RH Remote Control Switch** 55-66,68,69	(3)	**15**

6009	**O27 Uncoupling track** 53-55	(2)	**20**
6019	**O27 Remote Control Track** 48-66	(2)	**20**
6029	**O27 Remote Control Track** 55-63	(2)	**25**
6149	**O27 Remote Control Track** 64-66, 68,69	(2)	**10**

Transformers and Controllers

ECU-1	**Train Control Unit** Electronic set	(4)	**100**
KW	190 Watts 50-65	(4)	**175**
LW	125 Watts 55-66	(3)	**125**
Q	75 Watts 46	(2)	**60**
R	100 Watt or 110 Watt 46, 47	(3)	**80**
RW	110 Watt 48-54	(3)	**75**
S	80 Watts 47	(2)	**40**
SW	130 Watts 61-66	(4)	**100**
TW	175 Watts 53-60	(3)	**150**
V	150 Watts 46,47	(3)	**150**
VW	150 Watts 48,49	(3)	**200**
Z	250 Watts 45-47	(4)	**175**
ZW	250 Watts 48,49	(3)	**200**
ZW	275 Watts 50-66	(4)	**225**
88	**Controller** 46-50	(1)	**10**
90	**Controller** 55-66	(2)	**15**
91	**Circuit Breaker**	(3)	**25**
92	**Circuit Breaker**	(2)	**20**
96C	**Controller** 45-54	(2)	**20**
145C	**Contactor** 50-60	(1)	**7**
147	**Whistle Controller**	(2)	**13**
148-100	**Double Pole Switch** 57,58	(2)	**25**
153C	**Contactor** 46-66, 68,69	(1)	**5**
167	**Whistle Controller**	(2)	**15**
364C	**Switch** 59-64	(2)	**15**
390C	**Switch** 60-64	(3)	**30**
413	**Countdown Control Panel** Gray 62 (can be used with any operating car)	(3)	**75**
1010	35 Watt	(2)	**25**
1011	25 Watt	(2)	**25**
1012	35 Watt	(2)	**25**
1014	40 Watt	(2)	**25**
1015	45 Watt	(3)	**25**
1016	35 Watt	(3)	**25**
1025	45 Watt	(3)	**25**
1026	25 Watt	(2)	**25**
1032	75 Watt	(3)	**75**
1033	90 Watt	(3)	**75**
1034	75 Watt	(3)	**75**
1037	40 Watt	(2)	**40**
1041	60 Watt	(2)	**40**
1042	75 Watt	(3)	**50**
1043	50 Watt Black Case	(2)	**25**
1043-500	**Girls Train Transformer** 60 Watt (Ivory case)	(4)	**225▲**
1044	90 Watt	(3)	**75**
1053	60 Watt	(2)	**25**
1063	75 Watt	(3)	**50**
1073	60 Watt	(3)	**50**

Lionel Cataloged Sets 1945-1969

Note: Prices listed are for Excellent Boxed w/all inserts and packaging

463W	**O Gauge 4-Car Freight Set** 45 (224, 2466W, 2458, 2452, 2555, 2457)	(5)	**650**
1000W	**027 3-Car Set** 55 (2016, 6026W, 6014 red, 6012, 6017)	(4)	**225**
1001	**027 3-Car Set** 55 (610, 6012, 6014 red, 6017)	(3)	**325**
1111	**Lionel Scout Set** 48 (1001, 1001T, 1002 blue, 1005, 1007)	(3)	**200**
1112	**Lionel Scout Set** 48 (1101, 1001T, 1002 blue, 1004, 1005, 1007)	(4)	**250**
1113	**Lionel Scout Train** 50 (1120, 1001T, 1002 black, 1005, 1007)	(3)	**150**
1115	**Lionel Scout** 49 (1110, 1001T, 1002 black, 1005, 1007)	(4)	**150**
1117	**Lionel Scout** 49 (1110, 1001T, 1002 black, 1005, 1004, 1007)	(3)	**150**
1119	**Scout 3-Car Freight** 51, 52 (1110, 1001T, 1002 black, 1004, 1007)	(2)	**150**
1400	**Lionel 027 Passenger Set** 46 (221, 221T, two blue 2430s, blue 2431)	(4)	**675**
1400W	**Lionel 027 Passenger Set** 46 (221, 221W, two blue 2430s, blue 2431)	(5)	**800**
1401	**Lionel 027 Freight Outfit** 46 (1654, 1654T, 2452X, 2465, 2472)	(3)	**150**
1401W	**Lionel 027 Freight Outfit** 46 (1654, 1654W, 2452X, 2465, 2472)	(5)	**250**
1402	**Lionel 027 Passenger Set** 46 (1666, 2466T, two green 2440s, green 2441)	(4)	**500**
1402W	**Lionel 027 Passenger Set** 46 (1666, 2466W, two green 2440s, green 2441)	(5)	**600**
1403	**Lionel 027 Freight Train** 46 (221, 221T ,2411, 2465, 2472)	(4)	**425**
1403W	**Lionel 027 Freight Train** 46 (221, 221W, 2411, 2465, 2472)	(5)	**525**
1405	**Lionel 027 Freight Train** 46 (1666, 2466T, 2452X, 2465, 2472)	(3)	**185**
1405W	**Lionel 027 Freight Train** 46 (1666, 2466W, 2452X, 2465, 2472)	(5)	**250**
1407B	**Lionel 027 Switcher Bell Outfit** 46 (1665, 2403B, 2452X, 2560, 2419)	(5)	**900**
1409	**Lionel 027 Freight Train** 46 (1666, 2466T, 3559, 2465, 3454, 2472)	(4)	**425**
1409W	**Lionel 027 Freight Train** 46 (1666, 2466W, 3559, 2465, 3454, 2472)	(5)	**525**
1411W	**Freight Outfit** 46 (1666, 2466WX, 2452X, 2465, 2454, 2472)	(4)	**250**
1413WS	**Lionel 027 Freight Train** 46 (2020, 2020W, 2452X, 2465, 2454, 2472)	(3)	**350**
1415WS	**Lionel 027 Freight Set** 46 (2020, 2020W, 3459, 3454, 2465, 2472)	(4)	**550**
1417WS	**Lionel 027 Freight Outfit** 46 (2020, 2020W, 2465, 3451, 2560, 2419)	(4)	**750**
1419WS	**Lionel 027 Freight Train** 46 (2020, 2020W, 3459, 97, 2452X, 2560, 2419)	(5)	**900**
1421WS	**Lionel 027 Freight Train** 46 (2020, 2020W, 3451, 164, 2465, 3454, 2472)	(5)	**1000**

1423W	**Lionel 3-Car Freight Outfit** 48, 49		
	(1655, 6654W, 6452, 6465, 6257) 48	(3)	**150**
	(1655, 6654W, 6462, 6465, 6257) 49	(3)	**150**
1425B	**Switcher Freight** 48, 49		
	(1656, 6403B, 6456 black, 6465, 6257X) 48	(4)	**850**
	(1656, 6403B, 6456 black, 6465, 6257) 49	(4)	**850**
1426WS	**Lionel Passenger Set** 48, 49 (2026, 6466WX, two green 2440s, grn 2441)	(4)	**600**
1427WS	**Lionel Three-Car Freight Set** 48 (2026, 6466WX, 6465, 6454, 6257)	(3)	**250**
1429WS	**Four-Car Freight Set** 48 (2026, 6466WX, 3451, 6465, 6454, 6357)	(3)	**225**
1430WS	**Passenger Train** 48, 49 (2025, 6466WX, 2400, 2402, 2401)	(4)	**800**
1431	**Lionel Freight Train** 47 (1654, 1654T, 2452X, 2465, 2472)	(4)	**150**
1431W	**Lionel Freight Train** 47 (1654, 1654W, 2452X, 2465, 2472)	(4)	**150**
1432	**Lionel Passenger Set** 47 (221, 221T, two blue 2430s, blue 2431)	(4)	**900**
1432W	**Lionel Passenger Set** 47 (221, 221W, two blue 2430s, blue 2431)	(4)	**900**
1433	**Lionel Freight Train** 47 (221, 221T, 2411, 2465, 2472)	(4)	**400**
1433W	**Lionel Freight Train** 47 (221, 221W, 2411, 2465, 2472)	(4)	**400**
1434WS	**Passenger Train** 47 (2025, 2466WX , two green 2440s, green 2441)	(4)	**400**
1435WS	**Lionel Freight Train** 47 (2025, 2466WX, 2452X, 2454, 2472)	(3)	**250**
1437WS	**Lionel Freight Set** 47 (2025, 2466WX, 2452X, 2465, 2454, 2472)	(3)	**275**
1439WS	**Lionel Freight Outfit** 47 (2025, 2466WX, 3559, 2465, 3454, 2472)	(4)	**425**
1441WS	**De Luxe Work Outfit** 47 (2020, 2020W, 2461, 3451, 2560, 2419)	(4)	**550**
1443WS	**4-Car Freight** 47 (2020, 2020W, 3459, 3462, 2465, 2472)	(4)	**425**
1445WS	**4-Car Freight** 48 (2025, 6466WX, 3559, 6465, 6454, 6357)	(4)	**325**
1447WS	**De Luxe Work Train** 48, 49 (2020, 6020W, 3451, 2461, 2460, 6419) 48 (2020, 6020W, 3461, 6461, 2460, 6419) 49	(4)	**525**
1449WS	**5-Car Freight Outfit** 48 (2020, 6020W, 3462, 6465, 3459, 6411, 6357)	(4)	**450**
1451WS	**3-Car Freight** 49 (2026, 6466WX,6462, 3464, 6257)	(3)	**275**
1453WS	**4-Car Freight** 49 (2026, /6466WX, 3464, 6465, 3461, 6357)	(3)	**375**
1455WS	**4-Car 027 Freight** 49 (2025, 6466WX, 6462, 6465, 3472, 6357)	(3)	**400**
1457B	**4-Car Diesel Freight** 49, 50 (6220, 6462, 3464, 6520, 6419)	(4)	**625**
1459WS	**027 5-Car Freight Outfit** 49 (2020, 6020W, 6411, 3656, 6465, 3469, 6357)	(4)	**550**
1461S	**3-Car Freight With Smoke** 50 (6110, 6001T, 6002, 6004, 6007)	(2)	**175**
1463W	**027 3-Car Freight** 50 (2036, 6466W, 6462, 6465, 6257)	(2)	**175**
1463WS	**027 3-Car Freight** 51 (2026, 6466W, 6462, 6465, 6257)	(3)	**200**

1464W	**027 Diesel 3-Car Pullman** 50 (2023 AA yellow, 2481, 2482, 2483)	(4)	1200▼
1464W	**027 Diesel 3-Car Pullman** 51 (2023 AA silver, 2421, 2422, 2423 cars w/gray roof)	(4)	900
1464W	**3-Car Pullman** 52, 53 (2033 AA silver, 2421, 2422, 2423 cars w/silver roof)	(4)	800▼
1465	**3-Car Freight** (2034, 6066T, 6032, 6035, 6037) 52	(2)	175
1467W	**027 Diesel 4-Car Freight** 50, 51 (2023 AA yellow, 6656, 6465, 6456, 6357) 50 (2023 AA silver, 6656, 6465, 6456, 6357) 51	(3)	550▼
1467W	**4-Car Freight** 52, 53 (Twin 2032, 6656, 6456, 6465, 6357)	(4)	475▼
1469WS	**027 4-Car Freight** 50, 51 (2035, 6466W, 6462, 6465, 6456 black, 6257) 50 (2035, 6466W, 6462, 6465, 6456 maroon, 6257) 51	(2)	225
1471WS	**5-Car Freight** 50, 51 (2035, 6466W, 3469X, 6465, 6454, 3461X, 6357)	(3)	350
1473WS	**4-Car Freight** 50 (2046, 2046W, 3464, 6465, 6520, 6357)	(3)	400
1475WS	**5-Car Freight** 50 (2046, 2046W, 3656, 3461X, 6472, 3469X, 6419)	(3)	500
1477S	**027 3-Car Freight** 51, 52 (2026, 6466T, 6012, 6014 white, 6017)	(3)	200
1479WS	**027 4-Car Freight** 52 (2056, 2046W, 6462, 6465, 6456, 6257)	(3)	425
1481WS	**5-Car Freight** 51 (2035, 6466W, 3464, 6465, 3472, 6462, 6357)	(3)	375
1483WS	**5-Car Freight** 52 (2056, 2046W, 3472, 6462, 3474, 6465, 6357)	(4)	625
1484WS	**4-Car Pullman** 52 (2056, 2046W, 2421, 2422, 2429, 2423 w/silver roof)	(4)	800▼
1485WS	**027 3-Car Freight** 52 (2025, 6466W, 6462, 6465, 6257)	(3)	225
1500	**027 3-Car Freight** 53, 54 (1130, 6066T, 6032, 6034, 6037)	(1)	150
1501S	**027 3-Car Freight** 53 (2026, 6066T, 6032, 6035, 6037)	(2)	160
1502WS	**027 3-Car Pullman** 53 (2055, 2046W, 2421, 2422, 2423)	(4)	650▼
1503WS	**027 4-Car Freight** NDV, 53, 54 (2055, 6026W, 6462 blk, 6456 black, 6465, 6257) 53 (2055, 6026W, 6462 blk, 6456 maroon, 6465, 6257) 54	(2)	350
1505WS	**027 4-Car Freight** 53 (2046, 2046W, 6464-1, 6462, 6415, 6357)	(3)	450
1507WS	**027 5-Car Freight** 53 (2046, 2046W, 3472, 6415, 6462, 6468, 6357)	(3)	450
1509WS	**027 5-Car Freight** 53 (2046, 2046W, 3520, 6456, 3469, 6460, 6419)	(2)	500
1511S	**027 4-Car Freight** 53 (2037, 6066T, 6032, 3474, 6035, 6037)	(4)	300
1513S	**027 4-Car Freight** 54, 55 (2037, 6026T, 6012, 6014 red, 6015, 6017)	(1)	200
1515WS	**027 5-Car Freight** 54 (2065, 2046W, 6415, 6462, 6464-25, 6456, 6357)	(4)	400▼
1516WS	**027 3-Car Passenger** 54 (2065, 2046W, 2434, 2432, 2436)	(4)	650▼
1517W	**027 4-Car Freight** 54 (2245P/C AB, 6464-225, 6561, 6462 green, 6427)	(4)	1100
1519WS	**027 5-Car Freight** 54 (2065, 6026W, 3461, 6462 red, 6356, 3482, 6427)	(4)	550

1520W	**027 Texas Special 3-Car Passenger** 54 (2245P/C AB, 2432, 2435, 2436)	(5)	**1700▼**
1521WS	**027 5-Car Freight** 54 (2065, 2046W, 3620, 3562 black, 6561, 6460 black cab, 6419)	(4)	**700**
1523	**027 4-Car Work Train** 54 (6250, 6511, 6456 gray, 6460 red cab, 6419)	(4)	**700**
1527	**027 3-Car Work Train** 55 (1615, 1615T, 6462, 6560 gray cab, 6119)	(4)	**500**
1529	**027 3-Car Freight** (2028, 6311, 6436, 6257) 55	(5)	**750**
1531W	**027 4-Car Freight** 55 (2328, 6462 red, 6456, 6465, 6257)	(4)	**650**
1533WS	**027 Freight Hauler** 55 (2055, 6026W, 3562 yellow, 6436, 6465, 6357)	(4)	**450**
1534W	**027 3-Car Passenger** (2328, 2434, 2432, 2436) 55	(4)	**1000**
1536W	**027 3-Car Passenger** 55 (2245P/C AB, 2432, 2432, 2436)	(4)	**1700▼**
1537WS	**027 4-Car Freight** 55 (2065, 2046W, 3562 yellow, 3469, 6464-275, 6357)	(4)	**575**
1538WS	**027 4-Car Passenger** 55 (2065, 2046W, 2435, 2434, 2432, 2436)	(4)	**900**
1539W	**027 5-Car Freight** 55 (2243P/C AB, 3620, 6446, 6561, 6560, 6419)	(4)	**900**
1541WS	**027 5-Car Freight** 55 (2065, 2046W, 3482, 3461, 6415, 3494, 6427)	(4)	**600**
1542	**027 3-Car Freight** (520, 6014 red, 6012, 6017) 56	(3)	**250**
1543	**027 3-Car Freight** (627, 6121, 6112, 6017) 56	(4)	**225**
1545	**027 4-Car Freight** (628, 6424, 6014 red, 6257) 56	(4)	**325**
1547S	**027 Freight Hauler** 56 (2018, 6026T, 6121, 6112, 6014 red, 6257)	(4)	**200**
1549S	**027 3-Car Work Train** 56 (1615, 1615T, 6262, 6560, 6119 orange)	(4)	**900**
1551S	**027 4-Car Freight** (621, 6362, 6425, 6562, 6257) 56	(4)	**400**
1552	**027 Passenger** (629, 2434, 2432, 2436) 56	(5)	**1100**
1553W	**027 5-Car Freight** 56 (2338, 6430, 6462 red, 6464-425, 6346, 6257)	(4)	**700**
1555WS	**027 Freight Hauler** 56 (2018, 6026W, 3361, 6464-400, 6462 red, 6257)	(3)	**400**
1557W	**027 5-Car Work Train** 56 (621, 6436, 6511, 3620, 6560, 6119)	(4)	**525**
1559W	**027 5-Car Freight** 56 (2338, 6414, 3562 yellow, 6362, 3494-275, 6357)	(4)	**750**
1561WS	**027 5-Car Freight** 56 (2065, 6026W, 6430, 3424, 6262, 6562, 6257)	(4)	**550**
1562W	**027 4-Car Passenger** 56 (2328, 2442, 2442, 2444, 2446)	(4)	**2000**
1563W	**027 5-Car Freight** 56 (2240P/C AB, 6467, 3562 yellow, 3620, 6414, 6357)	(4)	**1750**
1565W	**027 5-Car Freight** 56 (2065, 6026W, 3662, 3650, 6414, 6346, 6357)	(4)	**600**
1567W	**027 5-Car Freight** 56 (2243P/C AB, 3356, 3424, 6672, 6430, 6357)	(4)	**1100**
1569	**027 4-Car Freight** 57 (202, 6014 white, 6111, 6112, 6017)	(3)	**300**
1571	**027 5-Car Freight** 57 (625, 6424, 6476, 6121, 6112, 6017)	(4)	**450**
1573	**027 5-Car Freight** 57 (250LT, 250T , 6025, 6112, 6464-425, 6476, 6017)	(4)	**250**

1575	**027 5-Car Freight** 57 (205P/T AA, 6111, 6121, 6112, 6560, 6119)	(4)	**400**
1577S	**027 6-Car Freight** 57 (2018, 1130T, 6121, 6464-475, 6111, 6014 red, 6112, 6017)	(4)	**250**
1578S	**027 3-Car Passenger** 57 (2018, 1130T, 2434, 2432, 2436)	(5)	**550**
1579S	**027 7-Car Freight** 57 (2037, 1130T, 6111, 6025, 6476, 6468, 6112, 6121, 6017)	(4)	**300**
1581	**027 7-Car Freight** 57 (611, 6476, 6024, 6424, 6464-650, 6025, 6560, 6119)	(4)	**500▼**
1583WS	**027 6-Car Freight** 57 (2037, 6026W, 6482, 6112, 6646, 6121, 6476 black, 6017)	(3)	**300**
1585W	**027 9-Car Freight Train** 57 (602, 6014 white,6121, 6025, 6464-525, 6112, 6024, 6476 gray, 6111, 6017)	(4)	**425**
1586	**027 3-Car Passenger** 57 (204P/T AA, 2432, 2432, 2436)	(4)	**700**
1587S	**Lady Lionel Pastel Train Set** 57, 58 (2037-500, 1130T-500, 6462-500, 6464-515, 6436-500, 6464-510, 6427-500)	(4)	**3800**
1589WS	**027 7-Car Freight** 57 (2037, 6026W, 6464-450, 6111, 6025 orange, 6024, 6424, 6112, 6017)	(4)	**450**
1590	**027 4-Car Steam Freight** 58 (249, 250T, 6014 red Bosco, 6151, 6112, 6017)	(3)	**300**
1591	**U.S. Marine Land & Sea Limited** 58 (212, 6809, 6807, 6803, 6017-50)	(4)	**1000▼**
1593	**5-Car UP Diesel Work Train** 58 (613, 6476, 6818, 6660, 6112, 6119)	(4)	**650**
1595	**027 Marine Battlefront Special** 58 (1625, 1625T, 6804, 6808, 6806, 6017 gray)	(5)	**1700**
1597S	**027 6-Car Coal King Smoking Freighter** 58 (2018, 1130T, 6014 orange, 6818, 6476 red, 6025 black, 6112 blue, 6017)	(4)	**350**
1599	**027 6-Car Texas Special Freight** 58 (210 AA, 6801-50 w/yellow hull boat, 6112-1 black, 6014 orange Bosco or red Frico, 6424-60, 6465-60 gray, 6017)	(3)	**450**
1600	**027 3-Car Burlington Passenger** 58 (216, 6572, 2432, 2436)	(4)	**900**
1601W	**027 5-Car Diesel Freight** 58 (2337, 6800, 6464-425, 6801, 6810, 6017)	(4)	**925**
1603WS	**027 5-Car Whistling Mountain Climber Steam Freight** 58 (2037, 6026W, 6424, 6014-60 white Bosco, 6818, 6112, 6017)	(4)	**375**
1605W	**027 6-Car Santa Fe Diesel Freight** 58 (208 AA, 6800, 6464-425, 6801, 6477, 6802, 6017)	(4)	**1000**
1607W	**027 6-Car Trouble Shooter Work Set** 58 (2037, 6026W, 6465, 6818, 6464-425, 6112, 6660, 6119)	(4)	**475**
1608W	**027 4-Car Merchants Limited Diesel Passenger** 58 (209P/T AA, 2434, 2432, 2432, 2436)	(5)	**1700**
1609	**027 3-Car Steam Freight** 59, 60 (246, 1130T, 6162-25 blue, 6476 red, 6057)	(2)	**125**
1611	**027 4-Car Alaskan Freight** 59 (614, 6825, 6162-50, 6465 black, 6027)	(3)	**650**
1612	**The General Old-Timer Outfit** 59, 60 (1862, 1862T, 1866, 1865)	(1)	**375**

1613S	**4-Car B&O Steam Freight** 59 (247, 247T, 6826, 6819, 6821, 6017)	(4)	**300**
1615	**5-Car Boston & Maine Diesel Freight** 59 (217P/C AB, 6800, 6464-475, 6812, 6825, 6017-100)	(4)	**625**
1617S	**5-Car Busy Beaver Steam Work Train** 59 (2018, 1130T, 6816, 6536, 6812, 6670, 6119)	(4)	**825**
1619W	**5-Car Santa Fe Diesel Freight** 59 (218P/T AA, 6819, 6802, 6801, 6519, 6017-185 gray)	(3)	**425**
1621WS	**5-Car Construction Special Steam Freight** 59 (2037, 6026W, 6825, 6519, 6062, 6464-475, 6017)	(3)	**325**
1623W	**5-Car NP Diesel Freight** 59 (2349, 3512, 3435, 6424, 6062, 6017)	(5)	**1300**
1625WS	**5-Car Action King Steam Freight** 59 (2037, 6026W, 6636, 3512, 6470, 6650, 6017)	(4)	**400**
1626W	**4-Car Santa Fe Diesel Passenger** 59 (208P/T AA, 3428, 2412 blue stripe, 2412 blue stripe, 2416 blue stripe)	(4)	**750**
1627S	**027 3-Car Steam Freight** 60 (244, 244T, 6062, 6825, 6017)	(1)	**125**
1629	**4-Car C & O Diesel Freight** 60 (225, 6650, 6470, 6819, 6219)	(1)	**325**
1631WS	**4-Car Industrial Steam Freight** 60 (243, 243W, 6519, 6812, 6465, 6017)	(2)	**325**
1633	**Land-Sea-Air 2-Unit Diesel Freight** 60 (224P/C AB, 6544, 6830, 6820, 6017-200)	(3)	**1100▼**
1635WS	**5-Car Heavy-Duty Special Steam Freight** 60 (2037, 243W, 6361, 6826, 6636, 6821, 6017)	(4)	**450**
1637W	**5-Car Twin Unit Diesel Freight** 60 (218P/T AA, 6475, 6175, 6464-475, 6801, 6017-185)	(4)	**550**
1639WS	**6-Car Power House Special Steam Freight** 60 (2037, 243W, 6816, 6817, 6812, 6530, 6560, 6119)	(5)	**1750**
1640W	**5-Car Presidential Campaign Special** 60 (218P/T AA, 3428, two 2412s blue stripe, 2416 blue stripe, 1640-100)	(3)	**700**
1641	**3-Car Headliner Steam Freight** 61 (246, 244T, 3362, 6162, 6057)	(1)	**150**
1642	**3-Car Circus Special Steam Freight** 61 (244, 1130T, 3376, 6405, 6119)	(2)	**200**
1643	**4-Car Sky-Scout Diesel Freight** 61 (230, 3509, 6050, 6175, 6058)	(2)	**275**
1644	**Frontier Special General Passenger** 61 (1862, 1862T, 3370, 1866, 1865)	(2)	**475**
1645	**027 4-Car Diesel Freight** 61 (229, 3410, 6465, 6825, 6059)	(3)	**250**
1646	**4-Car Utility Steam Freight** 61 (233, 233W, 6162, 6343, 6476 red, 6017)	(2)	**375**
1647	**Freedom Fighter Missile Launcher Outfit** 61 (45, 3665, 3519, 6830, 6448, 6814)	(4)	**950**
1648	**5-Car Supply Line Steam Freight** 61 (2037, 233W, 6062, 6465, 6519, 6476 red, 6017)	(2)	**275**
1649	**027 5-Car Two Unit Diesel Freight** 61 (218P/C AB, 6343, 6445, 6475, 6405, 6017)	(5)	**525**
1650	**5-Car Guardian Steam Freight** 61 (2037, 233W, 6544, 6470, 3330, 3419, 6017)	(4)	**475**
1651	**4-Car All Passenger Diesel** 61 (218P/T AA, 2414 blue stripe, two 2412s blue stripe, 2416 blue stripe)	(3)	**750**
1800	**The General Frontier Pack** 59, 60 (1862, 1862T, 1877, 1866, 1865, General Story Book)	(2)	**400**
1805	**Land-Sea-And Air Gift Pack** 60 (45, 3429, 3820, 6640, 6824)	(4)	**1900**

1809	**The Western Gift Pack** 61 (244, 1130 T, 3370, 3376, 1877, 6017)	(2)	**300**
1810	**The Space Age Gift Pack** 61 (231, 3665, 3519, 3820, 6017)	(2)	**550**
2100	**O Gauge 3-Car Passenger** 46 (224, 2466T, two brown 2442s, brn 2443)	(5)	**575**
2100W	**O Gauge 3-Car Passenger** 46 (224, 2466W, two brown 2442s, brn 2443)	(4)	**500**
2101	**O Gauge 3-Car Freight** 46 (224, 2466T, 2555, 2452, 2457)	(5)	**400**
2101W	**O Gauge 3-Car Freight** 46 (224, 2466W, 2555, 2452, 2457)	(4)	**350**
2103W	**O Gauge 4-Car Freight** 46 (224, 2466W, 2458, 3559, 2555, 2457)	(4)	**425**
2105WS	**3-Car Freight Outfit** 46 (671, 671W, 2555, 2454, 2457)	(4)	**450**
2110WS	**3-Car Passenger** (671, 671W, three 2625s) 46	(5)	**1800**
2111WS	**4-Car Freight** 46 (671, 671W, 3459, 2411, 2460, 2420)	(5)	**825**
2113WS	**O Gauge 3-Car Freight Outfit** 46 (726, 2426W, 2855, 3854, 2457)	(5)	**2000**
2114WS	**O Gauge 3-Car Passenger Outfit** 46 (726, 2426W, three 2625 Irvingtons)	(5)	**2500**
2115WS	**O Gauge 4-Car Work Train** with Smoke 46 (726, 2426W, 2458, 3451, 2460, 2420)	(5)	**1450**
2120S	**3-Car De Luxe Passenger** 47 (675, 2466T, two brown 2442s, brown 2443)	(5)	**500**
2120WS	**3-Car De Luxe Passenger** 47 (675, 2466WX, two brown 2442s, brown 2443)	(4)	**525**
2121S	**3-Car Freight** (675, 2466T, 2452, 2555, 2457) 47	(5)	**400**
2121WS	**3-Car Freight** (675, 2466WX, 2452, 2555, 2457) 47	(4)	**400**
2123WS	**4-Car Freight** 47 (675, 2466WX, 2458, 3559, 2555, 2457)	(4)	**475**
2124W	**3-Car Passenger** 47 (2625 Irvington, 2625 Madison, 2625 Manhattan)		
	1. With 2332 GG-1 Dark green	(4)	**3300**
	2. With 2332 GG-1 Black	(5)	**7500***
2125WS	**4-Car Freight** 47 (671, 671W, 2411, 2454, 2452, 2457)	(4)	**575**
2126WS	**3-Car Passenger** 47 (671, 671W, 2625 Irvington, 2625 Madison, 2625 Manhattan)	(4)	**1750**
2127WS	**Lionel Work Train** 47 (671, 671W, 3459, 2461, 2460, 2420)	(4)	**750**
2129WS	**4-Car Freight** 47 (726, 2426W, 3854, 2411, 2855, 2457)	(4)	**2100**
2131WS	**4-Car De Luxe Work Train** 47 (726, 2426W, 3462, 3451, 2460, 2420)	(4)	**1100**
2133W	**Twin Diesel O Gauge Freight** 48 (2333P/T AA, 2458, 3459, 2555, 2357)	(4)	**1250**
2135WS	**3-Car Freight** 48, 49 (675, 2466WX, 2456, 2411, 2357) 48 (675, 6466WX, 6456, 6411, 6457) 49	(3)	**350**
2136WS	**3-Car Passenger** 48, 49 (675, 2466WX, two brown 2442s, brown 2443) 48 (675, 6466WX, two brown 6442s, brown 6443) 49	(4)	**650**
2137WS	**4-Car De Luxe Freight** 48 (675, 2466WX, 2458, 3459, 2456, 2357)	(3)	**400**
2139W	**4-Car Freight** (2332, 3451, 2458, 2456, 2357) 48	(3)	**1500**
2139W	**O Gauge 4-Car Freight Outfit** 49 (2332, 6456, 3464, 3461, 6457)	(3)	**1400**

2140WS	**3-Car De Luxe Passenger** 48, 49 (671, 2671W, 2400, 2402, 2401)	(4)	**900**
2141WS	**4-Car Freight** 48, 49 (671, 2671W, 3451, 3462, 2456, 2357) 48 (671, 2671W, 3461, 3472, 6456, 6457) 49	(3)	**500**
2143WS	**4-Car De Luxe Work Train** 48 (671, 2671W, 3459, 2461, 2460, 2420)	(4)	**700**
2144W	**3-Car De Luxe Passenger Outfit** 48, 49 (2332, 2625, 2627, 2628)	(4)	**2500**
2145WS	**4-Car Freight** 48 (726, 2426W, 3462, 2411, 2460, 2357)	(4)	**850**
2146WS	**3-Car Pullman** (726, 2426W, 2625, 2627, 2628) 48,49	(5)	**1900▼**
2147WS	**4-Car Freight Set** 49 (675, 6466WX, 3472, 6465, 3469, 6457)	(3)	**450**
2148WS	**O Gauge 3-Car Deluxe Pullman** 50 (773, 2426W, 2625, 2627, 2628)	(5)	**4000▼**
2149B	**O Gauge 4-Car Diesel Work Train** 49 (622, 6520, 3469, 2460, 6419)	(4)	**750**
2150WS	**O Gauge Deluxe Passenger** 50 (681, 2671W, 2421, 2422, 2423)	(4)	**850**
2151W	**O Gauge 5-Car Diesel** 49 (2333P/T AA, 3464, 6555, 3469, 6520, 6457)	(3)	**900▼**
2153WS	**4-Car De Luxe Work Train** 49 (671, 2671W, 3469, 6520, 2460, 6419)	(4)	**600**
2155WS	**4-Car Freight** 49 (726, 2426W, 6411, 3656, 2460, 6457)	(4)	**850**
2159W	**5-Car Freight** 50 (2330, 3464, 6462, 3461X, 6456, 6457)	(5)	**2000**
2161W	**SF Twin Diesel Freight** 50 (2343 AA, 3469X, 3464, 3461X, 6520, 6457)	(3)	**1500**
2163WS	**4-Car Freight** 50, 51 (736, 2671WX, 6472, 6462, 6555, 6457) 50 (736, 2671WX, 6472, 6462, 6465, 6457) 51	(3)	**600**
2165WS	**O Gauge 4-Car Freight** 50 (736, 2671WX, 3472, 6456, 3461X, 6457)	(3)	**650**
2167WS	**3-Car Freight** 50, 51 (681, 2671W, 6462, 3464, 6457)	(3)	**425**
2169WS	**5-Car Freight** w/smoke and whistle 50 (773, 2426W, 3656, 6456, 3469X, 6411, 6457)	(5)	**2750**
2171W	**NYC Twin Diesel Freight** 50 (2344 AA, 3469X, 3464, 3461X, 6520, 6457)	(3)	**1250**
2173WS	**4-Car Freight** 50, 51 (681, 2671W, 3472, 6555, 3469X, 6457) 50 (681, 2671W, 3472, 6465, 3469X, 6457) 51	(3)	**575**
2175W	**5-Car Santa Fe Twin Diesel Freight** 50, 51 (2343 AA, 6456 black, 3464, 6555, 6462, 6457) 50 (2343 AA, 6456 maroon, 3464, 6465, 6462, 6457) 51	(3)	**1000▼**
2177WS	**3-Car Freight** (675, 2046W, 6462, 6465, 6457) 52	(4)	**325**
2179WS	**4-Car Freight** 52 (671, 2046WX, 3464, 6465, 6462, 6457)	(3)	**425**
2183WS	**4-Car Freight** 52 (726, 2046W, 3464, 6462, 6465, 6457)	(2)	**575**
2185W	**5-Car NYC Twin Diesel Freight** 50, 51 (2344 AA, 6456 black, 3464, 6555, 6462, 6457) 50 (2344 AA, 6456 maroon, 3464, 6465, 6462, 6457) 51	(3)	**1000▼**
2187WS	**5-Car Freight** 52 (671, 2046WX, 6462, 3472, 6456 maroon, 3469, 6457)	(4)	**500**
2189WS	**5-Car Transcontinental Fast Freight** 52 (726, 2046W, 3520, 3656, 6462, 3461, 6457)	(4)	**650**

2190W	**4-Car Super Speedliner Passenger** 52, 53 (2343 AA, 2533, 2532, 2534, 2531) 52 (2353 AA, 2533, 2532, 2534, 2531) 53	(3)	**2200**
2191W	**4-Car Diesel Freight** 52 (2343 AA, 2343C B Unit, 6462, 6656, 6456, 6457)	(3)	**1500**
2193W	**4-Car Diesel Freight** 52 (2344 AA, 2344C B-Unit, 6462, 6656, 6456, 6457)	(3)	**1200▼**
2201WS	**4-Car Freight** 53, 54 (685, 6026W, 6462, 6464-50, 6465, 6357) 53 (665, 6026W, 6462, 6464-50, 6465, 6357) 54	(3)	**700**
2203WS	**4-Car Freight** 53 (681, 2046WX, 3520, 6415, 6464-25, 6417)	(4)	**750**
2205WS	**5-Car Freight** 53 (736, 2046W, 3484, 6415, 6468 blue, 6456, 6417)	(3)	**700**
2207W	**Triple Diesel Freight** 53 (2353 AA, 2343C B Unit, 3484, 6415, 6462, 6417)	(3)	**1000▼**
2209W	**Triple Diesel Freight** 53 (2354 AA, 2344C B Unit, 3484, 6415, 6462, 6417)	(3)	**1500**
2211WS	**4-Car Freight** 53 (681, 2046WX, 3656, 3461, 6464-75, 6417)	(4)	**700**
2213WS	**5-Car Freight** 53 (736, 2046W, 3461, 3520, 3469, 6460, 6419)	(3)	**600**
2217WS	**O Gauge 4-Car Freight** 54 (682, 2046WX, 3562 gray, 6464-175, 6356, 6417)	(4)	**800▼**
2219W	**5-Car Fairbanks-Morse Power Giant Freight** 54 (2321, 6415, 6462 green, 6464-50, 6456 gray, 6417)	(4)	**1250**
2221WS	**O Gauge 5-Car Freight** 54 (646, 2046W, 3620, 3469, 6468 blue, 6456 gray, 6417)	(3)	**625**
2222WS	**O Gauge 3-Car Pullman** 54 (646, 2046W, 2530, 2532, 2531)	(4)	**1800**
2223W	**O Gauge 5-Car Freight** 54 (2321, 3482, 3461, 6464-100, 6462 red, 6417)	(5)	**2000▼**
2225WS	**5-Car Work Freight** 54 (736, 2046W, 3461, 3620, 3562 gray, 6460 black cab, 6419)	(4)	**800**
2227W	**O Gauge 5-Car Freight** 54 (2353 AA, 3562 gray, 6356, 6456 red, 6468 blue, 6417)	(3)	**1200▼**
2229W	**O Gauge 5-Car Freight** 54 (2354 AA, 3562 gray, 6356, 6456 red, 6468 blue, 6417)	(4)	**1200▼**
2231W	**O Gauge 5-Car Freight** 54 (2356 AA, 2356C B Unit, 6561, 6511, 3482, 6415, 6417)	(4)	**2200▼**
2234W	**4-Car Super-Streamliner** 54 (2353 AA, 2530, 2532, 2533, 2531)	(3)	**2500▼**
2235W	**O Gauge 4-Car Freight** 55 (2338, 6436, 6362, 6560 red, 6419)	(3)	**575**
2237WS	**O Gauge 3-Car Freight** 55 (665, 6026W, 3562 yellow, 6415, 6417)	(3)	**400**
2239W	**O Gauge Streak-Liner** 55 (2363P/C AB, 6672, 6464-125, 6414, 6517)	(4)	**2100**
2241WS	**O Gauge Freight Snorter** 55 (646, 2046W, 3359, 6446, 3620, 6417)	(4)	**550**
2243W	**O Gauge 5-Car Freight** 55 (2321, 3662, 6511, 6462 red, 6464-300, 6417)	(4)	**1500**
2244W	**3-Car Passenger** (2367P/C AB, 2530, 2533, 2531) 55	(4)	**3750**
2245WS	**O Gauge 5-Car Freight** 55 (682, 2046W, 3562, 6436, 6561, 6560, 6419)	(4)	**900**
2247W	**O Gauge 5-Car Freight** 55 (2367P/C AB, 6462 red, 3662, 6464-150, 3361, 6517)	(4)	**2200▼**
2249WS	**O Gauge 5-Car Freight** 55 (736, 2046W, 3359, 3562 yellow, 6414, 6464-275, 6517)	(4)	**750▼**

2251W	**O Gauge 5-Car Freight** 55 (2331, 3359, 3562 yellow, 6414, 6464-275, 6517)	(4)	**2250▼**
2253W	**O Gauge 5-Car Freight** 55 (2340-25 green, 3620, 6414, 3361, 6464-300, 6417)	(4)	**2500**
2254W	**The Congressional** 55 (2340-1 Tuscan, 2544, 2543, 2542, 2541)	(4)	**6000**
2255W	**O Gauge 4-Car Work Train** 56 (601, 3424, 6362, 6560, 6119 orange)	(4)	**625**
2257WS	**O Gauge 5-Car Freight** 56 (665, 2046W, 3361, 6346, 6467, 6462 red, 6427)	(3)	**500**
2259W	**O Gauge 5-Car Freight** 56 (2350, 6464-425, 6430, 3650, 6511, 6427)	(3)	**875**
2261WS	**O Gauge Freight Hauler**, 56 (646, 2046W, 3562 yellow, 6414, 6436, 6376, 6417)	(4)	**650**
2263W	**O Gauge 5-Car Freight** 56 (2350, 3359, 6468, 6414, 3662, 6517)	(4)	**1000**
2265WS	**O Gauge 5-Car Freight** 56 (736, 2046W, 3620, 6430, 3424, 6467, 6517)	(4)	**750**
2267W	**5-Car Freight** 56 (2331, 3562 yellow, 3359, 3361, 6560, 6419)	(4)	**1700**
2269W	**O Gauge 5-Car Freight** 56 (2368P/C AB, 3356, 6518, 6315, 3361, 6517)	(5)	**3000▼**
2270W	**3-Car Jersey Central Passenger** 56 (2341, 2533, 2532, 2531)	(5)	**4500▼**
2271W	**O Gauge 5-Car Freight** 56 (2360-25 green, 3424, 3662, 6414, 6418, 6417)	(4)	**2500▼**
2273W	**6-Car Milwaukee Road Diesel Freight** 56 (2378P/C AB, 342, 6342, 3562 yellow, 3662, 3359, 6517)	(5)	**3000▼**
2274W	**The Great Congressional** 56 (2360-1 Tuscan, 2544, 2543, 2542, 2541)	(5)	**4000▼**
2275W	**O Gauge 4-Car Freight** 57 (2339, 3444, 6464-475, 6425, 6427)	(3)	**750**
2276W	**Budd RDC Commuter Set** (404, 2559, 2559) 57	(4)	**3000▼**
2277WS	**O Gauge 4-Car Work Train** 57 (665, 2046W, 3650, 6446, 6560, 6119)	(4)	**550**
2279W	**O Gauge 5-Car Freight** 57 (2350, 6464-425, 6424, 3424, 6477, 6427)	(3)	**825**
2281W	**O Gauge 5-Car Freight** 57 (2243 AB, 3562 orange, 6464-150, 3361, 6560, 6119)	(3)	**1200**
2283WS	**O Gauge 5-Car Freight** 57 (646, 2046W, 3424, 3361, 6464-525, 6562 black, 6357)	(4)	**625**
2285W	**O Gauge 5-Car Freight** 57 (2331, 6418, 6414, 3662, 6425, 6517)	(4)	**1800**
2287W	**O Gauge 5-Car Freight** 57 (2351, 342, 6342, 6464-500, 3650, 6315, 6427)	(5)	**1800**
2289WS	**Super O 5-Car Freight** 57 (736, 2046W, 3359, 3494-275, 3361, 6430, 6427)	(4)	**750**
2291W	**Super O 5-Car Freight** 57 (2379P/C AB, 3562 orange, 3530, 3444, 6464-525, 6657)	(4)	**2800**
2292WS	**Super O Steam Luxury Liner** 57 (646, 2046W, 2530, 2533, 2532, 2531)	(4)	**1500**
2293W	**5-Car Freight** 57 (2360 Tuscan, 3662, 3650, 6414, 6518, 6417)	(5)	**2750**
2295WS	**6-Car Steam Freight** 57 (746, 746W, 342, 6342, 3530, 3361, 6560, 6419-100 no. 576419 on car)	(5)	**3000**
2296W	**Super O Diesel Luxury Liner** 57 (2373P/T AA, 2552, 2552, 2552, 2551)	(4)	**5500▼**

2297SW **The 16 Wheeler Class J** 57 (5) **2250▼**
(746, 746W, 264, 6264, 3356, 345, 6342, 3662, 6517)

2501W **Super O Work Train** 58 (4) **850**
(2348, 6464-525, 6802, 6560, 6119)

2502W **Super O Rail-Diesel Commuter** (400, 2559, 2550) 58 (5) **1900**

2503WS **Timberland Special Freight** 58 (4) **650**
(665, 2046W, 3361, 6434, 6801, 6536, 6357)

2505W **Super O 5-Car Freight** 58 (4) **1550**
(2329, 6805, 6519, 6800, 6464-500, 6357)

2507W **Super O 5-Car Diesel Freight** 58 (5) **2000**
(2242P/C AB, 3444, 6464-425, 6424, 6468-25, 6357)

2509WS **The Owl 5-Car Freight** 58 (4) **800**
(665, 2046W, 6414, 3650, 6464-475, 6805, 6357)

2511W **Super O 5-Car Electric Work Train** 58 (4) **1200**
(2352, 3562 orange, 3424, 3361, 6560, 6119)

2513W **Super O 6-Car Freight Train** 58 (5) **2000**
(2329, 6556, 6425, 6414, 6434, 3359, 6427-60)

2515WS **5-Car Mainliner Steam Freight** 58 (4) **825**
(646, 2046W, 3662, 6424, 3444, 6800, 6427)

2517W **Super O 5-Car Diesel Freight** 58 (5) **2500**
(2379 AB, 6519, 6805, 6434, 6800, 6657)

2518W **Super O 3-Car Passenger** 58 (5) **1700**
(2352, 2533, 2534, 2531)

2519W **Super O 6-Car Diesel Freight** 58 (4) **1900**
(2331, 6434, 3530, 6801, 6414, 6464-275, 6557)

2521WS **Super O 6-Car Freight** 58 (5) **2300**
(746, 746W, 6805, 3361, 6430, 3356, 6557)

2523W **Super O Super Chief Freight** 58 (5) **1500▼**
(2383 AA, 264, 6264, 6434, 6800, 3662, 6517)

2525WS **Super O 6-Car Work Train** 58 (5) **2500▼**
(746, 746W, 345, 342, 6519, 6518, 6560, 6419-100)

2526W **Super Chief Passenger** 58 (4) **2000**
(2383P/T AA, 2530, 2532, 2532, 2531)

2527 **Super O Missile Launcher Outfit** 59, 60 (3) **700**
(44, 3419, 6844, 6823, 6814, 943)

2528WS **5-Star Frontier Special Outfit** 59-61 (2) **725**
(1872, 1872T, 1877, 1876, 1875W)

2529W **5-Car Virginian Rectifier Work Train** 59 (4) **1300**
(2329, 3512, 6819, 6812, 6560, 6119)

2531WS **Super O 5-Car Steam Freight** 59 (5) **1300**
(637, 2046W, 3435, 6817, 6636, 6825, 6119)

2533W **5-Car Great Northern Electric Freight** 59 (5) **1850**
(2358, 6650, 6414, 3444, 6470, 6357)

2535WS **Super O 5-Car Hudson Steam Freight** 59 (4) **900▼**
(665, 2046W, 3434, 6823, 3672, 6812, 6357)

2537W **5-Car New Haven Diesel Freight** 59 (5) **2500**
(2242P/C AB, 3435, 3650, 6464-275, 6819, 6427)

2539WS **5-Car Hudson Steam Freight** 59 (5) **1200▼**
(665, 2046W, 3361, 464, 6464-825, 3512, 6812, 6357)

2541W **5-Car Super Chief Freight** 59 (5) **2350**
(2383P/T AA, 3356, 3512, 6519, 6816, 6427)

2543WS **6-Car Berkshire Steam Freight** 59 (5) **1750▼**
(736, 2046W, 264, 6264, 3435, 6823, 6434, 6812, 6557)

2544W **4-Car Super Chief Streamliner** 59, 60 (4) **3500▼**
(2383P/T AA, 2530, 2563 red stripe, 2562 red stripe, 2561 red stripe)

2545WS **6-Car N&W Space-Freight** 59 (5) **2200▼**
(746, 746W, 175, 6175, 6470, 3419, 6650, 3540, 6517)

2547WS **4-Car Variety Special Steam Freight** 60 (4) **675**
(637, 2046W, 3330, 6475, 6361, 6357)

2549W	**A Mighty Military Diesel Outfit** 60 (2349, 3540, 6470, 6819, 6650, 3535)	(2)	**1200**
2551W	**6-Car Great Northern Diesel Freight** 60 (2358, 6828, 3512, 6827, 6736, 6812, 6427)	(5)	**2250**
2553WS	**The Majestic Berkshire 5-Car Freight** 60 (736, 2046W, 3830, 3435, 3419, 3672, 6357)	(4)	**1200▼**
2555W	**Over & Under Twin Railroad Empire** 60 (2383P/T AA, 3434, 3366, 6414, 6464-900, 6357-50, 110-85) Includes matching set of Lionel HO trains	(5+)	**12000**
2570	**5-Car Husky Diesel Freight** 61 (616, 6822, 6828, 6812, 6736, 6130)	(4)	**650**
2571	**Fort Knox Special Steam Freight** 61 (637, 736W, 3419, 6445, 6361, 6119)	(4)	**670**
2572	**5-Car Space Age Diesel Freighter** 61 (2359, 6544, 3830, 6448, 3519, 3535)	(3)	**850**
2573	**5-Car TV Special Steam Freight** 61 (736, 736W, 3545, 6416, 6475, 6440, 6357)	(4)	**1200**
2574	**5-Car Defender Diesel Freight** 61 (2383P/T AA, 3665, 3419, 448, 6448, 3830, 6437)	(4)	**1500▼**
2575	**7-Car Dynamo Electric Freight** 61 (2360 single stripe, 6530, 6828, 6464-900, 6827, 6560, 6437)	(5)	**2500▼**
2576	**4-Car Super Chief Streamline** 61 (2383P/T AA, 2563, 2562, 2562, 2561)	(4)	**4000**
4109WS	**Electronic Control Set** 46, 47 (671R, 4671W, 4452, 4454, 5459, 4457)	(4)	**1500▲**
4110WS	**Lionel Electronic Railroad** 48, 49 (671R, 4671W, 4452, 4454, 5459, 4357, 97, 151)	(5)	**2250▲**
11201	**Fast Starter Steam Freight** 62 (242, 1060T, 6042-75, 6502, 6047)	(1)	**160**
11212	**4-Unit Cyclone Diesel Freight** 62 (633, 3349, 6825, 6057)	(2)	**250**
11222	**5-Unit Vagabond Steam Freight** 62 (236, 1050T, 3357, 6343, 6119)	(2)	**160**
11232	**027 5-Unit Diesel Freight** 62 (232, 3410, 6062, 6413, 6057-50 orange)	(4)	**425**
11242	**Trail Blazer Steam Freight** 62 (233, 233W, 6465, 6476 red, 6162, 6017)	(2)	**125**
11252	**027 7-Unit Diesel Freight** 62 (211 AA, 3509, 6448, 3349, 6463, 6057)	(4)	**600**
11268	**027 6-Unit Diesel Freight** 62 (2365, 3619, 3470, 3349, 6501, 6017)	(3)	**1050**
11278	**7-Unit Plainsman Steam Freight** 62 (2037, 233W, 6473, 6162, 6050-110, 6825, 6017)	(3)	**260**
11288	**7-Unit Orbitor Diesel Freight** 62 (229P/C AB, 3413, 6512, 6413, 6463, 6059)	(4)	**800**
11298	**7-Unit Vigilant Steam Freight** 62 (2037, 233W, 3419, 6544, 6448, 3330, 6017)	(4)	**450**
11308	**027 6-Unit Diesel Passenger** 62 (218P/T AA 2414 blue stripe, two 2412s blue stripe, 2416 blue stripe)	(3)	**650**
11311	**Value Packed Steam Freight** 63 (1062, 1061T, 6409-25, 6076-100, 6167)	(2)	**100**
11321	**027 5-Unit Diesel Freighter** 63 (221, 3309, 6076-75, 6042-75, 6167-50 yellow)	(2)	**250**
11331	**Outdoorsman Steam Freight** 63 (242, 1060T, 6473, 6476-25, 6142, 6059-50)	(2)	**150**
11341	**Space-Prober Diesel Freight** 63 (634, 3410, 6407, 6014-335 white, 6463, 6059-50)	(4)	**900▼**

11351	**Land Rover Steam Freight** 63 (237, 1060T, 6050-100, 6465-100, 6408, 6162, 6119-100)	(2)	**250**
11361	**Shooting Star Diesel Freight** 63 (211P/T AA, 3665-100, 3413-150, 6470, 6413, 6257-100)	(4)	**750**
11375	**Cargomaster Steam Freight** 63 (238, 234W, 6822-50, 6414-150, 6465-150, 6476-75, 6162, 6257-100)	(4)	**700**
11385	**Space Conqueror Diesel Freight** 63 (223P/218C AB, 3619-100, 3470-100, 3349-100, 6407, 6257-100)	(5)	**2000**
11395	**Muscleman Steam Freight** 63 (2037, 234W, 6464-725, 6469-50, 6536, 6440-50, 6560-50, 6119-100)	(4)	**600**
11405	**027 6 Unit Diesel Passenger** 63 (218 AA, 2414 blue stripe, two 2412s blue stripe, 2416 blue stripe)	(3)	**750**
11420	**4-Unit Steam Freight** 64 (1061, 1061T, 6042-250, 6167-25)	(2)	**125**
11430	**5-Unit Steam Freight** 64 (1062, 1061T, 6176, 6142, 6167-125)	(2)	**150**
11440	**5-Unit Diesel Freight** 64 (221, 3309, 6176-50 black, 6142-125 blue, 6167-100 red)	(2)	**225**
11450	**6-Unit Steam Freight** 64 (242, 1060T, 6473, 6142-75 grn, 6176-50 blk, 6059-50)	(2)	**150**
11460	**7-Unit Steam Freight** 64 (238, 234W, 6014-335 white, 6465-150 orange, 6142-100 blue, 6176-75 yellow, 6119-100)	(3)	**150**
11470	**7-Unit Steam Freight** 64 (237, 1060T, 6014-335 white, 6465-150 orange, 6142-100 blue, 6176-50 yellow, 6119-100)	(4)	**225**
11480	**7-Unit Diesel Freight** 64 (213P/T AA, 6473, 6176-50 black, 6142-150, 6014-335 white, 6257-100)	(4)	**700**
11490	**5-Unit Diesel Passenger** 64, 65 (212P/T AA, 2404, 2405, 2406)	(3)	**725**
11500	**7-Unit Steam Freight** 64-66 (2029, 234W, 6465-150 org, 6402-50, 6176-75 yell, 6014-335 wht, 6257-100) 64 (2029, 234W, 6465-150 org, 6402-50, 6176 blk, 6014-335 wht, 6059) 65 (2029, 234W, 6465-150 org, 6402-50, 6176-75 yell, 6014-335 wht, 6059) 66	(3)	**275**
11510	**7-Unit Steam Freight** 64 (2029, 1060T, 6465-150 orange, 6402-50, 6176-75 yellow, 6014-335 white, 6257-100)	(4)	**300**
11520	**6-Unit Steam Freight** 65, 66 (242, 1062T, 6176, 3364, 6142, 6059)	(2)	**150**
11530	**5-Unit Diesel Freight** 65, 66 (634, 6014-335 white, 6142, 6402, 6130)	(2)	**200▼**
11540	**6-Unit Steam Freight** 65, 66 (239, 242T, 6473, 6465, 6176, 6119)	(4)	**250**
11550	**6-Unit Steam Freight** 65, 66 (239, 234W, 6473, 6465, 6176, 6119)	(3)	**250**
11560	**7-Unit Diesel Freight** 65, 66 (211P/T AA, 6473, 6176, 6142, 6465, 6059)	(2)	**300**
11590	**5-Unit Illuminated Passenger** 66 (212P/T AA, 2408, 2409, 2410)	(3)	**750**
11600	**7-Unit Steam Freight** 68 (2029, 234W, 6014-335 white, 6476 yellow, 6315, 6560, 6130)	(3)	**700▼**

11710	**5-Unit Steam Freight** 69 (1061, 1062T, 6402, 6142, 6059)	(3)	**175**
11720	**5-Unit Diesel Freight** 69 (2024, 6142, 6402, 6176 yellow, 6057 brown)	(4)	**250**
11730	**6-Unit Diesel Freight** 69 (645, 6402, 6014-85 orange, 6142, 6176 black, 6167)	(3)	**325**
11740	**7-Unit Diesel Freight** 69 (2041 AA, 6315, 6142, 6014-410 white, 6476 yellow, 6057 brown)	(4)	**350**
11750	**7-Unit Steam Freight** 69 (2029, 234T, 6014-85 orange, 6476 black, 6473, 6315, 6130)	(5)	**400▼**
11760	**7-Unit Steam Freight** 69 (2029, 234W, 6014-410 white, 6315, 6476 black, 3376, 6119)	(3)	**300**
12502	**Prairie-Rider Gift Pack** 62 (1862, 1862T , 3376, 1877, 1866, 1865)	(4)	**600**
12512	**Enforcer Gift Pack** 62 (45, 3413, 3619, 3470, 3349, 6017)	(4)	**1100▲**
12700	**7-Unit Steam Freight** 64 Same as 12710 without transformer	(4)	**1100**
12710	**7-Unit Steam Freight** 64-66 (736, 736W, 6464-725, 6162-100 blue, 6414-75, 6476-135 yellow, 6437) 64 (736, 736W, 6464-725, 6162-100 blue, 6414, 6476-135 yellow, 6437) 65, 66	(4)	**1100**
12720	**7-Unit Diesel Freight** 64 Same as 12730 without transformer	(4)	**1500**
12730	**7-Unit Diesel Freight** 64-66 (2383P/T AA, 6464-725, 6162-100 blue, 6414-75, 6476-135 yell, 6437) 64 (2383P/T AA, 6464-725, 6162-100 blue, 6414, 6476-135 yellow, 6437) 65,66	(4)	**1500**
12740	**9-Unit Diesel Freight** 64 Same as 12750 without transformer	(5)	**1500**
12750	**9-Unit Diesel Freight** 64 (2383P/T AA, 3662, 6822, 6361, 6464-525, 6436-110, 6315-60, 6437)	(5)	**1500**
12760	**9-Unit Steam Freight** 64 Same as 12770 without transformer	(4)	**1200▼**
12770	**9-Unit Steam Freight** 64 (736, 736W, 3662, 6822, 6361, 6464-525, 6436-110, 6315-60, 6437)	(5)	**1200▼**
12780	**6-Unit Diesel Passenger** 64-66 (2383P/T AA, 2523, 2522, 2523, 2521)	(4)	**2800▼**
12800	**6-Unit Diesel Freight** 65, 66 (2346, 6428, 6436-110, 6464-475, 6415, 6017)	(2)	**650**
12820	**8-Unit Diesel Freight** 65 (2322, 3662, 6822, 6361, 6464-725, 6436-110, 6315, 6437)	(4)	**1500**
12840	**7-Unit Steam Freight** 66 (665, 736W, 6464-375, 6464-450, 6431, 6415, 6437)	(4)	**850▼**
12850	**8-Unit Diesel Freight** 66 (2322, 3662, 6822, 6361, 6464-725, 6436-110, 6315, 6437)	(4)	**1500**
13008	**6-Unit Champion Steam Freight** 62 (637, 736W, 3349, 6448, 6501, 6119)	(4)	**475**
13018	**6-Unit Starfire Diesel Freight** 62 (616, 6500, 6650, 3519, 6448, 6017-235)	(5)	**1250**
13028	**6-Unit Defender Diesel Freight** 62 (2359, 3665, 3349, 3820, 3470, 6017-100)	(2)	**875**
13036	**6-Unit Plainsman Steam Outfit** 62 (1872, 1872T, 6445, 3370, 1876, 1875W)	(4)	**950**

13048	**7-Unit Steam Freight** 62 (736, 736W, 6822, 6414, 3362, 6440, 6437)	(3)	**850**
13058	**7-Unit Vanguard Diesel Freight** 62 (2383P/T AA, 3619, 3413, 6512, 470, 6470, 6437)	(3)	**1650**
13068	**8-Unit Goliath Electric Freight** 62 (2360 single stripe, 6464-725, 6828, 6416, 6827, 6530, 6475, 6437)	(5)	**3000**
13078	**5-Unit Presidential Passenger** 62 (2360 single stripe, 2523, 2522, 2522, 2521)	(5)	**3500**
13088	**6-Unit Presidential Passenger** 62 (2383P/T AA, 2523, 2522, 2522, 2521)	(4)	**2600**
13098	**Goliath Steam Freight** 63 (637, 736W, 6469, 6464-900, 6414, 6446, 6447)	(5)	**2000**
13108	**Super O 7-Unit Diesel Freight** 63 (617, 3665, 3419, 6448, 3830, 3470, 6119-100)	(4)	**1050**
13118	**Super O 8-Unit Steam Freight** 63 (736, 736W, 6446-60, 6827, 3362, 6315-60, 6560, 6429)	(4)	**1500**
13128	**Super O 7-Unit Diesel Freight** 63 (2383P/T AA, 3619, 3413, 6512, 448, 6448, 6437)	(4)	**1825**
13138	**Majestic Electric Freight** 63 (2360 single stripe, 6464-725, 6828, 6416, 6827, 6315-60, 6436-110, 6437)	(5)	**3000**
13148	**Super Chief Passenger** 63 (2383 AA, 2523, 2523, 2522, 2521)	(4)	**2600**
13150	**Super O 9-Unit Steam Freight** NDV, 64-66 (773, 736W, 3434, 6361, 3662, 6415, 3356, 6436-110, 6437) 64 (773, 773W, 3434, 6361, 3662, 6415, 3356, 6436-110, 6437) 65, 66	(5)	**2500▼**

Postwar Boxes

Prices based on Excellent with inserts and all flaps intact. No Rarity Rating indicates not enough information to assign one.

ECU-1	**Electronic Control Unit**	(4)	**35**
ZW	**Transformer**	(2)	**25**
30	**Water Tower**	(3)	**40**
38	**Water Tower**	(4+)	**85**
41	**US Army Switcher**	(2)	**30**
42	**Picatinny Arsenal Switcher**	(4)	**70**
44	**US Army Mobile Missile Launcher**	(3)	**55**
45	**USMC Mobile Missile Launcher**	(3+)	**85**
50	**Gang Car (O&B)**	(3)	**25**
51	**Navy Yard Switcher**	(2+)	**65**
52	**Fire Fighting Car**	(3)	**85**
53	**Rio Grande Snow Plow**	(3)	**60**
54	**Ballast Tamper**	(3)	**50**
55	**Tie-Jector**	(3+)	**50**
56	**Minn. & St. Louis Min Steamer**	(4)	**170**
57	**AEC Switcher**	(4+)	**170**
58	**GN Rotary Snowplow**	(4)	**170**
59	**Minuteman Switcher**	(4+)	**170**
60	**Trolley**	(2)	**30**
65	**Motorized Handcar**	(3+)	**85**
68	**Executive Inspection Car**	(3)	**85**
69	**Motorized Maintenance Car**	(3+)	**120**
89	**Flagpole**	(4)	**25**
97	**Coal Elevator**	(3)	**40**
110-85	**Trestle Set**	(5)	**165**
114	**Newsstand with horn**	(3)	**40**

115	Lionel City Station	(3+)	50
118	Newsstand with whistle	(3)	35
128	Animated Newsstand	(2)	45
132	Passenger Station	(3)	25
133	Passenger Station	(2)	25
138	Water Tower	(3)	35
150	Telegraph Pole Set	(2)	25
164	Log Loader	(3)	45
175	Rocket Launcher	(3)	50
182	Magnetic Crane	(3)	50
192	Operating Control Tower	(4)	85
193	Industrial Water Tower	(3)	45
197	Rotating Radar Antenna	(3+)	35
202	Union Pacific A	(3+)	45
204P	Santa Fe Alco Powered A Unit	(3)	50
204T	Santa Fe Alco Dummy A Unit	(3)	50
205P	MP Alco Powered A Unit	(4)	55
205T	MP Alco Dummy A Unit	(4)	55
208P	Santa Fe Alco Powered A Unit	(3)	55
208T	Santa Fe Alco Dummy A Unit	(3)	55
209P	New Haven Alco Powered A Unit	(4+)	90
209T	New Haven Alco Dummy A Unit	(4+)	90
210P	Texas Special Alco Powered A	(2)	45
210T	Texas Special Alco Dummy A	(2)	45
211P	Texas Special Alco Powered A	(3)	30
211T	Texas Special Alco Dummy A	(3)	30
212	USMC Alco Powered A Unit	(3)	60
212T	USMC Alco Dummy A Unit	(5)	430
212P	Santa Fe Alco Powered A Unit	(4)	50
212T	Santa Fe Alco Dummy A Unit	(4)	50
213P	Minn. & Stl. Alco Powered A	(4)	80
213T	Minn. & Stl. Alco Dummy A	(4)	80
215	Santa Fe Alco Powered A Unit		
216P	Burlington Alco Powered A	(4+)	100
216	Minn & Stl. Alco Powered A		
217P	Boston & Maine Alco Powered A Unit	(3+)	50
217C	Boston & Maine Alco Dummy B Unit	(3+)	50
218P	Santa Fe Alco Powered A Unit	(2)	35
218C	Santa Fe Alco Dummy B Unit	(3+)	45
218T	Santa Fe Alco Dummy A Unit	(3)	40
219	Missouri Pacific Alco AA		
220P	Santa Fe Alco Powered A Unit	(4)	50
221	Rio Grande Alco Powered A		NOB
221	Santa Fe Powered A Unit		NOB
221	USMC Powered A Unit		NOB
221	2-6-4 Steamer	(3+)	50
221T	Tender	(3+)	60
221W	Tender	(3+)	45
222	Rio Grande Alco Powered A		NOB
223P	Santa Fe Alco Powered A Unit	(4)	75
224P	Navy Alco Powered A Unit	(4)	85
224C	Navy Alco Dummy B Unit	(4)	65
224	2-6-2 Steamer	(3)	40

225	C&O Alco Powered A Unit		
226	Boston & Maine Alco AB		135
227	CN Alco Powered A Unit		NOB
228	CN Alco Powered A Unit	(3)	40
229P	Minn. & St. Louis Alco Powered A Unit	(3+)	50
229C	Minn. & St. Louis Alco Dummy B Unit	(3+)	50
230	C&O Alco Powered A Unit		30
231	Rock Island Powered A Unit		40
232	New Haven Alco A		30
233	2-4-2 Steamer	(3)	35
233W	Tender	(3)	75
235	2-4-2 Steamer		NOB
236	2-4-2 Steamer	(2)	30
237	2-4-2 Steamer	(3)	30
238	2-4-2 Steamer	(3)	50
239	2-4-2 Steamer	(3)	30
240	2-4-2 Steamer		NOB
241	2-4-2 Steamer		NOB
242	2-4-2 Steamer		
242T	Tender	(3)	30
243	2-4-2 Steamer	(3)	45
243W	Tender	(3)	30
244	2-4-2 Steamer	(3)	35
244T	Tender	(4)	35
245	2-4-2 Steamer	(4)	40
247	2-4-2 Steamer	(3)	40
247T	Tender	(3)	25
248	2-4-2 Steamer	(3)	45
249	2-4-2 Steamer	(3)	40
250	2-4-2 Steamer	(3)	40
250T	Tender	(3)	30
251	2-4-2 Steamer		NOB
256	Freight Station	(2)	25
257	Freight Station with horn	(4)	65
264	Operating Forklift Platform	(3)	50
282	Gantry Crane	(3)	50
282R	Gantry Crane	(3+)	65
299	Code Transmitter Beacon Set	(2)	85
350-50	Transfer Table Extension	(4+)	85
313	Bascule Bridge	(3+)	150▲
334	Operating Dispatching Board	(3)	80
342	Operating Culvert Loader	(2)	55
345	Operating Culvert Unloader	(3)	55
346	Manual Culvert Unloader	(4+)	150▲
347	Cannon Firing Range		NOB
348	Manual Culvert Unloader	(4)	150▲
350	Transfer Table	(4)	85
352	Ice Depot	(2)	45
362	Barrel Loader	(2)	30
364	Lumber Loader	(3)	25
365	Dispatch Station	(2)	55
375	Turntable	(2)	40
397	Diesel Operating Coal Loader	(2)	35

400	**B&O Budd Car**	(3)	**70**
404	**B&O Budd Car**	(3+)	**85**
415	**Diesel Fueling Station**	(3)	**40**
419	**Heliport Control Tower**	(5+)	**175▲**
443	**Missile Launching Platform**	(3)	**30**
445	**Switch Tower**	(2+)	**25**
448	**Missile Firing Range Set**	(3)	**45**
452	**Gantry Signal**	(3+)	**40**
455	**Oil Derrick**	(2+)	**50**
456	**Coal Ramp**	(2)	**35**
460	**Piggyback Transportation**	(2)	**30**
460P	**Piggyback Platform**	(5)	**1200**
461	**Platform with truck and trailer**	(4)	**65**
462	**Derrick Platform Set**	(4)	**200▲**
463W	**O Gauge 4-Car Freight Set** 45		**220**
464	**Lumber Mill**	(2)	**40**
465	**Sound Dispatching Station**	(2+)	**35**
470	**Missile Launching Platform**	(2)	**30**
497	**Coaling Station**	(3+)	**50**
520	**Box Cab Electric**		**NOB**
600	**MKT GM Switcher**	(3)	**50**
601	**Seaboard GM Switcher**	(2+)	**45**
602	**Seaboard GM Switcher**	(2+)	**45**
610	**Erie GM Switcher**	(3)	**50**
611	**Jersey Central**	(3)	**45**
613	**Union Pacific GM Switcher**	(4)	**90**
614	**Alaska GM Switchers**	(4)	**80**
616	**Santa Fe GM Switcher**	(3+)	**65**
617	**Santa Fe GM Switcher**	(4)	**110**
621	**Jersey Central GM Switcher**	(3)	**45**
646-25	**Great Northern Boxcar**	(2)	**30**
622	**Santa Fe GM Switcher**	(3)	**55**
623	**Santa Fe GM Switcher**	(2+)	**50**
624	**C & O GM Switcher**	(3)	**45**
625	**Lehigh Valley GE 44-Ton**	(3+)	**45**
626	**Baltimore & Ohio GE 44-Ton**	(4)	**70**
627	**Lehigh Valley GE 44-Ton**	(3)	**45**
628	**Northern Pacific GE 44-Ton**	(3)	**45**
629	**Burlington GE 44-Ton**	(4)	**85**
633	**Santa Fe GM Switcher**	(4)	**45**
634	**Santa Fe GM Switcher**	(4)	**45**
635	**Union Pacific GM Switcher**		
637	**2-6-4 Steamer**	(3+)	**40**
645	**Union Pacific GM Switcher**		**NOB**
646	**4-6-4 Steamer**	(3)	**50**
665	**4-6-4 Steamer**	(2+)	**50**
671	**6-8-6 Steamer**	(2+)	**50**
671R	**6-8-6 Steamer**	(4)	**85**
671W	**Tender**	(3+)	**55**
675	**2-6-2 Steamer**	(3)	**40**
681	**6-8-6 Steamer**	(3)	**45**
682	**6-8-6 Steamer**	(3+)	**75**
685	**4-6-4 Steamer**	(2+)	**45**

726	**2-8-4 Steamer**	(3)	**65**
726RR	**2-8-4 Steamer**	(3)	**120**
736	**2-8-4 Steamer**	(2+)	**60**
736W	**Tender**	(4)	**85**
746	**4-8-4 N&W Steamer**	(4)	**120**
746W	**Tender** (Short Stripe)	(3+)	**85**
746WX	**Tender** (Long Stripe)	(4+)	**135**
773	**4-6-4 Hudson Steamer** (1950)	(4)	**250▲**
773	**4-6-4 Hudson Steamer** (1964)	(4)	**250▲**
773W	**Tender**	(4+)	**150**
920	**Scenic Display Set**	(2)	**25**
958	**Vehicle Set** (white box only)	(4+)	**120**
963-100	**Frontier Set**	(4)	**120**
970	**Ticket Booth**	(2)	**50**
986	**Farm Set**	(4)	**125**
987	**Town Set**	(4+)	**125**
988	**Railroad Structure Set**	(4+)	**125**
1000W	**027 3-Car Set,** 55	(2)	**35**
1001	**027 3-Car Set,** 55	(2)	**60**
1047	**Operating Switchman**	(4)	**60**
1050	**0-4-0 Steamer**		**NOB**
1050T	**Tender**		**NOB**
1055	**Texas Special Alco Powered A**		**NOB**
1065	**Union Pacific Alco Powered A**		**NOB**
1066	**Union Pacific Alco Powered A**		**NOB**
1111	**Lionel Scout Set,** 48	(2)	**25**
1112	**Lionel Scout Set,** 48		**35**
1113	**Lionel Scout Train,** 50		**25**
1115	**Lionel Scout,** 49		**35**
1117	**Lionel Scout,** 49		**25**
1119	**Scout 3-Car Freight,** 51, 52		**25**
1130T	**Tender**	(3)	**35**
1130T-500	**Tender (Girls Train)**	(5)	**170**
1400	**Lionel 027 Passenger Set,** 46		**225**
1400W	**Lionel 027 Passenger Set,** 46		**270**
1401	**Lionel 027 Freight Outfit,** 46		**35**
1401W	**Lionel 027 Freight Outfit,** 46		**35**
1402	**Lionel 027 Passenger Set** 46		**120**
1402W	**Lionel 027 Passenger Set** 46		**170**
1403	**Lionel 027 Freight Train** 46		**60**
1403W	**Lionel 027 Freight Train** 46		**60**
1405	**Lionel 027 Freight Train** 46		**35**
1405W	**Lionel 027 Freight Train** 46		**45**
1407B	**Lionel 027 Switcher Bell Outfit** 46		**170**
1409	**Lionel 027 Freight Train** 46		**60**
1409W	**Lionel 027 Freight Train** 46		**35**
1411W	**Freight Outfit** 46		**35**
1413WS	**Lionel 027 Freight Train** 46		**45**
1415WS	**Lionel 027 Freight Set** 46		**60**
1417WS	**Lionel 027 Freight Outfit** 46		**60**
1419WS	**Lionel 027 Freight Train** 46		**135**
1421WS	**Lionel 027 Freight Train** 46		**170**
1423W	**Lionel 3-Car Freight Outfit** 48, 49		**35**

1425B	**027 O Gauge Switcher Freight** 48, 49	**140**
1426WS	**Lionel Passenger Set** 48, 49	**120**
1427WS	**Lionel Three-Car Freight Set** 48	**35**
1429WS	**Four-Car Freight Set** 48	**35**
1430WS	**Passenger Train** 48, 49	**225**
1431	**Lionel Freight Train** 47	**35**
1431W	**Lionel Freight Train** 47	**35**
1432	**Lionel Passenger Set** 47	**220**
1432W	**Lionel Passenger Set,** 47	**225**
1433	**Lionel Freight Train** 47	**35**
1433W	**Lionel Freight Train** 47	**35**
1434WS	**Passenger Train** 47	**170**
1435WS	**Lionel Freight Train** 47	**35**
1437WS	**Lionel Freight Set** 47	**35**
1439WS	**Lionel Freight Outfit** 47	**45**
1441WS	**De Luxe Work Outfit** 47	**60**
1443WS	**Lionel Freight Set** 47	**60**
1445WS	**Lionel Freight Train,** 48	**35**
1447WS	**Lionel De Luxe Work Train Set** 48, 49	**60**
1449WS	**027 Lionel 5-Car Freight Outfit** 48	**60**
1451WS	**Three-Car Freight** 49	**35**
1453WS	**Four-Car Freight Train** 49	**45**
1455WS	**Four-Car 027 Freight Set** 49	**50**
1457B	**Diesel Freight** 49, 50	**120**
1459WS	**027 Gauge 5-Car Freight Outfit** 49	**60**
1461S	**3-Car Freight With Smoke,** 50	**25**
1463W	**Lionel 027 3-Car Freight,** 50	**35**
1463WS	**027 3-Car Freight,** 51	**35**
1464W	**027 Diesel 3-Car Pullman** 50	**440**
1464W	**027 Diesel 3-Car Pullman** 51	**220**
1464W	**3-Car Pullman** 52, 53	**220**
1465	**3-Car Freight** 52	**25**
1467W	**027 Diesel 4-Car Freight** 50, 51	**110**
1467W	**4-Car Freight** 52, 53	**110**
1469WS	**Lionel 027 4-Car Freight** 50, 51	**35**
1471WS	**Lionel 5-Car Freight Set** 50, 51	**35**
1473WS	**Lionel 4-Car Freight** 50	**35**
1475WS	**Lionel 5-Car Freight Set** 50	**60**
1477S	**027 3-Car Freight** 51, 52	**35**
1479WS	**027 4-Car Freight** 52	**50**
1481WS	**5-Car Freight** 51	**50**
1483WS	**5-Car Freight** 52	**60**
1484WS	**4-Car Pullman** 52	**225**
1485WS	**027 3-Car Freight** 52	**35**
1500	**027 3-Car Freight** 53, 54	**25**
1501S	**027 3-Car Freight** 53	**35**
1502WS	**027 3-Car Pullman** 53	**175**
1503WS	**027 4-Car Freight** 53	**35**
1505WS	**027 4-Car Freight** 53	**60**
1507WS	**027 5-Car Freight** 53	**60**
1509WS	**027 5-Car Freight** 53	**60**
1511S	**027 4-Car Freight** 53	**35**
1513S	**027 4-Car Freight** 54, 55	**35**

1515WS	**027 5-Car Freight** 54	**60**
1516WS	**027 3-Car Passenger** 54	**125**
1517W	**027 4-Car Freight** 54	**175**
1519WS	**027 5-Car Freight** 54	**60**
1520W	**The Flashing Star of the South West** 54	**340**
1521WS	**027 5-Car Freight** 54	**80**
1523	**Lionel Work Train** 54	**170**
1527	**027 3-Car Work Train** 55	**85**
1529	**027 3-Car Freight** 55	**125**
1531W	**027 4-Car Freight** 55	**125**
1533WS	**027 Freight Hauler** 55	**60**
1534W	**027 Passenger Train** 55	**175**
1536W	**Pride of the Katy and Frisco** 55	**330**
1537WS	**027 4-Car Freight** 55	**60**
1538WS	**027 Passenger Train** 55	**120**
1539W	**027 5-Car Freight** 55	**120**
1541WS	**027 5-Car Freight** 55	**60**
1542	**027 3-Car Freight** 56	**40**
1543	**027 3-Car Freight** 56	**50**
1545	**027 4-Car Freight** 56	**50**
1547S	**027 Freight Hauler** 56	**35**
1549S	**027 3-Car Work Train** 56	**120**
1551S	**027 4-Car Freight** 56	**60**
1552	**027 Passenger Train** 56	**170**
1553W	**027 5-Car Freight** 56	**85**
1555WS	**027 Freight Hauler** 56	**45**
1557W	**027 5-Car Work Train** 56	**60**
1559W	**027 5-Car Freight Train** 56	**85**
1561WS	**027 5-Car Freight Train** 56	**60**
1562W	**027 Passenger Train** 56	**330**
1563W	**027 5-Car Freight** 56	**270**
1565W	**027 5-Car Freight** 56	**85**
1567W	**The Pride of the Santa Fe** 56	**120**
1569	**027 4-Car Freight** 57	**35**
1571	**027 5-Car Freight** 57	**60**
1573	**027 5-Car Freight** 57	**35**
1575	**027 5-Car Freight** 57	**60**
1577S	**027 6-Car Freight** 57	**60**
1578S	**027 Passenger Train** 57	**120**
1579S	**027 7-Car Freight** 57	**35**
1581	**027 7-Car Freight** 57	**85**
1583WS	**027 King of the High Iron** 57	**60**
1585W	**027 9-Car Freight Train** 57	**60**
1586	**027 Passenger Train** 57	**120**
1587S	**Lady Lionel Pastel Train Set** 57, 58	**450**
1589WS	**027 King of the High Iron** 57	**25**
1590	**027 4-Car Steam Freight** 58	**45**
1591	**U.S. Marine Land & Sea Limited** 58	**135**
1593	**5-Car Diesel Work Train** 58	**85**
1595	**027 Marine Battlefront Special** 58	**170**
1597S	**6-Car Coal King Smoking Freighter** 58	**35**
1599	**027 6-Car Freight** 58	**60**
1600	**027 3-Car Passenger Set** 58	**170**

1601W	**027 5-Car Diesel Freight** 58		120
1603WS	**Whistling Mountain Climber** 58		50
1605W	**027 6-Car Diesel Freight** 58		120
1607W	**Trouble Shooter Work Set** 58		60
1608W	**Merchants Limited Diesel Passenger Set** 58		220
1609	**027 3-Car Steam Freight** 59, 60		25
1611	**027 4-Car Alaskan Freight** 59		85
1612	**The General Old-Timer Outfit** 59, 60		60
1613S	**4-Car B&O Steam Freight** 59		35
1615	**0-4-0 Steamer**	(2+)	50
1615T	**Tender**	(3)	60
1615	**5-Car B&M Diesel Freight** 59		85
1617S	**5-Car Busy Beaver Steam Work Train** 59		85
1619W	**5-Car Santa Fe Diesel Freight** 59		60
1621WS	**Construction Special Steam Freight** 59		35
1623W	**5-Car Northern Pacific Diesel Freight** 59		120
1625	**0-4-0 Steamer**	(4)	100
1625T	**Tender**	(4)	85
1625WS	**5-Car Action King Steam Freight** 59		50
1626W	**4-Car Santa Fe Diesel Passenger** 59		120
1627S	**027 3-Car Steam Freight** 60		35
1629	**4-Car C & O Diesel Freight** 60		45
1631WS	**4-Car Industrial Steam Freight** 60		35
1633	**Land-Sea-Air Two Unit Diesel Freight** 60		120
1635WS	**Heavy-Duty Special Steam Freight** 60		60
1637W	**5-Car Twin Unit Diesel Freight** 60		60
1639WS	**Power House Special Steam Freight** 60		175
1640W	**Presidential Campaign Special** 60		125
1640-100	**Presidential Kit**	(3)	60
1641	**3-Car Headliner Steam Freight** 61		25
1642	**3-Car Circus Special Steam Freight** 61		35
1643	**4-Car Sky-Scout Diesel Freight** 61		35
1644	**Frontier Special General Passenger** 61		85
1645	**027 4-Car Diesel Freight** 61		35
1646	**4-Car Utility Steam Freight** 61		35
1647	**Freedom Fighter Missile Launcher Outfit** 61		120
1648	**5-Car Supply Line Steam Freight** 61		35
1649	**027 5-Car Two Unit Diesel Freight** 61		60
1650	**5-Car Guardian Steam Freight** 61		45
1651	**4-Car All Passenger Diesel** 61		120
1656	**0-4-0 Steamer**	(4+)	75
1665	**0-4-0 Steamer**	(4)	85
1666	**2-6-2 Steamer**	(3)	40
1800	**The General Frontier Pack** 59, 60		85
1805	**Land-Sea-And Air Gift Pack** 60		185
1809	**The Western Gift Pack** 61		60
1810	**The Space Age Gift Pack** 61		85
1862	**4-4-0 Steamer**	(4)	60
1862T	**Tender**	(4)	60
1865	**W & A Passenger Car**	(3)	50
1866	**W & A Passenger Car**	(3)	40
1872	**4-4-0 Steamer**	(4)	70
1872T	**Tender**	(4)	45

1875	**W & A Passenger Car**	(5)	**170**
1875W	**W & A Passenger Car**	(3)	**85**
1876	**W & A Passenger Car**	(3)	**35**
1877	**Flat with horses and fences**	(2)	**35**
1882	**4-4-0, 1882T**		**NOB**
1885	**W & A Passenger Car**		**NOB**
1887	**Flat Car w/horses and fences**		**NOB**
2016	**2-6-4 Steamer**	(3)	**60**
2018	**2-6-4 Steamer**	(2)	**35**
2020	**6-8-6 Steamer**	(2+)	**45**
2020W	**Tender**	(3)	**45**
2023(MC)	**Union Pacific Alco AA**	(3)	**95**
2024	**C&O Alco A**		**NOB**
2025	**2-6-2 Steamer**	(2)	**35**
2026	**2-6-2 Steamer**	(2)	**35**
2026X	**2-6-2 Steamer**		
2028	**Pennsylvania GP-7**	(3)	**75**
2029	**2-6-4 Steamer**	(2+)	**40**
2031(MC)	**Rock Island Alco AA**	(3)	**85**
2032(MC)	**Erie Alco AA**	(3)	**85**
2033(MC)	**Union Pacific Alco AA**	(4)	**95**
2034	**2-4-2 Steamer**	(2)	**35**
2035	**2-6-4 Steamer**	(2)	**35**
2036	**2-6-4 Steamer**	(3)	**35**
2037	**2-6-4 Steamer**	(2)	**35**
2037-500	**2-6-4 Steamer** (Girls Train)	(4+)	**170**
2041	**Rock Island Alco AA**		**120**
2046	**4-6-4 Steamer**	(2+)	**50**
2046W	**Tender**	(2)	**40**
2046WX	**Tender**	(4)	**50**
2046W-50	**PRR Tender**	(4)	**50**
2055	**4-6-4 Steamer**	(3)	**45**
2056	**4-6-4 Steamer**	(3)	**50**
2065	**4-6-4 Steamer**	(2)	**50**
2100	**Lionel O Passenger Train** 46		**120**
2100W	**Lionel O Passenger Train** 46		**120**
2101	**Lionel O Gauge Freight Set** 46		**60**
2101W	**Lionel O Gauge Freight Set** 46		**60**
2103W	**Lionel O Gauge Freight Set** 46		**60**
2105WS	**Lionel Freight Outfit** 46		**60**
2110WS	**Lionel Passenger Train** 46		**225**
2111WS	**Lionel Freight Train** 46		**125**
2113WS	**Lionel O Gauge Freight Outfit** 46		**225**
2114WS	**O Passenger Outfit** 46		**325**
2115WS	**Lionel O Gauge Freight Work Train w/smoke** 46		**175**
2120S	**De Luxe Passenger** 47		**120**
2120WS	**De Luxe Passenger** 47		**120**
2121S	**Lionel Freight Set** 47		**45**
2121WS	**Lionel Freight Set** 47		**45**
2123WS	**Lionel Freight Set** 47		**60**
2124W	**Lionel Passenger Set** 47		**380**
2125WS	**Lionel Freight Train** 47		**85**
2126WS	**Lionel Passenger Set** 47		**225**

2127WS **Lionel Work Train** 47 85

2129WS **Lionel Freight Set** 47 225

2131WS **De Luxe Work Train** 47 135

2133W **4-Car Twin Diesel O Gauge Freight Train** 48 135

2135WS **Lionel Freight Train** 48, 49 50

2136WS **Passenger Train** 48, 49 120

2137WS **De Luxe Freight Train** 48 60

2139W **Lionel Four-Car Freight Set** 48 135

2139W **O Gauge Four-Car Freight Outfit** 49 135

2140WS **De Luxe Passenger Set** 48, 49 120

2141WS **Four-Car Freight Train** 48, 49 60

2143WS **De Luxe Work Train** 48 85

2144W **3-Car De Luxe Passenger Outfit** 48, 49 330

2145WS **Four-Car Freight Set** 48 110

2146WS **Lionel Pullman Train** 48, 49 275

2147WS **Four-Car Freight Set** 49 60

2148WS **Lionel O Deluxe Pullman Set** 50 575

2149B **O Gauge Four-Car Diesel Work Train** 49 120

2150WS **O Deluxe Passenger Set** 50 120

2151W **Five-Car O Gauge Diesel Set** 49 135

2153WS **Four-Car De Luxe Work Train** 49 85

2155WS **Four-Car Freight Train** 49 120

2159W **Lionel 5-Car Freight** 50 225

2161W **Twin Diesel Freight** 50 135

2163WS **4-Car Freight** 50, 51 120

2165WS **O 4-Car Freight Set** 50 120

2167WS **3-Car Freight** 50, 51 60

2169WS **Lionel 5-Car Freight w/smoke and whistle** 50 340

2171W **Twin Diesel Freight** 50 135

2173WS **Lionel 4-Car Freight** 50 60

2175W **Magnificent Lionel Twin Diesel Freights** 50, 51 175

2177WS **3-Car Freight** 52 50

2179WS **4-Car Freight** 52 50

2183WS **4-Car Freight** 52 60

2185W **Magnificent Lionel Twin Diesel Freights** 50, 51 135

2187WS **5-Car Freight** 52 60

2189WS **Transcontinental Fast Freight** 52 85

2190W **Lionel Super Speedliner** 52, 53 275

2191W **4-Car Diesel Freights** 52 170

2193W **4-Car Diesel Freights** 52 170

2201WS **Highballing Freight** 53, 54 85

2203WS **Highballing Freight** 53 85

2205WS **5-Car Freight** 53 85

2207W **Triple Diesel Freight** 53 170

2209W **Triple Diesel Freight** 53 170

2211WS **4-Car Freight** 53 85

2213WS **5-Car Freight** 53 85

2217WS **O Gauge 4-Car Freight** 54 120

2219W **Fairbanks-Morse Power Giant** 54 175

2221WS **O Gauge 5-Car Freight,** 54 85

2222WS **Lionel O Gauge 3-Car Pullman Set** 54 225

2223W **O Gauge 5-Car Freight** 54 275

2225WS **Lionel O Gauge 5-Car Work Freight** 54 85

2227W	**O Gauge 5-Car Freight** 54		**175**
2229W	**O Gauge 5-Car Freight** 54		**175**
2231W	**O Gauge 5-Car Freight** 54		**275**
2234W	**Super-Streamliner** 54		**325**
2235W	**O Gauge 4-Car Freight** 55		**85**
2237WS	**O Gauge 3-Car Freight** 55		**60**
2239W	**O Gauge Streak-Liner** 55		**220**
2240P	**Wabash F3 Powered A Unit**	(3)	**170**
2240C	**Wabash F3 Dummy B Unit**	(3+)	**170**
2241WS	**O Gauge Freight Snorter** 55		**60**
2242P	**New Haven F3 Powered A Unit**	(4)	**185**
2242C	**New Haven F3 Dummy B Unit**	(4)	**185**
2243P	**Santa Fe F3 Powered A Unit**	(2+)	**75**
2243C	**Santa Fe F3 Dummy B Unit**	(3)	**75**
2243W	**The High and the Mighty** 55		**170**
2244W	**The Sweetest Sight on Rails** 55		**275**
2245P	**Texas Special F3 Powered A**	(3)	**135**
2245C	**Texas Special F3 Dummy B Unit**	(3+)	**135**
2245WS	**Whistles While She Works** 55		**85**
2247W	**O Gauge 5-Car Freight** 55		**275**
2249WS	**O Gauge 5-Car Freight** 55		**120**
2251W	**The High and the Mighty** 55		**275**
2253W	**A Miracle of Modeling Accuracy** 55		**275**
2254W	**The Congressional** 55		**825**
2255W	**O Gauge 4-Car Work Train** 56		**85**
2257WS	**O Gauge 5-Car Freight** 56		**60**
2259W	**O Gauge 5-Car Freight** 56		**120**
2261WS	**O Gauge Freight Hauler** 56		**85**
2263W	**O Gauge 5-Car Freight** 56		**120**
2265SW	**O Gauge 5-Car Freight** 56		**85**
2267W	**Proud Giant of the Rails** 56		**225**
2269W	**Majestic O Gauge Freight Set** 56		**600**
2270W	**Proud Giant of the Rails,** 56		**775**
2271W	**O Gauge 5-Car Freight Train** 56		**450**
2273W	**From the Midwest to the East** 56		**670**
2274W	**The Great Congressional** 56		**775**
2275W	**O Gauge 4-Car Freight** 57		**175**
2276W	**Budd RDC Commuter Set** 57		**275**
2277SW	**O Gauge 4-Car Work Train** 57		**85**
2279W	**O Gauge 5-Car Freight** 57		**120**
2281W	**O Gauge 5-Car Freight** 57		**135**
2283WS	**O Gauge 5-Car Freight** 57		**85**
2285W	**O Gauge 5-Car Freight** 57		**230**
2287W	**O Gauge 5-Car Freight** 57		**230**
2289WS	**Super O Freight Train** 57		**120**
2291W	**Dream-Liner of the Western Roads** 57		**335**
2292WS	**Crack Super O Luxury Liner** 57		**270**
2293W	**Pride of the Eastern Lines** 57		**225**
2295WS	**The Grand Daddy of all Steamers** 57		**335**
2296W	**Crack Super O Luxury Liner** 57		**775**
2297WS	**The 16 Wheeler Class J** 57		**350**
2340-25	**GG-1/Green 5 gold stripes**	(4)	**270**
2321	**Lackawanna FM**	(3)	**135**

2322	Virginian FM	(3)	120
2328	Burlington GP-7	(2+)	95
2329	Virginian Electric	(4)	175
2330	GGI	(4+)	275
2331	Virginian FM	(3)	170
2332	GGI	(3)	135
2333P	Santa Fe F-3 Powered A Unit	(2+)	75
2333T	Santa Fe F-3 Dummy A Unit	(3)	75
2333P	NYC F-3 Powered A Unit	(3)	85
2333T	NYC F-3 Dummy A Unit	(3+)	85
2360-25	GG-1 Brunswick green	(4)	300
2337	Wabash GP-7	(4)	85
2338	Milwaukee Road GP-7	(2)	75
2339	Wabash GP-7	(3+)	85
2340-1	GG-1/Tuscan 5 gold stripes	(4)	275
2341	Jersey Central FM	(4+)	575
2343P	Santa Fe F-3 Powered A Unit	(2)	75
2343T	Santa Fe F-3 Dummy A Unit	(3)	75
2343C	Santa Fe F3 Dummy B Unit	(2+)	85
2344P	NYC F-3 Powered A Unit	(3)	80
2344T	NYC Dummy A Unit	(3+)	80
2344C	NYC Dummy B Unit	(3)	90
2345P	Western Pacific F-3 Powered A	(3+)	190
2345T	Western Pacific F-3 Dummy A	(4)	190
2346	Boston & Maine GP-7	(4)	95
2347	C&0 GP-7	(5)	330
2348	Minn & St. Louis GP-9	(3+)	110
2349	Northern Pacific GP-9	(3)	110
2350	New Haven EP-5	(2+)	95
2351	Milwaukee Road EP-5	(3+)	135
2352	Pennsylvania EP-5	(3+)	165
2353P	Santa Fe F-3 Powered A Unit	(2)	85
2353T	Santa Fe F-3 Dummy A Unit	(3)	85
2354P	NYC F-3 Powered A Unit	(3)	95
2354T	NYC F-3 Dummy A Unit	(3+)	95
2355P	Western Pacific F-3 Powered A	(3+)	195
2355T	Western Pacific F-3 Dummy A	(4)	195
2356P	Southern F-3 Powered A Unit	(3)	170
2356T	Southern F-3 Dummy A Unit	(3+)	170
2356C	Southern F-3 Dummy B Unit	(3+)	195
2358	Great Northern EP-5	(4+)	280
2359	Boston & Maine GP-9	(3)	95
2360-1	GG-1	(4)	275
2363P	Illinois Central F-3 Powered A	(3)	170
2363C	Illinois Central F-3 Dummy B	(3+)	170
2365	Chesapeake & Ohio GP-7	(3+)	105
2367P	Wabash F-3 Powered A Unit	(3)	150
2367C	Wabash F-3 Dummy B Unit	(3+)	150
2368P	B&O F-3 Powered A Unit	(4)	295
2368C	B&O F-3 Dummy B Unit	(4)	295
2373P	Canadian Pacific F-3 Powered A	(4)	270
2373T	Canadian Pacific F-3 Dummy A	(4)	270
2378P	Milwaukee Road F-3 Powered A	(4)	295

2378C	**Milwaukee Road F-3 Dummy B**	(4)	**295**
2379P	**Rio Grande F-3 Powered A Unit**	(3)	**175**
2379C	**Rio Grande F-3 Dummy B Unit**	(3+)	**175**
2383P	**Santa Fe F-3 Powered A Unit**	(3)	**75**
2383T	**Santa Fe F-3 Dummy A Unit**	(2)	**75**
2400	**Maplewood Pullman**	(4)	**60**
2401	**Hillside Observation**	(4)	**60**
2402	**Chatham Pullman**	(4)	**60**
2403B	**Tender**	(4)	**85**
2404	**Santa Fe Vista Dome**	(3+)	**35**
2405	**Santa Pullman**	(3+)	**40**
2406	**Santa Fe Observation**	(3+)	**35**
2408	**Santa Vista Dome**	(4)	**35**
2409	**Santa Fe Pullman**	(4)	**40**
2410	**Santa Fe Observation**	(4)	**35**
2412	**Santa Fe Vista Dome**	(3)	**40**
2414	**Santa Fe Pullman**	(3)	**40**
2416	**Santa Fe Observation**	(3)	**35**
2419	**DL&W Work Caboose**	(3)	**30**
2420	**DL&W Work Caboose**	(3)	**30**
2421	**Maplewood Pullman**	(2)	**30**
2422	**Chatham Pullman**	(2)	**30**
2423	**Hillside Observation**	(2)	**25**
2426	**Tender**	(4)	**250**
2429	**Livingston Pullman**	(3)	**40**
2430	**Pullman**	(3+)	**35**
2431	**Observation**	(3+)	**30**
2432	**Clifton Vista Dome**	(2+)	**30**
2434	**Newark Pullman**	(2+)	**30**
2435	**Elizabeth Pullman**	(2+)	**30**
2436	**Mooseheart Observation**	(3)	**40**
2440	**Observation**	(3)	**30**
2441	**Observation**	(3)	**30**
2442	**Pullman**	(3)	**30**
2442	**Clifton Vista Dome**	(4)	**50**
2443	**Observation**	(3)	**30**
2444	**Newark Pullman**	(4)	**60**
2445	**Elizabeth Pullman**	(5-)	**120**
2446	**Summit Observation**	(4)	**50**
2454	**Pennsylvania Boxcar**	(4)	**60**
2460	**Bucyrus Erie Crane Car**	(3+)	**50**
2461	**Transformer Car**	(3)	**35**
2466T	**Tender**	(3)	**35**
2466W	**Tender**	(3)	**35**
2466WX	**Tender**	(4)	**40**
2481	**Plainfield Pullman**	(4+)	**135**
2482	**Westfield Pullman**	(4+)	**135**
2483	**Livingston Observation**	(4+)	**135**
2501W	**Super O Work Train,** 58		**120**
2502W	**Super O Rail-Diesel Commuter** 58		**275**
2503WS	**Timberland Special Freight** 58		**85**
2505W	**5-Car Super O Freight** 58		**195**
2507W	**5-Car Super O Diesel Freight** 58		**225**
2509WS	**The Owl 5-Car Freight** 58		**85**

2511W	Super O Electric Work Train 58		135
2513W	6-Car Super O Freight Train 58		225
2515WS	5-Car Mainliner Steam Freight 58		120
2517W	5-Car Super O Diesel Freight 58		330
2518W	Super O Passenger Train 58		270
2519W	6-Car Super O Diesel Freight 58		220
2521	President McKinley Obsv	(3+)	95
2521WS	6-Car Super O Freight Train 58		275
2522	President Harrison Vista Dome	(3+)	95
2523	President Garfield Pullman	(3+)	110
2523W	Super O Super Chief Freight, 58		225
2525WS	6-Car Super O Work Train, 58		375
2526W	Super Chief Passenger, 58		275
2527	Super O Missile Launcher Outfit 59, 60		120
2528WS	5-Star Frontier Special Outfit 59-61		120
2529W	5-Car Virginian Rectifier Work Train 59		175
2530	Baggage Car (B & O)	(2+)	70
2530	Baggage Car (OPerf)	(5)	175
2531	Silver Dawn Observation	(2)	40
2531WS	Super O 5-Car Steam Freight 59		135
2532	Silver Range Vista Dome	(2)	45
2533	Silver Cloud Pullman	(2+)	45
2533W	5-Car GN Electric Freight 59		225
2534	Silver Bluff Pullman	(2+)	45
2535WS	Super O 5-Car Hudson Steam Freight 59		120
2537W	5-Car New Haven Diesel Freight 59		275
2539WS	5-Car Hudson Steam Freight 59		170
2541	Alexander Hamilton Observation	(3)	110
2541W	5-Car Super Chief Freight 59		275
2542	Betsy Ross Vista Dome	(3+)	110
2543	William Penn Pullman	(3+)	110
2543WS	6-Car Berkshire Steam Freight 59		175
2544	Molly Pitcher Pullman	(3+)	110
2544W	4-Car Super Chief Streamliner 59, 60		450
2545WS	6-Car N&W Space-Freight 59		340
2547WS	4-Car Variety Special Steam Freight 60		85
2549W	A Mighty Military Diesel Outfit 60		140
2550	Baltimore & Ohio Budd	(4)	120
2551	Banff Park Observation	(4)	120
2551W	6-Car GN Diesel Freight 60		240
2552	Skyline 500 Vista Dome	(4)	130
2553	Blair Manor Pullman	(4+)	190
2553WS	The Majestic Berkshire 5-Car Freight 60		165
2554	Craig Manor	(4+)	190
2555	Sunoco Tank Car	(3+)	30
2555W	Over & Under Twin Railroad Empire 60		1200
2559	Baltimore & Ohio Budd	(3+)	95
2560	Lionel Lines Crane	(4)	40
2561	Vista Valley Observation	(4)	120
2562	Regal Pass Vista Dome	(4)	125
2563	Indian Falls Pullman	(4)	125
2570	5-Car Husky Diesel Freight, 61		85
2571	Fort Knox Special Steam Freight 61		60

2572	**5-Car Space Age Diesel Freighter** 61		**120**
2573	**5-Car TV Special Steam Freight** 61		**135**
2574	**5-Car Defender Diesel Freight** 61		**190**
2575	**7-Car Dynamo Electric Freight** 61		**330**
2576	**4-Car Super Chief Streamline** 61		**450**
6517-1966	**TCA 1966 Conv Car**	(4)	**40**
2625	**Irvington** (1946-1949)	(3)	**95**
2625	**Irvington** (1950)	(4+)	**110**
2625	**Madison** (1947)	(3)	**95**
2625	**Manhattan** (1947)	(3)	**95**
2627	**Madison** (1948,1949)	(3)	**95**
2627	**Madison** (1950)	(4+)	**120**
2628	**Manhattan** (1948, 1949)	(3)	**95**
2628	**Manhattan** (1950)	(4+)	**120**
2671W	**Tender**	(3)	**40**
2671WX	**Tender**	(4)	**50**
2755	**Sunoco Tank Car aluminum**	(3)	**30**
2758	**Pennsylvania Automobile Boxcar**	(2)	**25**
2855	**Sunoco Tank Car**	(4)	**70**
3330	**Flat Car with Operating Sub Kit**	(3)	**60**
3330-100	**Operating Submarine Kit**	(4)	**135**
3349	**Turbo Launching Car**	(3)	**25**
3356	**Operating Horse Car w/corral**	(2)	**40**
3356-2	**Operating Horse Car**	(4)	**30**
3356-150	**Operating Horse Car Corral**	(5)	**135**
3357	**Cop and Hobo Car**	(2)	**30**
3359-55	**Lionel Lines Twin Dump Car**	(3)	**35**
3360	**Burro Crane**	(3)	**50**
3366	**Operating Circus Car w/corral**	(3+)	**85**
3370	**Sheriff & Outlaw Car**	(3+)	**40**
3376	**Operating Giraffe Car**	(2)	**30**
3376-160	**Operating Giraffe Car**	(4)	**40**
3386	**Operating Giraffe Car**		**NOB**
3409	**Operating Helicopter Car**		**NOB**
3410	**Operating Helicopter Car**		**NOB**
3413	**Mercury Capsule Car**	(4)	**40**
3419	**Operating Helicopter Car**	(2+)	**30**
3424	**Wabash Brakeman Car**	(2)	**25**
3428	**US Mail Car**	(3+)	**35**
3429	**USMC Helicopter Launch Car**		**NOB**
3434	**Operating Chicken Car**	(3)	**35**
3435	**Aquarium Car**	(3)	**70**
3444	**Erie Animated Gondola**	(3)	**45**
3454	**PRR Merchandise Car**	(3+)	**85**
3460	**Flatcar with trailors**	(3)	**30**
3470	**Aerial Target Launching Car**	(3)	**30**
3474	**Western Pacific Op. Boxcar**	(3)	**30**
3484	**PRR Operating Boxcar**	(3)	**25**
3484-25	**Santa Fe Operating Boxcar**	(3)	**35**
3494-1	**NYC Operating Boxcar**	(3)	**30**
3494-150	**Missouri Pacific Op. Boxcar**	(3+)	**40**
3494-275	**State Of Maine Op. Boxcar**	(2+)	**35**
3494-550	**Monon Operating Boxcar**	(4)	**95**

3494-625	Soo Operating Boxcar	(4)	95
3509	Satellite Car	(5)	120
3510	Satellite Car		NOB
3512	Operating Fireman and Ladder Car	(3)	60
3519	Operating Satellite Car	(3)	35
3530	Operating Generator Car	(3)	35
3535	AEC Security Car	(3)	30
3540	Operating Radar Car	(4)	45
3545	Operating TV Monitor Car	(4)	45
3562-1	Operating Barrel Car	(3)	30
3562-25	Operating Barrel Car	(2)	25
3562-50	Operating Barrel Car	(2)	25
3562-75	Operating Barrel Car	(3)	30
3619	Helicopter Reconnaissance Car	(3+)	45
3665	Minuteman Missile Launching Car	(3)	35
3666	Cannon Box Car		NOB
3672	Operating Bosco Milk Car	(3+)	85
3820	Operating Submarine Car		NOB
3830	Operating Submarine Car	(3)	35
3854	Pennsylvania Merchandise Car	(4)	95
3927	Track Cleaning Car	(2)	25
4109WS	Electronic Control Set 46, 47		140
4110WS	Lionel Electronic Railroad 48, 49		250
4357	SP Caboose	(4)	75▲
4452	Pennsylvania Gondola	(4)	100▲
4454	Baby Ruth Boxcar	(4)	125▲
4457	Pennsylvania Caboose	(4)	75▲
5459	Operating Dump Car	(4)	50
6014	Chun King Boxcar		
6014-60	Bosco Boxcar	(4)	40
6014-100	Airex Boxcar	(3)	30
6014-150	Wix Boxcar	(4+)	85
6014-410	Frisco Boxcar	(4)	30
6017-50	USMC Caboose	(3)	40
6017-85	Lionel Lines Caboose	(4)	50
6017-100	Boston & Maine Caboose	(3+)	30
6017-200	US Navy Caboose	(4+)	100▲
6020W	Tender	(3)	50
6024-60	RCA Whirlpool Boxcar	(4)	40
6026T	Tender	(3)	25
6026W	Tender	(3)	30
6027	Alaska Caboose	(4)	95
6044-1X	McCall/Nestle's Boxcar	(5)	220
6050	Libby's Tomato Juice Boxcar		NOB
6119	DL&W Work Caboose	(2+)	25
6119-25	DL&W Work Caboose	(3)	25
6119-50	DL&W Work Caboose	(3)	25
6119-100	DL&W Work Caboose	(3)	25
6119-125	Lionel Rescue Unit		NOB
6151	Flat Car w/Range Patrol Truck	(3)	35
6162-60	Alaska Gondola	(3)	45

6162-110	**NYC Blue Gondola**	(3)	**25**
6162-110	**NYC Red Gondola (Paste-On-Label)**	(4+)	**40**
6175	**Flat Car with rocket**	(3)	**30**
6220	**Santa Fe GM Switcher**	(3)	**70**
6250	**Seaboard GM Switcher**	(3)	**70**
6257X	**SP Caboose**	(4)	**60**
6262	**Wheel Car**	(3)	**30**
6264	**Lumber Car**	(4+)	**130**
6311	**Flat Car with pipes**	(4)	**85**
6315	**Gulf Tank Car**	(2)	**30**
6343	**Barrel Ramp Car**	(3)	**25**
6346-56	**Alcoa Covered Hopper**	(3)	**35**
6352-25	**Ice Car**	(5)	**85**
6356	**NYC Stock Car**	(2+)	**25**
6357-50	**AT&SF**	(4+)	**140**
6362	**Railway Truck Car**	(3+)	**35**
6376	**Circus Car**	(3)	**30**
6401	**Flat Car**	(5)	**125**
6403B	**Tender**	(3+)	**70**
6405	**Flat with trailer**	(4)	**40**
6406	**Flat Car with single auto**		**NOB**
6407	**Flat Car with missile**	(5-)	**140**
6408	**Flat Car with pipes**		**NOB**
6409	**Flat Car with pipes**		**NOB**
6409-25	**Flat Car with pipes**		**NOB**
6411	**Flat Car with logs**		
6413	**Mercury Capsule Car**	(3+)	**40**
6414	**Automobile Car (B&O)**	(2+)	**35**
6414	**Automobile Transport Car (OPerf)**	(4)	**50**
6414	**Automobile Transport Car (OPix)**	(3)	**35**
6414	**RS 6414 on end flap (WB)**	(4)	**85**
6414-25	**Four Autos**	(4)	**120**
6414-85	**Automobile Transport Car**	(5-)	**120**
6416	**Boat Loader**	(3+)	**60**
6417	**NYC Porthole Caboose**	(2)	**25**
6417-50	**Lehigh Valley Caboose**	(3)	**40**
6418	**Machinery Car**	(3+)	**40**
6419-100	**DL&W Work Caboose**	(3)	**25**
6420	**DL&W Work Caboose**	(3)	**40**
6424-110	**Flat Car with two autos**	(2+)	**30**
6427-60	**Virginian**	(4)	**95**
6427-500	**Pennsylvania Caboose**	(4+)	**120**
6429	**DL&W**	(4+)	**170**
6430	**Flat Car with trailers**	(3)	**35**
6431	**Piggy-Back Car with Midge Toy Tractor**	(4)	**120**
6434	**Poultry Car**	(3)	**35**
6436	**Lehigh Valley Hopper**	(2+)	**25**
6436-25	**Lehigh Valley Hopper**	(2+)	**25**
6436-110	**Lehigh Valley Hopper**	(3)	**30**
6436-500	**Lehigh Valley Hopper**	(4+)	**120**
6440	**Pullman**	(3)	**35**
6441	**Observation**	(3)	**35**

6442	Pullman	(3)	35
6443	Observation	(3)	35
6445	Fort Knox Gold Bullion Car	(3+)	40
6446	N&W Covered Hopper (B&O)	(2+)	25
6446	Cement Car (OPR)	(4+)	40
6446-25	N&W Covered Hopper	(2+)	25
6446-60	Lehigh Valley Covered Hopper	(5-)	95
6447	Pennsylvania Caboose	(5+)	200▲
6448	Exploding Boxcar	(2+)	25
6454	Baby Ruth Boxcar	(4)	85
6460	Bucyrus Erie Crane Car	(2)	30
6461	Transformer Car	(3+)	30
6462-500	NYC Gondola (Girls Train)	(4+)	175▲
6463	Rocket Fuel Tank Car	(3+)	40
6464-1	Western Pacific Boxcar	(2)	35
6464-50	M&STl. Boxcar	(2)	30
6464-75	Rock Island Boxcar	(3)	30
6464-100	WP Boxcar (Yellow Feather)	(3)	40
6464-125	New York Central Boxcar	(3)	40
6464-150	Missouri Pacific Boxcar	(3)	45
6464-175	Rock Island Boxcar (50, Silver, Overstamp)	(3+)	35
6464-175	Rock Island Boxcar (175 Stamped on Box)	(4+)	75
6464-175	Rock Island Boxcar (C)	(3)	25
6464-200	Pennsylvania Boxcar (B&O)	(3+)	45
6464-200	Pennsylvania Boxcar (C)	(3)	35
6464-225	Southern Pacific Boxcar	(2+)	35
6464-250	Western Pacific Boxcar (WB)	(3)	45
6464-250	Western Pacific Boxcar (B&O)	(5)	195
6464-275	State of Maine Boxcar	(3)	40
6464-300	Rutland Boxcar	(3)	45
6464-325	Sentinel Boxcar	(4)	145
6464-350	MKT Boxcar	(4)	85
6464-375	Central of GeorgiaBoxcar (B&O)	(3)	35
6464-375	Central of Georgia Boxcar (WB)	(2)	30
6464-400	B&O Boxcar (B&O)	(3)	35
6464-400	Baltimore & Ohio Boxcar (C)	(3)	30
6464-425	New Haven Boxcar	(2)	25
6464-450	Great Northern Boxcar (B&O)	(3)	35
6464-450	Great Northern Boxcar (WB)	(2)	30
6464-475	Boston & Maine Boxcar	(3)	25
6464-475	Boston & Maine Boxcar (OPerf)	(2+)	40
6464-500	Timken Boxcar (B&O)	(3)	35
6464-500	Timken Boxcar (C)	(3)	30
6464-510	NYC Pacmaker Boxcar (Girls Train)	(4+)	225▲
6464-515	Katy Boxcar Type	(4+)	225▲
6464-525	M&STl. Boxcar	(3)	25
6464-650	Rio Grande Boxcar (B&O)	(3)	65
6464-650	Rio Grande Boxcar (WB)	(3)	40
6464-700	Santa Fe Boxcar (OPI)	(3+)	40
6464-700	Santa Fe Boxcar (WB)	(3)	25
6464-725	New Haven Boxcar (735 on box) (OPix)	(2+)	25
6464-725	New Haven Boxcar (735 on box) (WB)	(3+)	30
6464-725	New Haven Boxcar (425 on box) (C)	(4)	45

6464-825	Alaska Boxcar	(4)	135
6464-900	NYC Boxcar	(3)	30
6464-1965	TCA Pittsburgh Boxcar	(4)	50
6466W	Tender	(3)	25
6466WX	Tender	(4)	40
6467	Miscellaneous Car	(3)	25
6468	Baltimore & Ohio Boxcar	(2)	25
6468X	Baltimore & Ohio Boxcar	(5-)	105
6469	Liquified Gas Car	(4)	85
6475	Pickle Car	(2)	25
6475	Libbys Pickle Car		NOB
6475	Heinz Pickle Car		
6477	Miscellaneous Car with pipes	(3)	35
6480	Exploding Boxcar		NOB
6500	Beechcraft Bonanza Transport Car (OPix)	(4+)	170
6500	Beechcraft Bonanza Transport Car (OPP)	(5-)	170
6501	Jet Boat Car	(3+)	60
6502	Girder Car, Black/white		NOB
6502-50	Girder Car, Blue/white		NOB
6502-75	Girder Car, Light blue/white		NOB
6511	Flatcar with pipes	(3)	25
6512	Cherry Picker Car	(3+)	45
6517	Lionel Lines Bay Window Caboose	(2)	35
6517-75	Erie Bay Window Caboose	(4)	120
6518	Transformer Car	(3+)	40
6519	Allis Chalmers Car	(3+)	30
6520	Searchlight Car	(3)	25
6530	Fire And Safety Training Car	(3+)	40
6544	Missile Launching Car	(3)	30
6556	Katy Stock Car	(4)	65
6557	Lionel Smoking Caboose	(3)	45
6560	Bucyrus Erie Crane Car	(2)	25
6560-25	Bucyrus Erie Crane Car	(3)	25
6561	Cable Car	(3)	30
6572	Railway Express Car (B&O)	(3+)	40
6572	Railway Express Car (OPix)	(3)	35
6630	Missile Launcher		NOB
6640	USMC Missile Launcher		NOB
6650	Missile Launching Flat Car	(3)	30
6651	USMC Cannon Car		NOB
6657	Rio Grande Caboose	(3+)	50
6660	Boom Car	(4)	30
6670	Derrick Car	(4)	30
6672	Refrigerator Car	(3)	30
6736	Detroit & Mackinac Hopper	(3+)	35
6800	Airplane Car (B&O)	(3)	40
6800	Airplane Car (OPix)	(4+)	60
6800-60	Airplane	(4)	175
6801	Flat Car with boat	(3)	30
6801-50	Flat Car with boat	(3+)	30
6801-75	Flat Car with boat	(3)	30
6802	Flat Car with girders	(4)	25
6803	Flat Car with Military Units	(3+)	50

6804	Flat Car with Military Units	(3+)	50
6805	Radioactive Waste	(3+)	40
6806	Flat Car with Military Units	(3+)	50
6807	Flat Car with Military Unit	(3)	40
6808	Flat Car with Military Units	(3+)	50
6809	Flat Car with Military Units	(3+)	50
6810	Flat Car with van	(3)	30
6812	Track Maintenance Car	(3)	30
6814	First Aid Medical Car	(3)	35
6816	Flatcar with bulldozer	(4)	200▲
6816-100	Bulldozer (B&O)	(5)	1100*
6816-100	Bulldozer (Photo Box*)	(5)	1100*
6817	Flatcar with scraper	(4)	200▲
6817-100	Scraper (PWB)	(5)	1100*
6817-100	Scraper (Photo Box)	(5)	1100*
6819	Flat Car with helicopter	(3+)	35
6820	Missile Transport Car	(4)	120
6821	Flat Car with crates	(3+)	30
6822	Nightcrew Searchlight Car	(3)	25
6823	Flat Car with missiles	(3)	30
6824	USMC First Aid Medical Car		NOB
6824-50	First Aid Medical Car		NOB
6825	Flat Car with trestle	(3)	25
6826	Flat Car with Christmas Trees	(3+)	35
6827	Flat Car w/P&H Steam Shovel	(3)	50
6827	Power Shovel	(3)	40
6828	Flat Car with P&H Crane	(3)	50
6828	Truck Crane	(3)	40
6830	Flat Car with submarine	(3+)	40
6844	Flat Car with missiles	(3)	30
11201	Fast Starter Steam Freight, 62		25
11212	4-Unit Cyclone Diesel Freight 62		45
11222	5-Unit Vagabond Steam Freight 62		35
11232	027 5-Unit Diesel Freight, 62		45
11242	Trail Blazer Steam Freight 62		25
11252	027 7-Unit Diesel Freight 62		60
11268	027 6-Unit Diesel Freight 62		120
11278	7-Unit Plainsman Steam Freight 62		35
11288	7-Unit Orbitor Diesel Freight 62		120
11298	7-Unit Vigilant Steam Freight 62		60
11308	027 6-Unit Diesel Passenger 62		120
11311	Value Packed Steam Freighter 63		25
11321	027 5 Unit Diesel Freighter 63		35
11331	Outdoorsman Steam Freight 63		35
11341	Space-Prober Diesel Freight 63		170
11351	Land Rover Steam Freight 63		35
11361	Shooting Star Diesel Freight 63		120
11375	Cargomaster Steam Freight 63		85
11385	Space Conqueror Diesel Freight 63		225
11395	Muscleman Steam Freight 63		85
11405	027 6 Unit Diesel Passenger 63		120
11420	4-Unit Steam Freight 64		25
11430	5-Unit Steam Freight 64		25

11440	**5-Unit Diesel Freight 64**	35
11450	**6-Unit Steam Freight 64**	25
11460	**7-Unit Steam Freight 64**	25
11470	**7-Unit Steam Freight 64**	35
11480	**7-Unit Diesel Freight** 64	60
11490	**5-Unit Diesel Passenger** 64, 65	120
11500	**7-Unit Steam Freight** 64-66	35
11510	**7-Unit Steam Freight** 64	35
11520	**6-Unit Steam Freight** 65, 66	25
11530	**5-Unit Diesel Freight** 65, 66	35
11540	**6-Unit Steam Freight** 65, 66	25
11550	**6-Unit Steam Freight** 65, 66	35
11560	**7-Unit Diesel Freight** 65, 66	60
11590	**5-Unit Illuminated Passenger Set** 66	120
11600	**7-Unit Steam Freight Set** 68	340
11710	**Value Packed Steam Freighter** 69	25
11720	**5 Unit Diesel Freighter** 69	35
11730	**6 Unit Diesel Freight** 69	45
11740	**7 Unit Diesel Freight** 69	45
11750	**7 Unit Steam Freight** 69	60
11760	**7 Unit Steam Freight** 69	35
12502	**Prairie-Rider Gift Pack** 62	120
12512	**Enforcer Gift Pack** 62	120
12700	**7-Unit Steam Freight** 64	135
12710	**7-Unit Steam Freight** 64-66	135
12720	**7-Unit Diesel Freight** 64	135
12730	**7-Unit Diesel Freight** 64-66	135
12740	**9-Unit Diesel Freight** 64	135
12750	**9-Unit Diesel Freight** 64	135
12760	**9-Unit Steam Freight** 64	135
12770	**9-Unit Steam Freight** 64	135
12780	**6-Unit Diesel Passenger** 64-66	340
12800	**6-Unit Diesel Freight** 65, 66	85
12820	**8-Unit Diesel Freight** 65	135
12840	**Back by Popular Demand** 66	120
12850	**8-Unit Diesel Freight** 66	135
13008	**6-Unit Champion Steam Freight** 62	45
13018	**6-Unit Starfire Diesel Freight** 62	170
13028	**6-Unit Defender Diesel Freight** 62	130
13036	**6-Unit Plainsman Steam Outfit** 62	120
13048	**7-Unit Super O Steam Freight** 62	120
13058	**7-Unit Vanguard Diesel Freight** 62	175
13068	**8-Unit Goliath Electric Freight** 62	340
13078	**5-Unit Presidential Passenger** 62	340
13088	**6-Unit Presidential Passenger** 62	340
13098	**Goliath Steam Freight** 63	220
13108	**7 Unit Super O Diesel Freight** 63	120
13118	**8 Unit Super O Steam Freight** 63	170
13128	**7 Unit Super O Diesel Freight** 63	220
13138	**Majestic Electric Freight** 63	330
13148	**Super Chief Passenger** 63	330
13150	**9-Unit Super O Steam Freight** 64-66	330

Lionel HO, 1957-1966

by Charles Sommer

A combination of diminishing sales in the mid 1950's and a growing interest in the HO scale among the train buying public led The Lionel Corporation to launch an HO line in 1957. Lacking the necessary experience with HO production, Lionel contracted with the Italian firm Rivarossi to furnish them with the cars used in their 1957 line.

In 1958, Athearn made most of Lionel's HO line and in 1959, Lionel manufactured their own line of HO, using tooling purchased from Hobby-line. Starting with the Poultry car in 1959, Lionel introduced a series of HO versions of their O gauge operating cars. While these cars were appealing to kids, they ended any interest HO modelers may have had with Lionel. Lionel discontinued their HO line in 1966.

Today, Lionel HO is drawing interest from collectors because prices are still relatively low and it's still possible to find mint/boxed pieces. In the late 60s, large inventories of Lionel HO were sold in bulk by hobby shops trying to dump the poor-selling line. Many buyers stored the items, waiting for that day when there was enough demand to bring them out. That day is here.

Since very little Lionel HO is purchased to operate, condition is crucial. There is a dramatic drop (50% or more) in price after Mint/boxed. Exceptions would be the very scarce cars that remain in demand no matter what their condition.

Most Lionel HO has a Rarity Rating of 2 or 3. For some of the very scarce variations, we have assigned a Rarity Rating of 4 or 5. Some items have no price because no sales have been reported.

The HO engines and cars made for Lionel by Rivarossi and Athearn were supposed to be stamped with the Lionel "L" trademark.

Rivarossi was vigilant about this policy while Athearn was lax. Only Rivarossi's SP, T&P and C&NW FM units, the 0600 switcher, and the 0610 Consolidation were sold without the "L". Athearn shipped cars without the "L" in Lionel boxes, shipped cars with the "L" in Athearn boxes and some cars have surfaced with the Lionel markings on one side only.

Obviously, for Lionel collectors, the cars with the Lionel "L" trademark, packaged in Lionel boxes, are the most desirable.

1957

Diesels

Fairbanks-Morse Units

None of the FM units supplied by Rivarossi to Lionel's HO line in 1957 were numbered using the assigned catalog number for the unit or with any other number. To distinguish the diesel locomotives supplied to Lionel from its own HO line sold in the US, all units in the Western Pacific, Wabash and Illinois Central road names intended for Lionel were marked with an encircled "L." The prices shown here assumes the presence of this marking for these road names. The Southern Pacific, Texas and Pacific and the Chicago and Northwestern diesels are not known marked in that manner and are priced accordingly. Any of these three roadnames with the Lionel "L" would bring a premium price.

0500	**Chicago and Northwestern Powered A Unit** Green-yellow/orange	**150**
0501	**Texas and Pacific Powered A Unit** Light blue-white/white	**450**
0502	**Wabash Powered A Unit** with L Dark blue-gray-white/gold	**120**
0503	**Western Pacific Powered A Unit** with L Gray-orange/black	**110**
0504	**Southern Pacific Powered A Unit** Red-gray/black	**500**
0505	**Illinois Central Powered A Unit** with L Brown-orange-yellow/brown	**110**
0510	**Chicago and Northwestern Dummy A Unit** decorated as 0500	**135**

0511	**Texas and Pacific Dummy A Unit** decorated as 0501		450
0512	**Wabash Dummy A Unit** decorated as 0502, with L		100
0513	**Western Pacific Dummy A Unit** decorated as 0503		100
0514	**Southern Pacific Dummy A Unit** with L decorated as 0504		400
0515	**Illinois Central Dummy A Unit** with L decorated as 0505		100
0520	**Chicago and Northwestern Dummy B Unit** decorated as 0500		120
0521	**Texas and Pacific Dummy B Unit** decorated as 0501		250
0522	**Wabash Dummy B Unit** decorated as 0502, with L		60
0523	**Western Pacific Dummy B Unit** with L decorated as 0503		70
0524	**Southern Pacific Dummy B Unit** decorated as 0504		375
0525	**Illinois Central Dummy B Unit** with L decorated as 0505		100

Steamers

0600	**Two Axle Shunting Loco** Dockside Switcher (unnumbered)		125
0610LT	**2-8-0 Consolidation and Tender** 280 on Tender, Black/white, lighted. *Note that the motor for the consolidation engine was located in the tender and a shaft ran from the motor through the cab to power the drive wheels. Unfortunately, the metal floor of the tender was prone to expansion, cracking the tender and rendering the unit inoperable. This may help explain the extreme scarcity of this engine in any condition grade.*		
	1. Cab has rounded windows and was supplied to Lionel's HO line. No Lionel L. The engine was screw mounted to a wooden frame which served as the "liner" in its Lionel HO box. The box is as scarce as the engine.	(5)	875
	2. Cab has rectangular windows - believed to be late Rivarossi production and never sold by Lionel. Value about $50 in excellent condition.	(2)	50

Rolling Stock

Boxcars

0864-1	**Seaboard** (15412) Brown/white, with L		150
0864-25	**New York Central Pacemaker** (174478) Gray-red/white, with L		125
0864-50	**State of Maine** (2300)		
	1. Red-white-blue/white w/L		60
	2. With Maine Potatoes decal	(5)	*
0864-75	**B&O Sentinel** (466464) Silver-blue/blue-white, with L		100
0864-100	**New Haven** (36409) Black/white with orange door, with L		100
0864-125	**Rutland** (104) Yellow-green/green-yellow, with L		120
0864-150	**Minneapolis & St. Louis** (54652) with L Red/white with red door		90
0864-175	**Timken** (646450) Yellow-white/black-blue, with L		100

Cabooses

0819	**Pennsylvania Work Caboose** (6475) Gray/black, with L	**50**
0857	**Reading Bobber-Type 4-wheel Caboose** (90258) Red/white, with L	**50**

Crane and Miscellaneous Car

0860	**Pennsylvania Crane Car** (489690) Gray/black, with L	**60**
0877	**Illinois Central Miscellaneous Car** (63234) Black/white, with L	**50**

Flatcars

0811-1	**Pennsylvania** w/stakes (unnumbered) Gray/black, with L	**50**
0811-25	**Reading** w/stakes (91306) Red/white, with L	**40**

Gondolas

0862-1	**Pennsylvania** (357843) Tuscan/white, with L	**30**
0862-25	**Michigan Central** (15317) Black/white, with L	**30**

Reefers

0871-1	**Fruit Growers Express** (39783) Yellow/black, with L	**100**
0872-25	**Illinois Central** (51604) Silver/green, with L	**75**
0872-50	**A.T.S.F.** (8175) Orange-black/black, with L	**60**

Stock Cars

0866	**MKT Cattle Car** (502) Yellow-brown/black, with L	**50**

1958

While some Rivarossi produced items continued to be listed in the 1958 catalog, the vast majority of Lionel's HO line was produced by Athearn. Since the same cars were often offered under Athearn's name, the encircled Lionel L was again employed to distinguish items intended for sale by Lionel. Despite this, quite a few unmarked Athearn cars were packaged in Lionel boxes. Some cars, such as the 0815 Gulf Chemical Tank Car, are unknown with the identifying encircled L marking. As a result, unmarked cars in a Lionel box are often acceptable, but at a reduced price, when the piece is known to exist with the L trademark.

Diesels

F-7 Units with Belt (Hi-F) Drive

0530	**(D&RG) Rio Grande** (unnumbered) with L Silver-orange yellow/black	**80**
0531	**Milwaukee Road Powered A Unit** (2376) with L Gray-red-yellow/yellow	**70**
0532	**B&O Powered A Unit** (unnumbered) Dark blue-gray-blue-yellow/yellow	
	1. Without Lionel L but in correct Lionel box	**75**
	2. With Lionel L	**190**
0533	**NH (New Haven) Powered A Unit** (0272) Black-orange-white/orange	
	1. Same size Lionel L each side	**60**
	2. Different size L symbol each side	**85**
0540	**(D&RG) Rio Grande Dummy B Unit** (unnumbered) decorated as 0530	
	1. Without Lionel L, but in correct Lionel box	**60**
	2. With Lionel L - *does it exist?*	*

0541	**Milwaukee Road Dummy B Unit** (unnumbered) decorated as 0531, with L *Note: Can be found with the L marking on one side only.*	**100**
0542	**B&O Dummy B Unit** (unnumbered) decorated as 0532, with L	**75**
0543	**NH (New Haven) Dummy B Unit** (unnumbered) decorated as 0533, with L	**90**
0550	**Rio Grande Dummy A Unit** (unnumbered) decorated as 0530, with L	**85**
0551	**The Milwaukee Road Dummy A Unit** (2376) decorated as 0531, with L	**85**
0552	**Baltimore and Ohio Dummy A Unit** (unnumbered) decorated as 0532	
	1. Without Lionel L, but in correct Lionel box	**60**
	2. With Lionel L	**170**
0553	**NH (New Haven) Dummy A Unit** (0272) decorated as 0533 with L	**80**

GP-9 Units with Belt (Hi-F) Drive

0580	**Wabash GP-9** with headlight (452) Dark blue-gray-white with L. In addition to the Lionel L, the unit sold by Lionel has a gray cab while the geep marketed by Athearn had a dark blue cab.	**160**
0585	**Milwaukee Road GP-9** (unnumbered) Black-orange/black-white, w/headlight, with L	**250**

Husky Diesel Switchers with Belt (Hi-F) Drive

0560	**Rio Grande Snow Plow Switcher** (unnumbered) with light with L under cab window. Has separate painted orange plastic plow which snaps on to front of the shell, this is often missing.	
	1. Black shell, side of cab painted yellow	**200**
	2. Black shell, side of cab painted orange like plow	**225**
0570	**Navy Yard (New York) Switcher** with light (51) Blue/white, with L	**150**

Electrics

0590	**Virginian Rectifier with Belt (Hi-F) Drive** w/pantograph and headlight, (unnumbered). The diesel sold by Lionel had "Built by Lionel" alongside the cab door at the short end. This slogan was absent on the Virginian sold by Athearn. Ironically, the number 0590 appeared either upright or inverted on the unit sold by Athearn and not on the Lionel Rectifier.	**150**

Steamers

0615 LT	4-6-2 **Pacific** w/tender, headlight, cataloged with Boston and Maine tender. The Athearn company experienced difficulties developing their 4-6-2 Pacific in time to meet the demands of Lionel's HO train line in 1958. Athearn would offer this engine in later years in their own line of HO trains, it was never sold by Lionel. Using modified dies acquired from Hobbyline, Lionel introduced the 0625LT 4-6-2 Southern Pacific in 1959.	**NM**

Passenger Cars

Note: Add $40 to excellent price if boxed. The New Haven cars do not carry the identifying Lionel L. Since these cars were sold by Athearn in their HO line for years, this poses a problem for the collector in determining which cars were sold by Lionel. The cars supplied to Lionel came from the early production of these units and should have a dark red stripe and a separate, snap in floor without a battery box. Cars with a battery box as part of the floor could not have been sold by Lionel.

0700 **New Haven Baggage** (3406) Silver-dark red/black 15

0701 **New Haven Pullman Coach** (3150) Silver-dark red/black 15

0702 **New Haven Vista Dome** (500) Silver-dark red/black 15

0703 **New Haven Observation** (3246) Silver-dark red/black 15

Rolling Stock

Boxcars

0864-25 **New York Central Pacemaker** (174477) Red-gray/white, with L 70

0864-50 **State of Maine** (5206) Red-white-blue/black-white, with L
1. "and" in white section of door 65
2. "and" absent from white section of door 65

0864-150 **M&St.L** (52673) Red/white, black door, with L 70

0864-175 **Timken** (88) Yellow-white/brown, with L *Roller Freight* herald 120

0864-200 **Monon** (3029) Brown/white, with L 60

0864-225 **Central of Georgia** (7402) with L Brown-silver/brown-silver 40

0864-250 **Wabash** (6287) Blue/white, *Wabash* herald, with L 50

Cabooses

0817 **The Milwaukee Road** (01924) Silver/black, with L 40

0817-25 **Virginian** (1217) Dark blue/white, with L 55

0817-50 **(D&RG) Rio Grande** (01439) Silver/black, with L 45

Work Cabooses

0819-1 **Pennsylvania** Cataloged in 1958. *Does it exist?* *
Cataloged but not pictured in 1958 catalog. Does this car exist with the Lionel L marking and/or does a Lionel HO box exist stamped 0819-1?
Athearn Pennsylvania Gray/black without L 5

0819-25 **U.S. Navy** (1013) Blue/white. 70
This car is not known to have been marked with a Lionel L; however, since Athearn did not market a Navy work caboose in their HO line, the entire production of this item was intended for distribution by Lionel.

0819-50 **Wabash** (WAB 615) Blue/white, with L 50

0819-75 **Baltimore and Ohio** (MWC-17) Blue/white, with L 50

0819-100 **Boston and Maine** (MW 24) Reddish blue/white, with L 55

Crane and Miscellaneous Cars

0860-1 **Pennsylvania Derrick Car** Gray/black
1. (489711) on side with Lionel L 65
2. (425500) on side with Lionel L, scarce (5) *

0877-1 **Illinois Central Miscellaneous Car** (63210) Black/white, with Lionel L 45

0879	**Union Pacific Wrecker Crane Car** Red/white		
	1. (03043) without Lionel L, in correct Lionel box		**50**
	2. (03043) with Lionel L		**60**
	3. (787) with Lionel L *(Ken Fairchild collection)*	(5)	*

Flatcars

0800	**Nickel Plate Road** w/Airplane (1958) Black/white, with L	
	1. Original Athearn orange plane	**70**
	2. Original Athearn silver plane	**50**
0801	**Seaboard** w/Boat (42806) Brown/white, with L	**60**
0811-25	**Reading** w/Stakes (9440) Brown/white, with L	**60**
0814	**Evans Four Auto Transport Car**	
	1. NYC (499300) Brown/white, with L	**65**
	2. Reading (40125) Brown/white, with L	**65**
0824	**Erie** w/Two Autos (74286) Black/white, with L	**50**
0830	**Flat Car w/Two *Cooper-Jarrett Inc.* Vans**	
	1. Reading (40125) Brown/white with L	**75**
	2. NYC (499300) Brown/white, with L	**75**

Gondolas

0865	**Michigan Central** w/five canisters (350623)	
	1. Tuscan body, decorated in white, with L	**40**
	2. Black body, decorated in white, with L	**40**

Hoppers

0836	**Lehigh Valley** (4127) Brown/white, no load	
	1. Without Lionel L, but in correct Lionel box (without the Lionel L) and unboxed is worth under $5	**90**
	2. With Lionel L - *Does this item exist?*	

Reefers

0872-1	**Fruit Growers Express** (9253) with L Yellow-brown/black,	**90**
0872-50	**Santa Fe** Orange-black/black (cataloged as the El Capitan Reefer Car)	
	1. "El Capitan" on one side, with L	**60**
	2. "Super Chief " on one side, with L	**130**

Stock Car

0866-25	**AT&SF** (50656) Pale green/yellow. w/Lionel L	**60**

Tank Car

0815	**Gulf Chemical Car** (2605) Orange-black/black, black frame and dome, does not have Lionel L marking. Not known to have been produced with the Lionel L marking, so it is critical to purchase only with the appropriate Lionel box. Gulf tank car **without** the Lionel box is valued at $5 or less.	**75**

1959-1966

Lionel Corporation Production 1959-1966

When John English's Hobbyline series of HO trains ceased production in 1959, Lionel acquired several of their dies, including those for the Alco diesel, the Pacific tank engine, the small switcher steam locomotive, and the bodies for the gondola, hopper and boxcar. Some of these were modified, such as the dies for the steam engines which were re-worked to accommodate the Lionel motors. The airplane, boat, auto and canister loads continued to be supplied by Athearn. Athearn passenger car body shells were decorated in both Texas Special and Pennsylvania paint schemes, but, unlike the New Haven cars, carried their Lionel catalog numbers on the side of the car.

Diesels

Alcos

0535	**Santa Fe Powered A Unit** (0535) Silver-red-yellow/black	**60**
0535W	**Santa Fe Dummy B Unit w/Horn** (0535) Silver-red-yellow/black	**75**
0536	**Santa Fe Powered A Unit** (0536) Silver-red-yellow/black	**95**
0537	**Santa Fe Powered A Unit** Cataloged in 1966. Was it ever produced?	*
0555	**Santa Fe Powered A Unit** (0555) Silver-red-yellow/black, powered by a Helic drive	**75**
0556	**Santa Fe Powered A Unit** (0556) Silver-red-yellow/black, direct gear drive for the rear truck	**80**
0564	**Chesapeake and Ohio Powered A Unit** (0564) Blue-yellow/blue-yellow	**50**
0565	**Santa Fe Powered A Unit** (0565) Silver-red-yellow/black	**50**
0566	**Texas Special Powered A Unit** (0566) Red-white/red	**50**
0567	**Alaska Railroad Powered A Unit** (0567) Dark blue/yellow	**75**
0568	**Union Pacific Powered A Unit** (0568) Yellow-gray/red	**100**
0569P	**Union Pacific Powered A Unit** (0569) Yellow-gray/red	**60**
0571P	**Pennsylvania Powered A Unit** (0571) Maroon plastic/yellow	**250**
0575	**Santa Fe Dummy B Unit** (0575) Silver-red-yellow/black	**40**
0576	**Texas Special Dummy B Unit** (0576) Red-white/red	**40**
0577	**Alaska Railroad Dummy B Unit** (0577) Dark blue/yellow	**40**
0586	**Texas Special Dummy A Unit** (0586) Red-white/red	**140**
0587	**Alaska Railroad Dummy A Unit** (0587) Dark blue/yellow Questions persist as to whether true heat stamped 0587's exist. Known pieces in collections typically resemble a 0567 with the "6" touched up to look like an "8".	**85**
0595	**Santa Fe Dummy A Unit** (0595) Silver-red-yellow/black	**40**

Geeps

0592	**Santa Fe Powered GP-9** (0592) Blue/yellow	**100**
0593P	**Northern Pacific Powered GP-9** (0593) Black-gold/red-white gold	**125**
0593T	**Northern Pacific Dummy GP-9** (0593) Black-gold/red-white gold	**125**
0594P	**Santa Fe Powered GP-9** (0594) Blue/yellow	**75**
0596	**New York Central Powered GP-9** (0596) 2-tone gray/white	**80**
0597	**Northern Pacific Powered GP-9** (0597) Black-gold/red-white-gold	**75**
0598	**New York Central Powered GP-7** (0598) 2-tone gray/white	**60**

Electrics

0581	**Pennsylvania Rectifier** (0581) Tuscan/yellow	**175**
0591	**New Haven Rectifier** (0591) e Black-orange-white/orange-white	**175**

Husky Locomotive and Powered Units

0050	**Lionel Lines Gang Car** (0050) w/small blue plastic figure		
	1. All orange with white lettering		**125**
	2. Orange top, gray bottom, white lettering		**75**
	3. Orange top, gray bottom, bluish-black lettering		**75**
	4. Gray top, orange bottom, white lettering		**75**
0054	**Canadian Pacific Husky** Cataloged in 1961. No proof it was produced.		
0055	**Minneapolis and St. Louis** (0055) Red/white		**50**
0056	**A. E. C. Husky** (0056) White/red		
	1. Normal production		**60**
	2. Special NBC promotional A.E.C. husky with special billboard (billboard is typically missing)	(5)	**1400***
0057	**Union Pacific Husky** (0057) Yellow-gray/red		**70**
0058	**Rock Island Husky** (0058) Black-red/white		**75**
0059	**U.S. Air Force Husky** (0059) White/blue, Minuteman and Air Forceinsignia under cab		**125**
0068	**Executive Inspection Car** (unnumbered) Red/white		**120**
0545	**Erie Lackawanna GE-44 Switcher** Black/white, headlight, (herald and 0545)		**75**
0561	**M&St. L Snow Blower** (0561) Red-white/red		**200**

Steamers

0602(LT)	**Pennsylvania 0-6-0 Switcher** w/tender, light		**60**
0605	**0-4-0 Tank Switcher**		
	1. 0605 heat stamped under cab window		**60**
	2. 0605 and Lionel heat stamped under cab window	(5)	*
0625(LT)	**Southern Pacific** w/tender, light		**50**
	Some found with working smoke unit and boiler shell used for smoking locomotives		**100**
0626(LT)	**Southern Pacific** w/tender, light		**90**
0635(LT)	**Southern Pacific** w/tender, light, smoke unit		**75**
0636(LTS)	**Southern Pacific** w/tender, light, smoke unit		**85**
0637(LTS)	**Southern Pacific** w/tender, light, smoke unit, 0637 in white on black paper sticker under cab window		**90**
0642(LT)	**2-4-2 Steam Switcher** w/unlettered tender, headlight and combination belt and gear drive		**50**
0643(LT)	**2-4-2 Steam Switcher** w/unlettered tender, headlight and Helic drive (set only)		**110**

0645(LTS) Southern Pacific w/0645W tender, smoke unit, light — **140**

0645W **Plastic Whistle Tender** Long Haul Type w/whistle. This tender's metal six wheel trucks have a tendency towards severe corrosion and even disintegration. Beware of replacements using the more common four wheel trucks utilized for the short Pacific tenders. — **25**

0646(LTS) Southern Pacific w/0645W tender, smoke unit, light — **110**

0647(LTS) Southern Pacific w/0645W tender, smoke unit, light
1. Black paper sticker/white 0647 under cab window — **95**
2. Heat stamped 0647 under cab window — **120**

Passenger Cars

Athearn passenger car body shells were utilized for production of the Texas Special and Pennsylvania series. By 1961 Lionel had developed its own series of streamlined passenger car bodies. These were used for the Santa Fe and the 1963 Pennsylvania series.

0704 **Texas Special Baggage** (0704) Silver-red/red, no battery box in floor — **35**

0705 **Texas Special Pullman Coach** (0705) Silver-red/red
1. Without battery box in floor — **30**
2. With battery box in floor — **30**

0706 **Texas Special Vista Dome** (0706) Silver-red/red
1. Without battery box in floor — **30**
2. With battery box in floor — **30**

0707 **Texas Special Observation** (0707) Silver-red/red
1. Without battery box in floor — **30**
2. With battery box in floor — **30**

0708 **Pennsylvania Baggage** (0708) Tuscan/yellow — **50**

0709 **Pennsylvania Vista Dome** (0709) Tuscan/yellow — **50**

0710 **Pennsylvania Observation** (0710) Tuscan/yellow — **50**

0711 **Pennsylvania Pullman** (0711) Tuscan/yellow — **125**

0712 **Santa Fe Baggage Car** (0712) Silver/red
1. Red stripe above the windows and illuminated — **40**
2. Without red stripe and unlighted — **55**

0713 **Santa Fe Pullman Coach** (0713) Silver/red
1. Red stripe above the windows and illuminated — **40**
2. Without red stripe and unlighted — **55**

0714 **Santa Fe Vista Dome Car** (0714) Silver/red
1. Red stripe above the windows and illuminated — **40**
2. Without red strip and unlighted — **50**

0715 **Santa Fe Observation** (0715) Silver/red
1. Red stripe above the windows and illuminated — **40**
2. Without red strip and unlighted — **50**

0723 **Pennsylvania Pullman Coach** (0723) Silver/maroon
1. Silver roof (set only) — **60**
2. Maroon roof (set only) — **75**

0725 **Pennsylvania Observation Car** (0725) Silver/maroon
1. Silver roof (set only) — **70**
2. Maroon roof (set only) — **80**

0733 **SF Pullman Coach** (0713) Silver/maroon, no stripe,
30
unlighted, numbered 0713 not 0733 in maroon (set only)

0735 **SF Observation Car** (0715) Silver/maroon, no stripe,unlighted, numbered 0715 not 0735 in maroon (set only) — **30**

Rolling Stock

Boxcars

0864-275	**State of Maine** Cataloged in 1962. No proof it was produced.	
0864-285	**State of Maine** Lionel box exists with end flap printed "0864-285 State of Maine Box Car", however no car with that number has been identified.	
0864-300	**The Alaska Railroad** (0864300) Dark blue/yellow	**60**
0864-325	**Duluth, South Shore & Atlantic** (0864325) Red-black/white	**45**
0864-350	**State of Maine** (0864350) Red-white-blue/black	**50**
0864-400	**Boston and Maine** (0864400) Blue-black/white	**75**
0864-700	**Santa Fe** (0864-400) Red/white	**50**
0864-900	**New York Central** (0864900) Jade green/black-red	**50**
0864-935	**New York Central** (0864900) Jade green/black-red, similar to 0864-900 with 0864-935 on box end flap	**50**

Note: The previously listed boxcars were all produced by Lionel using dies acquired from Hobbyline. The following boxcars (0874 series) appeared after 1963 and utilized dies developed by Lionel. These cars had a separate floor and an upper body shell of very thin plastic. It is not uncommon to find excellent and even new pieces with cracks in the door guides.

0874	**New York Central** (0874) Jade green/black-red	**40**
0874-25	Same as **0874** except box flap is stamped 0874-25	**40**
0874-60	**Boston and Maine** (0874) Blue/white	**80**

Cabooses

In 1959, Athearn caboose body shells and floors continued in use for the 0817 series. The AEC, Alaska Railroad, Texas Special, and early New Haven cabooses used a shell with a separate roof walk and a floor with visible metal weight and plastic cross bracing. Beginning in 1960, Lionel developed its own caboose with a roof walk molded to the body and underframe marked "Lionel".

0817-150	**AT&SF** (0817) Red/white	**15**
0817-200	**Atomic Energy Commission** (0817) White/red	**30**
0817-225	**Alaska Railroad** (0817) Blue/yellow	**55**
0817-250	**Texas Special** (0817) Red/white	**50**
0817-275	**New Haven** (0817) Black/orange-white	
	1. Athearn body shell & floor w/separate cross bracing	**40**
	2. Lionel caboose body shell w/Lionel name cast into separate floor	**30**
0817-300	**Southern Pacific** (0817) Maroon/yellow	**30**
0817-325	**Union Pacific** (0817) Yellow-gray/red	**30**
0817-350	**Rock Island** (0817) Red-black/white	**30**
0827	**Safety First** (0827) Illuminated, Red/white	**40**
0827-50	**A.E.C.** (0827) Illuminated, White/red (set only)	**70**
0827-75	**AT&SF** (0827) Illuminated, Red/white (set only)	**80**
0837	**M&St.L** (0837) Red/white	**15**
0837-110	Same as **0837** with 0837-110 on box end flap	**10**
0838	**Erie** (E in diamond shaped herald) (0838) Gray/red (set only)	**30**
0840	**NYC** (0840) Black/white (set only)	**25**
0841	**Unlettered** but numbered 0841 Red/white	**15**
0841-50	**Union Pacific** (0841) Yellow-gray/red (set only)	**45**
0841-85	**AT&SF** (0841) painted Red/white (set only)	**20**

0841-125	**A.E.C.** (0841) White/red (set only) ***Note: The unpainted white plastic shell is prone to discoloration. These are worth less than the values given.***	**25**
0841-185	**AT&SF** (0841) unpainted red plastic/white, 0841-185 on box end flap	**20**

Work Cabooses

0819-200	**Boston & Maine** (0819200) Blue/white	**40**
0819-225	**Santa Fe** (08192255) Gray/yellow-red	**35**
0819-250	**Northern Pacific** (0819250) Red-black/white-black	**30**
0819-275	**Chesapeake and Ohio** (0819275) Blue/yellow	**25**

Crane and Derrick Cars

0860-200	**Pennsylvania Derrick Car** (0860200)	**40**
0889	**Illinois Central Wrecker Crane Car** (0889) Orange-black green	**50**

Flatcars

0800-200	**Seaboard Airplane Car** (0800200) Black/white	
	1. Orange top of airplane, black undercarriage	**60**
	2. Silver top of airplane, black undercarriage	**30**
0801-200	**Seaboard Boat Car** (0801200) Black /white, Athearn boats have a white top w/either red or blue hull	**30**
0806	**Southern Pacific** w/Helicopter (0806) Black/white,	
45		
	helicopter also usedfor O Gauge 6819, comes both with and without blue "NAVY" heat stamp.	
0807	**NYC w/"Matchbox Series" Bulldozer** (0807) Tuscan/white. Lesney Caterpillar Bulldozer number 18	**130**
0808	**NYC w/"Matchbox Series" Tractor** (0808) Tuscan/white. Lesney Tractor number 4	**130**
0809	**Helium Tank Transport Car** Black (unlettered and unnumbered) Three silver painted wooden cylinders. Black hopper car base.	**20**
0810	**SP Emergency Transport Generator** (0810) Black/white. Plastic orange generator used on O gauge 3520/3530 generator cars.	**45**
0813	**Seaboard Mercury Capsule Carrying Car** (0813200) Blue/white. Twosoft plastic silver capsules (used on O gauge 3413 Capsule Launching Car)	**120**
0814-200	**SP Four Auto Transport Car** (0814200) Tuscan/white, four Athearn Autos.	**50**
0821	**Pipe Transport Car** (unlettered and unnumbered) Three plastic pipes on hopper car underframe.	
	1. Gray plastic pipes	**20**
	2. Yellow plastic pipes	**20**
	3. Gray plastic pipes painted yellow	**90**
0823	**Southern Pacific Twin Missile Carrying Car** (0823) Red/white, two white missiles as used with O gauge 448 Missile Firing Range.	**30**
0824-200	**NYC** w/Two Autos (0824200) Black/white, two Athearn autos	**40**
0842	**Culvert Piper Transport Car** (lettered TLCX, numbered 0842) black tank car underframe. Three metal culvert pipes (also used with O gauge cars and accessories)	**30**
0861	**Timber Transport Car** (unlettered and unnumbered) Black hopper frame w/three logs	**20**
0863	**Southern Pacific Rail Trucks Car** (0863) Red/white, w/three trucks	**35**

0870	**Pennsylvania Maintenance Car** w/Generator (0870) Tuscan/white, graybase and yellow platform. Generator load was produced in both gray and dark gray plastic.	**45**
0875	**Seaboard Flat Car with Missile** (0875) Black/white, brown carriage load is large missile used on O gauge 6650 flat car.	
	1. White rocket with blue end	**35**
	2. Red and white rocket with blue end	**40**

Gondolas

0862-200	**Michigan Central** (0862200) Black/white		
	1. With load of scrap metal		**50**
	2. With red plastic crates (R. Kughn collection)	(5)	*
0862-250	**Michigan Central** (0862200) Black/white, similar to 086200 #1 with 862-250 box on end flap		**40**
0865-200	**Michigan Central** (0865200) Tuscan /gold, five red canisters		**75**
0865-225	**Michigan Central Gondola** (0865225) load of scrap metal		
	1. Red plastic body shell, white lettering (set only)		**20**
	2. Gray plastic body shell, black lettering		**25**
0865-250	**Michigan Central** (0865250) Red/white, tan plastic crates		**15**
0865-400	**Michigan Central** (0865250) Blue plastic shell decorated in white. Cataloged as 0865-400 in 1964 as part of sets and then as 0865 in the 1965-66 catalogs. This blue and white gondola was listed as 0865-435 when listed for individual sale. (set only)		**10**
0865-435	**Michigan Central** (0865-250) Blue/white (see 0865-400 above). Only box end flap stamped 0865-435 when offered for individual sale.		**10**

Hoppers

0836(1)	**Alaska Hopper** (08361)	
	1. Black/orange without load	**25**
	2. Black/orange with load of scrap metal	**30**
	3. Red plastic/white	**10**
	4. Painted red on red plastic shell/white	**20**
	5. Painted red on gray plastic shell/white	**35**
0836-100	**Alaska Hopper** (08361) Red/white w/nonsprung trucks. The 0836-100 is catalog number only as car still carries 08361.	**15**
0836-110	**Alaska Hopper** (08361) Red/white w/nonsprung trucks. The 08361-110 appears on end flap of box only. Car is similar to 0836-100 above. Found in sets 14300 and 14310.	**15**

Operating Cars

0039	**Southern Pacific Track Cleaning Car** (TC-0039) Black-orange/whitewith track cleaning fluid in plastic bottle used for the O gauge car, abrasive pads and cleansing sponges	**50**
0300	**TLCX Operating Lumber Car** (0300) Red/white w/three wood logs and dark brown plastic tray. Used with the 0900 unloading platform.	**30**
0301	**Pennsylvania Operating Coal Dump Car** (0301) Gray/black, black framew/bag of coal and brown plastic tray. Used with 0900 unloading platform	**30**
0319	**SP Operating Helicopter Launching Car** (0319) Blue/white, red plastic helicopter (also used with the O-gauge 3619), metal track trip included.	**50**

0319-110	**Operating Helicopter Launching Car** (0319) Similar to 0319 except nonsprung trucks. Both brake wheel and rear tail support for helicopter now at the same end of car. 0319-110 is stamped on box end flap.	**60**
0333	**Southern Pacific Satellite Launching** (0333) Blue/white, with satellite (used on the O gauge satellite car), metal track trip also included.	**50**
0337	**Animated Circus Giraffe Car** (0337) White/red, with magnet and telltale	**40**
0349	**Operating Turbo Missile Firing Car** (no numbers or letters) Blue launcher and turbo support w/two turbos.	
	1. Red plastic car body	**40**
	2. Maroon plastic car body	**100**
0357	**Cop and Hobo Car** (0357) Blue/white, black trestle bridge, platformw/no roof is gray plastic. Comes with figures of cop and hobo.	**60**
0365	**"Minuteman" Missile Launching Car** (0365) White/blue-red w/StrategicAir Command and insignia on left and U.S. Air Force Minuteman on the right, thin blue tipped white missile. The compressed spring launching mechanism often broken. Check even in "Mint/Boxed" cars.	**70**
0366	**Operating Milk Can Unloading Car** (0366) White/black w/eight metalmilk cans. Doors are often broken. Operated w/0900 unloading platform	**50**
0370	**Animated Sheriff and Outlaw Car** (0370) Red/yellow, sheriff andoutlaw alternately appear through cutouts in the car's roof as the car moves.	**50***
0805	**Illuminated Radioactive Waste Disposal Car** (0805) Black-red/white, single gray plastic waste container lettered in red.	
	1. Numbered (0805)	**30**
	2. Numbered (0805200) (4)	*
0834	**Poultry Car** (0834) Red/white, gray painted doors, chickens pictured on plastic inserts, lighted	**30**
0847	**Exploding Box Car** (0847) Red/white, explodes when bull's-eye target on side is hit by missile	**15**
0847-100	**Exploding Box Car** same as 0847 except nonsprung trucks and number0847-100 on end flap of box	**20**
0850	**U.S. Army Missile Launching Car** (0850) Red missile launcher mounted on gray flat car lettered in black, comes with single small white plastic missile (as used with O gauge 448 Missile Firing Range).	**20**
0850-110	**U.S. Army Missile Launching Car** (0850) similar to 0850 except nonsprung trucks and 0850-110 on box end flap	**20**
0873	**Rodeo Car** (0873) w/two bobbing horse heads	
	1. Yellowish-orange plastic body w/red lettering	**30**
	2. Same as 1 but maroon lettering	**80**
	3. Translucent lemon yellow body, maroon lettering	**85**
0880	**Pennsylvania Maintenance Car** (0880) with Light yellow platform mounted to gray base which snaps into black flat car lettered in white.	**50**

Reefer

0872-200	**Railway Express Reefer** (0872200) Dk green/gold, red-white herald,thin black plastic door, door guides frequently broken and missing doors.	**50**

Mint Car

0845	**Gold Bullion Transport Car/Fort Knox Reserve** (0845) painted silveron clear plastic/black. Same body shell as 0872-200 REA.		120

Stock Car

0866-200	**Circus Car** (0866-200) White plastic/red w/white painted doors, red painted roof walk. Non-operating version of the 0337 Giraffe car.		30

Tank Cars

0815-50	**Rocket Fuel Tank Car** (0815) White/red tank mounted on blackplastic frame with black platform around dome.		30
0815-60	**Rocket Fuel Tank Car**		
	1. Same as 0815-50 except in box with end flap stamped 0815-60		30
	2. Can be found in sets 14300 and 14310) but without heat stamped 0815	(5)	*
0815-75	**Lionel Lines Tank Car** (0815200) Painted tank, Dark orange/black, black plastic platform around dome		60
0815-85	**Lionel Lines Tank Car** (0815200) Orange plastic/black tank, no platform		50
0815-110	**SUNOCO Tank Car** (uncataloged 25064) Black plastic/yellow-white tank with SUNOCO herald and black platform around dome. Can be found in sets 14310 and 14300 in place of 0815-60.		250
0816	**Rocket Fuel Tank Car** (0816) White/red tank, black plastic frame,without platform around dome.		30

HO Sets

1957

5700	**Three-Car Steam Work Train** SRP: $25.00 0600 Dockside Switcher Shunting Loco, 0862-1 Pennsylvania Gondola, 0860 Pennsylvania Derrick, 0819 Pennsylvania Work Caboose. (11) sections 0989 18" radius curved track, 1 section 0975 18" radius curved terminal track, 0950 Re-Railer, 0929 Uncoupling track	325
5701	**Five-Car Illinois Central Diesel Set** SRP: $29.95 0505 Illinois Central Powered A FM Unit, 0811-25 Reading Flatcar with stakes, 0862-25 Michigan Central Gondola, 0866 MKT Stock Car, 0872-25 Illinois Central Reefer, 0857 Reading Caboose, (11) sections 0989 18" radius curved track, 1 section 0975 18" radius curved terminal track, 0950 Re-Railer, 0929 Uncoupling track	375
5702	**Five-Car Wabash Work Train** SRP: $39.95 0502 Wabash Powered A FM Unit, 0522 Wabash Dummy B FM Unit, 0862-25 Michigan Central Gondola, 0860 Pennsylvania Derrick, 0864-50 State of Maine Boxcar, 0877 Illinois Central Miscellaneous Car, 0819 Pennsylvania Work Caboose, (11) sections 0989 18" radius curved track, 1 section 0975 18" radius curved terminal track, 0950 Re-Railer, 0929 Uncoupling track	425

5703	**Five-Car Western Pacific ABA Train** SRP: $45.00 0503, 0523, 0513 Western Pacific ABA FM Units, 0862-1 Pennsylvania Gondola, 0864-75 B&O Sentinel Boxcar, 0872-50 Santa Fe Reefer, 0877 Illinois Central Miscellaneous Car, 0857 Reading Caboose, (11) sections 0989 18" radius curved track, 1 section 0975 18" radius curved terminal track, 0950 Re-Railer, 0929 Uncoupling track, (4) sections 0909 9" straight track	**525**
5704	**Six-Car Steam Work Train** SRP: $49.95 0610LT Consolidation Steam Loco and Tender, 0811-1 Pennsylvania Flatcar with stakes, 0860 Pennsylvania Derrick, 0862-25 Michigan Central Gondola, 0864-1 Seaboard Boxcar, 0866 MKT Stock Car, 0819 Pennsylvania Work Caboose, (11) sections 0989 18" radius curved track, 1 section 0975 18" radius curved terminal track, 0950 Re-railer, 0929 uncoupling track, (2) sections 0909 9" straight track.	**1,200**

1958

5705	**Four-Car Navy Switcher Freight** SRP: $25.00 0570 Navy Yard Switcher, 0800 Flatcar with Airplane, 0801 Flatcar with Boat, 0864-225 Central Georgia Boxcar, 0819-25 Navy Yard Work Caboose, (11) sections 0989 18" radius curved track, 1 0975 18" curved terminal track, 0950 Re-railer track, 0929 uncoupling track, 0101 1 1/4 AMP DC, AC Power Pack	**375**
5707	**Four-Car Wabash GP-9 Work Train** SRP: $29.95 0580 Wabash GP-9 Diesel, 0862-25 MC Black Gondola, 0864-250 Wabash Box Car, 0860 Pennsylvania Derrick, 0819-50 Wabash Work Caboose, (11) sections 0989 18" radius curved track, 1 0975 18" curved terminal track, 0950 Re-railer track, 0929 uncoupling track, 0101 1 1/4 AMP DC, AC Power Pack	**375**
5709	**Milwaukee Road F-7 Freight** SRP: $29.95 0531 Milwaukee Road Powered A F-7 Diesel, 0801 Flatcar with Boat, 0824 Flatcar with 2 autos, 0864-150 Minn. & St. Louse Boxcar, 0866-25 Santa Fe Cattle Car, 0817 Milwaukee Road Caboose, (11) sections 0989 18" radius curved track, 1 0975 18" curved terminal track, 0950 Re-railer track, 0929 uncoupling track, 0101 1 1/4 AMP DC, AC Power Pack	**350**
5711	**Six-Car Virginian Rectifier Freight** SRP: $35.00 0590 Virginian Rectifier with Pantograph, 0811-25 Flatcar with stakes, 0814 Auto transport with four autos, 0864-50 State of Main Boxcar, 0872-50 El Capitan Reefer, 0877 Miscellaneous Car, 0817-25 Virginian Caboose, (11) sections 0989 18" radius curved track, 1 0975 18" curved terminal track, 0950 Re-railer track, 0929 uncoupling track, 0101 1 1/4 AMP DC, AC Power Pack	**525**
5713	**Five-Car B&O AB Work Train** SRP: $35.00 1. 0532 B&O Powered A F-7 Diesel, 0542 B&O Dummy B Unit, 0824 Flat with 2 autos, 0860 Pennsylvania Derrick, 0864-200 Monon Boxcar, 0872-1 Fruit Growers Express Reefer, 0819-75 B&O Work Caboose, (11) sections 0989 18" radius curved track, 1 0975 18" curved terminal track, 0950 Re-railer track, 0929 uncoupling track, 0101 1 1/4 AMP DC, AC Power Pack	**475**
	2. If 0532 B&O Powered A Units have the Lionel "L" trademark on the Engine	**550**

5714	**A-A Powered NH F-7 Four-Car Passenger Set** SRP: $39.95, (2) 0533 F-7 NH Powered A Units, 0700 NH Baggage Car, 0701 NH Coach, 0702 VistaDome Car, 0703 NH Observation Car, (11) sections 0989 18" radius curved track, 1 0975 18" curved terminal track, 0950 Re-railer track, 0929 uncoupling track, 0101 1 1/4 AMP DC, AC Power Pack	450
5715	**Five-Car D& RG AA Freight Set** SRP: $39.95 (2) 0530 F-7 D&RG Powered A Units, 0800 Flatcar with Airplanes, 0815 Gulf Chemical Tank Car, 0830 Flatcar with 2 vans, 0864-25 NYC Boxcar, 0817-50 D&RG Caboose, (11) sections 0989 18" radius curved track, 1 0975 18" curved terminal track, (2) sections 0909 9" long straight track, 0950 Re-railer track, 0929 uncoupling track, 0101 1 1/4 AMP DC, AC Power Pack	425
5717	**Six-Car Pacific Steam Work Train** SRP: $45.00 0615 LT Pacific Steam Loco & Tender, 0814 Auto Transport with 4 autos, 0836 Hopper, 0864-175 Timken Boxcar, 0865 Gondola with Canisters, 0879 Wrecker Crane, 0819-100 B & M Work Caboose - This set was NEVER PRODUCED in 1958	NM

1959

5717	**Six-Car Pacific Steam Freight** SRP: $39.95 0625 LT Southern Pacific Locomotive and Tender with Headlight, 0860-200 Flatcar with Airplane (orange), 0805 Radioactive Waste Disposal Car, 0806 Flatcar with Helicopter, 0834 Illuminated Poultry Car, 0872-200 Railway Express Reefer, 0817-300 Southern Pacific, (11) sections 0989 18" radius curved track, 0975 curved terminal track, 0950 Re-Railer track, 0919 Uncoupler Re-Railer track, 0101 1 1/4 Amp Power Pack	425
5719	**Three-Car AEC Switcher Freight Set** SRP: $19.95 0056 AEC Husky Switcher, 0806 Flatcar with Helicopter, 0875 Flatcar with Missile, 0817-200 AEC Caboose, (11) sections 0989 18" radius curved track, 0975 curved terminal track, 0103 800 Milliamp Power Pack	250
5721	**Four-Car Texas Special Freight** SRP: $25.00 0566 Texas Special Powered A Alco Unit with Headlight, 0805 Radioactive Waste Disposal Car, 0866-200 Circus Car, 0864-325 DSSA Boxcar, 0817-250 Texas Special Caboose, (11) sections 0989 18" radius curved track, 0975 curved terminal track, 0909 straight track, 0950 Re-Railer track,0103 800 Milliamp Power Pack (* This set is pictured in the catalog with 0864-175 Timken Boxcar)	275
5723	**Four-Car Steam Switcher Freight** SRP: $29.95 0605 0-4-0 Steam Switcher with headlight, 0808 Flatcar with Matchbox Tractor, 0862-200 Pennsylvania Derrick, 0870 Maintenance Car with Generator, 0819-100 B & M Work Caboose, (11) sections 0989 18" radius curved track, 0975 curved terminal track, 0950 Re-Railer track, 0919 Uncoupler Re-Railer track, 0103 800 Milliamp Power Pack	400
5725	**Five-Car New Haven Rectifier Freight** SRP: $29.95, 0591 New Haven Rectifier with Headlight and Pantograph, 0834 Illuminated Poultry Car, 0836 Alaskan Hopper, 0864-325 DSSA Boxcar, 0875 Flatcar with Missile, 0817-275 New Haven Caboose (Athearn body), (11) sections 0989 18" radius curved track, 0975 curved terminal track, 0950 Re-Railer track, 0909 straight track, 0103 800 Milliamp Power Pack	425

5727	**Five-Car NYC GP-9 Freight** SRP: $35.00 0596 New York Central GP-9 with Headlight, 0807 Flatcar with Matchbox Bulldozer, 0865-200 MC Gondola with Canisters, 0860-200 Pennsylvania Derrick, 0880 Maintenance Car with Light, 0819-200 Boston & Main Work Caboose, (11) sections 0989 18" radius curved track, 0975 curved terminal track, 0950 Re-Railer track, 0919 Uncoupler Re-Railer track, 0101 1 1/4 Amp Power Pack	475
5729	**Five-Car Alaskan "AB" Freight Set** SRP: $39.95 with Graduated Over and Under Trestle Set 0567 Alaskan Powered A Unit Alco with Headlight and 0577 Alaskan Dummy B Unit, 0801-200 Flatcar with Boat, 0834 Illuminated Poultry Car, 0865- MC Gondola, 0864-300 Alaskan Boxcar, 0817-225 Alaskan Caboose, 0110 Graduated Trestle Set, (20) sections 0989 18" radius curved track, (3) sections 0909 straight track, 0925 straight terminal track, 0950 Re-Railer track, 0919 Uncoupler Re-Railer track, 0101 1 1/4 Amp Power Pack	425
5731	**Five-Car Pacific Steam Freight Set** SRP: $49.95 with Graduated Over and Under Trestle 0625 LT Pacific Steam Locomotive and Tender with Headlight, 0806 Flatcar with Helicopter, 0814 Auto Transport Car with four autos, 0805 Radioactive Waste Disposal Car, 0880 Maintenance Car with Light, 0817-300 Southern Pacific Caboose, 0110 Graduated Trestle Set, (20) sections 0989 18" radius curved tract, (3) sections 0909 straight track, 0925 straight terminal track, 0950 Re-Railer track, 0919 Uncoupler Re-Railer track, 0100 "Multi-Volt" 2 1/12 Amp DC, AC Power Pack	375
5732	**Four-Car Texas Special "ABA" Two Motored Passenger Set** SRP: $49.95 (2) 0566 Texas Special Powered A Alco Units with Headlight, 0576 Texas Special Dummy B Alco Unit, 0704 Texas Special Baggage Car, 0705 Texas Special Pullman Coach, 0706 Texas Special Vista Dome, 0707 Texas Special Observation Car, (11) sections 0989 18" radius curved track, 0975 curved terminal track, 0950 Re-Railer track, 0919 Uncoupler Re-Railer track, 0100 "Multi-Volt" 2 1/2 Amp DC/AC Power Pack	350
5733	**Seven-Car Santa Fe "ABA" Two Motored Work Train** with Figure 8 Layout, SRP: $59.95 (2) 0565 Santa Fe Powered A Alco Unit with Headlight, 0575 Santa Fe Dummy B Unit, 0814 Auto Transport with four Autos, 0815 Chemical Tank Car, 0824 Flat with two Autos, 0834 Illuminated Poultry Car, 0880 Maintenance Car with Light, 0879 UP Wrecker Crane, 0819-225 Santa Fe Work Caboose, 0990 90 degree crossing, (18) sections 0989 18" radius curved track, 0909 straight tract, (4) sections 0906 (2/3) straight track, 0925 straight terminal track, 0950 Re-Railer track, 0919 Uncoupler Re-Railer track, 0100 "Multi-Volt" 2 1/2 Amp DC/AC Power Pack	575

1960

5735	**Three-Car Rock Island Husky Freight** SRP: $19.95, 0058 Rock Island Husky with Headlight, 0865-250 Gondola with Crates, 0861 Timber Transport Car, 0817-350 Rock Island Caboose, (11) sections 0989 curved track, 0975 Curved terminal track, 0103 800 Milliamp Power Pack	200

5737	**Three-Car 0-4-0 Steam Switcher Freight** SRP: $25.00, 0605 0-4-0 Steam Switcher with Headlight, 0319 Operating Helicopter Launching Car, 0821 Pipe Transport Car, 0819-225 S.F. Work Caboose, (11) sections 0989 curved track, 0975 Curved terminal track, 0103 800 Milliamp Power Pack	225
5739	**Four-Car C&O Diesel Freight** SRP: $29.95 0564 C & O Powered A Unit, 0850 U.S. Army Missile Launching Car, 0847 Exploding Target Car, 0823 Twin Missile Transport Car, 0819-275 C&O Work Caboose, (11) sections 0989 curved track, 0975 curved terminal track, 0909 straight track, 0919 Uncoupler Re-Railer, 0103 800 Milliamp Power Pack	200
5741	**Four-Car 0-6-0 Steam Switcher Freight** SRP: $35.00, 0602LT 0-6-0 Steam Switcher, 0301 Coal Dump Car, 0842 Culvert Pipe Transport, 0865-225 MC Gondola with Scrap Metal, 0819-225 Santa Fe Work Caboose, (11) sections 0989 curved track, 0975 curved terminal, 0919 uncoupler Re-railer, 0900 remote control track section, 0101 1 1/4 AMP DC/AC Power Pack	225
5742	**Three-Car Pennsylvania Rectifier Passenger** with Automatic Gateman SRP: $39.95 0581 Pennsylvania Rectifier, 0708 Pennsylvania Baggage Car, 0709 Pennsylvania Vista-Dome, 0710 Pennsylvania Observation (16) 0982 22" radius curved track, 0925 straight terminal track, 0909 straight track, 0919 uncoupler re-railer, 0145 Automatic Gateman, 0101 1 1/4 AMP DC/AC Power Pack	325
5743	**Five-Car Northern Pacific GP-9 Diesel Freight** SRP: $39.95, 0597 GP-9 Northern Pacific, 0301 Operating Coal Dump Car, 0865-250 MC Gondola with Crates, 0300 Operating Log Dump Car, 0860-200 Pennsylvania Derrick, 0819-250 Northern Pacific Work Caboose, (11) sections curved track, 0975 curved terminal, 0919 uncoupler Re-railer, 0900 remote control track section, 0214 Girder Bridge, 0101 1 1/4 AMP DC/AC Power Pack	325
5745	**Five-Car Pacific Steam Freight** SRP: $39.95 0625LT Pacific Steam Locomotive & Tender, 0850 US Army Missile Launching Car, 0319 Operating Helicopter Car, 0847 Exploding Target Car, 0865-250 MC Gondola with Crates, 0817-150 ATSF Caboose, (11) sections 0989 curved track, 0975 curved terminal track, 0909 straight track, 0919 uncoupler Re-Railer, 0103 800 Milliamp Power Pack	275
5747	**Five-Car Santa Fe AB Diesel Freight** SRP: $49.95 Dog BoneLayout w/IRBM Missile Launching Platform 0565 S.F. Powered A Unit, 0575 S.F. Dummy B Unit, 0319 Operating Helicopter Launching Car, 0805 Radioactive Waste Car, 0875 Missile Transport Car, 0817-150 S.F. Caboose, 0470 IRBM Missile Launching Platform with 0847 Exploding Target Car, (24) sections 0989 curved track, (2) sections 0909 straight track, 0925 straight terminal track, 0919 Uncoupler re-railer, 0214 Girder Bridge, 0101 1 1/4 AMP DC/AC Power Pack.	375

5749	**Six-Car 0-6-0 Steam Switcher Work Train** with Rotary Beacon SRP: $49.95 0602LT 0-6-0 Steam Switcher, 0301 Coal Dump Car, 0300 Log Dump Car, 0836 Alaska Hopper, 0863 Rail Truck Transport Car, 0879 Wrecker Crane, 0819-225 SF Work Caboose, (11) sections 0989 curved track, 0975 curved terminal track, 0919 uncoupler Re-railer, 0900 remote control track section, 0494 Rotary Beacon, 0214 Girder Bridge, 0101 1 1/4 AMP DC/AC Power Pack	375
5770	**Four-Car Texas Special ABA Diesel** SRP: $49.95 0566 Texas Special Powered A (2 Units), 0576 Texas Special Dummy B, 0705 Texas Special Pullman Coach, 0706 Texas Special Vista-Dome (2), 0707 Texas Special Observation, (12) sections 0982 22" radius curved track, 0925 straight terminal track, 0919 uncoupler re-railer, 0101 1 1/4 AMP DC/AC Power Pack	350
5771	**Six-Car Pacific Steam Freight** SRP: $59.95 with Automatic Gateman 0625LT Pacific Steam Locomotive with Tender, 0300 Operating Lumber Car, 0301 Operating, Coal Dump Car, 0860-200 Pennsylvania Derrick, 0872-200 Railway Express Reefer, 0880 Maintenance Car with Light, 0817-150 S.F. Caboose, (11) sections 0989 curved track, 0975 curved terminal track, 0919 Uncoupler Re-railer, (2) 0900 remote control track section 0145 Automatic Gateman, 0100 Multi-Volt 2 1/2 AMP DC/AC Power Pack	375

1961

5750	**Three-Car M&St. L Husky Freight** SRP: $19.95 0055 Minneapolis & St. Louis Husky Switcher with Headlight, 0861 Timber Transport Car, 0865 -225 MC Gondola with Scrap Iron, 0837 Minn. And St. Louis Caboose, (5) sections 0988 18" radius curved track (18" long), 0976 curved terminal track (18" long), 0103 800 milliamp Power Pack	150
5751	**Three-Car Lackawanna Diesel Switch Freight** SRP: $25.00, 0545 Lackawanna GE-44 Diesel Switcher with Headlight, 0865-250 MC Gondola with Crates, 0337 Animated Circus Giraffe Car with Telltale Signal, 0838 Lackawanna Caboose, (5) sections 0988 18" radius curved track (18" long), 0976 curved terminal track (18" long), 0103 800 Milliamp Power Pack.	*
5752	**Four-Car 2-4-2 Military Steam Freight** SRP: $29.95, 0642 LT 2-4-2 Steam Locomotive and Slope Back Tender with headlight, 0847 Exploding Target Car, 0850 US Army Missile Launching Car, 0875 Flatcar with Missile, 0841 Caboose, (5) sections 0988 18" radius curved track (18" long), 0976 curved terminal track (18" long), 0103 800 milliamp Power Pack	200
5753	**Four-Car C&O Diesel Freight** SRP: $29.95 0564 C & O Alco Diesel with Headlight, 0319 Helicopter Launching Car, 0805 Illuminated Radioactive Waste Disposal Car, 0809 Helium Tank Transport Car, 0819-275 C & O Work Caboose, (5) sections 0988 18" radius curved track (18" long), 0976 curved terminal track (18" long), 0103 800 milliamp Power Pack	225

5754	**Five-Car "Heavy Weapon" Steam Freight** SRP: $39.95, 0625 LT Pacific Steam Locomotive and Tender with Headlight, 0333 Satellite Launching Car, 0809 Helium Tank Transport Car, 0847 Exploding Target Car, 0850 US Army Missile Launching Car, 0841 Caboose, (5) sections 0988 18" radius curved track (18" long), 0976 curved terminal track (18" long), 0909 straight track, 0919 Uncoupler Re-Railer, 0103 800 milliamp Power Pack	250
5755	**Five-Car NYC GP-7 Diesel Freight** SRP: $39.95 0598 NY Central GP-7 Diesel with headlight, 0301 Operating Coal Dump Car, 0366 Operating Milk Car, 0836 Alaskan Hopper, 0821 Pipe Transport Car, 0840 NY Central Caboose, (5) sections 0988 18" radius curved track (18" long), 0976 curved terminal track (18" long), 0900 Remote Control Operating Platform, 0919 Uncoupler Re-Railer, 0101 1 1/4 Amp DC/AC Power Pack	225
5756	**Three-Car Steam Passenger** with Smoke SRP: $39.95, 0635 LT Pacific Steam Locomotive and Tender with Headlight and Smoke, Pennsylvania Passenger Cars 0708 Baggage Car, 0709 Vista Dome Car, 07010 Observation Car, (5) sections 0988 18" radius curved track (18" long), 0976 curved terminal track (18" long), 0909 straight track, 0919 Uncoupler Re-Railer, 0103 800 milliamp Power Pack	275
5757	**Five-Car Smoke Puffing Steam Freight** with Illuminated Caboose, SRP: $49.95 0635 LT Pacific Steam Locomotive and Tender with Headlight and Smoke, 0300 Operating Log Unloading Car with Bin, 0366 Operating Milk Can Unloading Car, 0842 Culvert Pipe Transport Car, 0865-250 MC Gondola with Crates, 0827 Safety First Illuminated Caboose, (5) sections 0988 18" radius curved track (18" long), 0976 curved terminal track (18" long), 0900 Remote Control Operating Platform, 0919 Uncoupler Re-Railer, 0101 1 1/4 Amp DC/AC Power Pack	325
5758	**Six-Car Santa Fe "AB" Diesel Freight** with Missile Launching Platform, SRP: $49.95 0565 Santa Fe Powered A Alco Diesel with Headlight, Matching 0575 Santa Fe Dummy B Unit, 0333 Satellite Launching Car, 0805 Illuminated Radioactive Waste Disposal Car, 0823 Twin Missile Carrying Car, 0850 US Army Missile Launching Car, 0817-150 Santa Fe Caboose, 0470 Missile Firing Platform with 0847 Exploding Target Boxcar, (5) sections 0988 18" radius curved track (18" long), 0976 curved terminal track (18" long), 0909 straight track, 0919 Uncoupler Re-Railer, 0101 1 1/4 Amp DC/AC Power Pack	375
5759	**Four-Car Santa Fe "AA" Diesel Passenger** with Illuminated Coaches SRP: $49.95 0565 Santa Fe Powered A Alco Diesel with Headlight, Matching 0595 Santa Fe Dummy A unit, 0712 Illuminated Santa Fe Baggage Car, 0713 Illuminated Santa Fe Pullman Car, 0714 Illuminated Santa Fe Vista Dome Car, 0715 Illuminated Santa Fe Observation Car, (5) sections 0988 18" radius curved track (18" long), 0976 curved terminal track (18" long), (3) sections 0909 straight track, 0919 Uncoupler Re-Railer, 0101 1 1/4 Amp DC/AC Power Pack	400

5762	**Seven-Car Steam Freight** with Smoke SRP: $39.95 0635 LT Pacific Locomotive and Tender with Headlight and Smoke, 0039 Motorized Track Cleaning Car, 0319 Helicopter Launching Car, 0810 Emergency Generator Transport Car, 0863 Rail Truck Car, 0880 Maintenance Car with Light, 0889 Crane, 0819-200 B & M Work Caboose, (5) sections 0988 18" radius curved track (18" long), 0976 curved terminal track (18" long), 0909 straight track, 0919 Uncoupler Re-Railer, 0101 1 1/4 Amp DC/AC Power Pack	500
5767	**Valise Pack** SRP: $39.95 0642 LT 2-4-2 Steam Locomotive and Slopeback Tender with Headlight, 0319 Helicopter Launching Car, 0337 Operating Giraffe Car, 0841 Caboose, (11) sections 0989 18" radius curved track, 0875 18" radius curved terminal track, 0103 800 milliamp Power Pack. Set comes in 5765-15 Carrying Valise	1400

1962

14003	**Four-Unit M&St. L Husky Freight** SRP: $19.95 0055 Minneapolis & St. Louis Husky Switcher with Headlight, 0821 Pipe Transport Car, 0865-250 Gondola with Crates, 0837 Minn. & St. Louis Caboose, (5) sections 0988 18" radius curved track (18" long), 0976 curved terminal track (18" long), 0103 800 Milliamp Power Pack	150
14013	**Four-Unit Erie & Lackawanna Diesel Switcher Freight** SRP: $25.00 0545 Erie & Lackawanna GE-44 Diesel Switcher with Headlight, 0847 Exploding Target Car, 0850 US Army Missile Launching Car, 0838 Erie Caboose, (5) sections 0988 18" radius curved track (18" long), 0976 curved terminal track (18" long), 0103 800 Milliamp Power Pack	200
14023	**Six-Unit 2-4-2 "Heavy Cargo" Steam Freight** SRP: $29.95, 0642LT Steam Switcher with Slope Back Tender and Headlight, 0357 Cop and Hobo Car, 0861 Timber Transport Car, 0865-225 Gondola with Scrap Iron, 0841 Caboose, (5) sections 0988 18" radius curved track (18" long), 0976 curved terminal track (18" long) 0103 800 Milliamp Power Pack	225
14033	**Five-Unit Pacific Military Diesel Freight** SRP: $29.95, 0568 Union Pacific Diesel with Headlight, 0365 Minuteman Missile Firing Car, 0809 Helium Tank Transport Car, 0813 Mercury Capsule Carrying Car, 0841-50 Union Pacific Caboose, (5) sections 0988 18" radius curved track (18" long), 0976 curved terminal track (18" long), 0103 800 Milliamp Power Pack	375
14043	**Six-Unit "Weapons Carrier" Steam Freight** SRP: $39.95, 0635 LT Pacific Steam Locomotive and Tender with Headlight and Smoke, 0349 Turbo Missile Firing Car, 0805 Illuminated Radioactive Waste Disposal Car, 0847 Exploding Target Car, 0841 Caboose, (5) sections 0988 18" radius curved track (18" long), 0976 curved terminal track (18" long), 0909 straight track, 0919 Uncoupler re-railer, 0103 800 Milliamp Power Pack	275

14054	**Five-Unit Diesel Passenger** SRP: $39.95 0566 Texas Special Powered A Unit Diesel with Headlight, 0704 Texas Special Baggage Car, (2) 0706 Texas Special Vista-Dome, 0707 Texas Special Observation, (5) sections 0988 18" radius curved track (18" long), 0976 curved terminal track (18" long), 0909 straight track, 0919 Uncoupler re-railer, 0101 1 1/4 AMP DC/AC Power Pack., No 950 U.S.Railroad Map	**325**
14064	**Northern Pacific GP-9 Diesel Freight** SRP: $49.95 0597 Northern Pacific GP-9 Diesel with Headlight, 0365 Minuteman Missile Launching Car, 0366 Operating Milk Can Car, 0319 Helicopter Launching Car, 0301 Operating Coal Dump Car, 0841 Caboose, (5) sections 0988 18" radius curved track (18" long), 0976 curved terminal track (18" long) 0919 Uncoupler re-railer, 0900 Remote Control Platform, 0101 1 1/4 AMP DC/AC Power Pack.	**325**
14074	**Six-Unit Pacific Freight** SRP: $49.95 with Smoke and Whistle 0645LTS Pacific Locomotive Tender with Headlight, Smoke, Whistle and Whistle Controller, 0861 Timber Transport Car, 0865-250 MC Gondola with Crates, 0873 Rodeo Car, 0841 Caboose, (5) sections 0988 18" radius curved track (18" long), 0976 curved terminal track (18" long), (2) 0909 straight track, 0771-100 uncoupling set with ramp, Magnet and 10 coupler Magnets, 0103 800 Milliamp Power Pack	**275**
14084	**Seven-Unit Santa Fe Diesel Freight** SRP: $49.95 with Horn 0535 Santa Fe Powered A Unit Diesel, 0535W Santa Fe Dummy B Unit with Horn, 0370 Sheriff and Outlaw Car, 0821 Pipe Transport Car, 0845 Gold Bullion Transport Car, 0865-225 Gondola with Scrap Iron, 0841-85 Santa Fe Caboose, (5) sections 0988 18" radius curved track (18" long), 0976 curved terminal track (18" long), (2) 0909 straight track, 0214 Girder Bridge, 0771-100 uncoupling set with ramp, Magnet and 10 coupler Magnets, 0103 800 Milliamp Power Pack	**475**
14098	**Seven-Unit Fire Power Steam Freight** with Smoke and Whistle, SRP: $59.95 0645LTS Pacific Locomotive and Tender with Headlight, Smoke, Whistle and Whistle Controller, 0319 Helicopter Launching Car, 0349 Turbo Missile Firing Car, 0365 Minuteman Missile Launching Car, 0847 Exploding Target Car, 0841 Caboose, (5) sections 0988 18" radius curved track (18" long), 0976 curved terminal track (18" long), (2) 0909 straight track, 0771-100 uncoupling set with ramp, magnet and 10 coupler magnets, 0101 1 1/4 AMP DC/AC Power Pack	**400**
14108	**Six-Unit Santa Fe Passenger** w/Horn SRP: $59.95 0535 Santa Fe Powered A, 0535W Santa Fe Dummy B with Horn and Horn Controller, 0712 Illuminated Santa Fe Baggage Car, 0713 Illuminated Santa Fe Pullman Coach, 0714 Illuminated Santa Fe Vista Dome, 0715 Illuminated Santa Fe Observation, (5) sections 0988 18" radius curved track (18" long), 0976 curved terminal track (18" long), 0909 straight track, 0919 Uncoupler re-railer, 0100 2 1/2 AMP DC/AC Power Pack.	**425**

14133	**Five-Unit "Mohawk" Steam Freight** SRP: $19.95 0643 LT Steam Locomotive and Slope Back Tender with Headlight and Helic Drive, 0861-100 Timber Transport Car, 0865-375 MC Gondola, 0837-100 M&St. L Caboose, (5) sections 0988 18" radius curved track (18" long), 0976 curved terminal track (18" long), 0103 800 Milliamp Power Pack	225
14143	**Six-Unit Santa Fe Diesel Freight** SRP: $24.95 0594P Santa Fe GP-9 Diesel with Headlight and Helic Drive, 0815-50 Rocket Fuel Tank Car, 0865-400 Gondola with Crates, 0847-100 Exploding Target Car, 0850-100 US Army Missile Launching Car, 0841-175 ATSF Caboose, (5) sections 0988 18" radius curved track (18" long), 0976 curved terminal track (18" long), 0909 straight track, 0919 Uncoupler re-railer, 0103 800 Milliamp Power Pack	225
14153	**Eight-Unit Pacific Steam Freight** SRP: $29.95 0626 LT Pacific Locomotive and Tender with Headlight, 0815-75 Lionel Lines Tank Car, 0836-100 Alaskan Hopper, 0861-100 Timber Transport Car, 0873 Rodeo Car, 0865-375 MC Gondola, 0817-275 New Haven (Lionel Body) Caboose, (5) sections 0988 18" radius curved track (18" long), 0976 curved terminal track (18" long), 0909 straight track, 0919 Uncoupler re-railer, 0103 800 Milliamp Power Pack	300
14163	**Four-Unit Pennsylvania Diesel Passenger** SRP: $24.95, 0571P Pennsylvania Powered A Unit Diesel with Headlight and Helic Drive, (2) 0723 Pennsylvania Pullman Coach, 0725 Pennsylvania Observation, (5) sections 0988 18" radius curved track (18" long), 0976 curved terminal track (18" long), 0909 straight track, 0919 Uncoupler re-railer, 0103 800 Milliamp Power Pack	625
14173	**Six-Unit Santa Fe Diesel Passenger** SRP: 39.95 0555P Santa Fe Powered A with Headlight and Helic Drive, 0595 Santa Fe Dummy A, 0712 Illuminated Santa Fe Baggage Car, 0713 Illuminated Santa Fe Pullman Coach, 0714 Illuminated Santa Fe Vista Dome, 0715 Illuminated Santa Fe Observation, (5) sections 0988 18" radius curved track (18" long), 0976 curved terminal track (18" long), 0909 straight track, 0919 Uncoupler re-railer, 0101 1 1/4 AMP DC/AC Power Pack.	350
14183	**Ten-Unit Steam Freight** with Smoke SRP: $39.95 0636 LTS Pacific Steam Locomotive and Tender with Headlight and Smoke, 0810 Emergency Generator Transport Car, 0815-75 Lionel Lines Tank Car, 0836-100 Alaskan Hopper, 0864-935 New York Central Boxcar, 0865-250 Gondola with Crates, 0861-100 Timber Transport Car, 0873 Rodeo Car, 0827-50 Illuminated AEC Caboose, 0214 Girder Bridge (5) sections 0988 18" radius curved track (18" long), 0976 curved terminal track (18" long), 0909 straight track, 0919 Uncoupler re-railer, 0101 1 1/4 AMP DC/AC Power Pack	425
14193	**Nine-Unit Northern Pacific GP-9 Diesel Freight** SRP: $39.95, 0593P and 0593T Northern Pacific Powered and Dummy GP-9 Diesels, 0365 Minuteman Missile Launching Car, 0815-50 Rocket Fuel Tank Car, 0821-100 Pipe Transport Car, 0847-100 Exploding Target Car, 0865-350 MC Gondola, 0889 Illinois Central Crane, 0819-285 C & O Work Caboose, (5) sections 0988 18" radius curved track (18" long), 0976 curved terminal track (18" long), 0909 straight track, 0919 Uncoupler re-railer, 0101 1 1/4 AMP DC/AC Power Pack	475

14203	**Ten-Unit Santa Fe Diesel** with Horn, SRP: $49.95 0536 P Santa Fe Powered Unit, 0535W Dummy B Unit with Horn, 0595 Dummy A, Horn Controller, 0319-125 Operating Helicopter Car, 0815-50 Rocket Fuel Car, 0836-100 Alaskan Hopper, 0861-100 Timber Transport Car, 0864-400 B & M Boxcar, 0865-300 Gondola with Crates, 0827-75 A.T.S.F. Illuminated Caboose, (5) sections 0988 18" radius curved track (18" long), 0976 curved terminal track (18" long), (4) 0909 straight track, 0771-100 uncoupling set (with ramp, magnet, 10 coupler magnets), 0101 1 1/4 AMP DC/AC Power Pack	**475**
14233	**Ten-Unit Pacific Steam Freight** SRP: $59.95 with Smoke and Whistle 0646LTS Pacific Steam Locomotive and Tender with Headlights, smoke, whistle and whistle controller, 0300 Operating Lumber Car, 0301 Operating Coal Car, 0366 Operating Milk Can Car, 0815-75 Lionel Lines Tank Car, 0836-100 Alaskan Hopper, 0864-935 NYC Boxcar, 0889 Illinois Central Crane, 0819-285 C & O Work Caboose, (5) sections 0988 18" radius curved track (18" long), 0976 curved terminal track (18" long), (3) 0909 straight track, 0900 Remote Control Platform, 0101 1 1/4 AMP DC/AC Power Pack	**400**

1964

14240	**Four-Unit Husky Freight** SRP: $17.50 0055 M&St.L Husky Switcher with Headlight, 0821-50 Pipe Transport Car, 0865-400 MC Gondola, 0837-100 Minn. & St. Louis Caboose, (5) sections 0988 18" radius curved track (18" long), 0976 curved terminal track (18" long), 0103 800 Milliamp Power Pack	**125**
14250	**Four-Unit Husky Freight** without Power Pack SRP: $11.95, 0055 Minn. & St. Louis Husky Switcher with Headlight, 0821-50 Pipe Transport Car, 0865-400 MC Gondola, 0837-100 M&St.L Caboose, (5) sections 0988 18" radius curved track (18" long), 0976 curved terminal track (Cataloged only in 1964 same as 14240 set but without the power pack)	*
14260	**Five-Unit Diesel Freight** SRP: $21,95 0594P Santa Fe GP-9 Diesel with Headlight, 0836-100 Alaskan Hopper, 0861-100 Timber Transport Car, 0865-400 MC Gondola, 0837-100 M& St.L Caboose, (5) sections 0988 18" radius curved track (18" long), 0976 curved terminal track (18" long), 0103 800 Milliamp Power Pack	**175**
14270	**Six-Unit Steam Freight** SRP: $24.95 0626LT Pacific Steam Locomotive and Tender with Headlight, 0836-100 Alaskan Hopper, 0864-925 New York Central Boxcar, 0865-400 MC Gondola, 0837-100 Minn. & St. Louis Caboose, (5) sections 0988 18" radius curved track (18" long), 0976 curved terminal track (18" long) 0909 straight track, 0950 Re-railer track, 0103 800 Milliamp Power Pack	**200**
14280	**Eight-Unit Steam Freight** SRP: $29.95 0636 LTS Pacific Locomotive and Tender with Headlight and Smoke, 0836-100 Alaska Hopper, 0865-400 MC Gondola, 0861-100 Timber Transport Car, 0864-925 NY Central Boxcar, 0873 Rodeo Car, 0837-100 Minn. & St. Louis Caboose, (5) sections 0988 18" radius curved track (18" long), 0976 curved terminal track (18" long), 0909 straight track, 0950 Re-railer track, 0103 800 Milliamp Power Pack	**250**

14290	**Four-Unit Diesel Passenger** SRP: $29.95 0555 P Santa Fe Powered A Unit Diesel with Headlight, (2) 0733 Santa Fe Pullman Coaches, 0735 Santa Fe Observation Car, (5) sections 0988 18" radius curved track (18" long), 0976 curved terminal track (18" long), 0909 straight track, 0950 Re-railer track, 0103 800 Milliamp Power Pack	**275**
14300	**Nine-Unit Steam Freight** SRP: $39.95 0646 LTS Pacific Steam Locomotive and tender with Headlight, Smoke, Whistle and Whistle Controller, 0815-50 Rocket Fuel Tank Car, 0836-100 Hopper, 0861-100 Timber Transport Car, 0865-400 MC Gondola, 0864-925 New York Central Boxcar, 0873 Rodeo Car, 0837-100 Minn. & St. Louis Caboose, (5) sections 0988 18" radius curved track (18" long), 0976 curved terminal track (18" long), (3) 0909 straight track, 0950 Re-railer track, 0101 1 1/4 AMP DC/AC Power Pack	**300**
14310	**Ten Unit Diesel Freight** SRP: $39.95 0555P Santa Fe Powered A, 0535W Santa Fe Dummy B with Horn and Horn Controller, 0595 Dummy A, 0815-50 Rocket Fuel Tank Car, 0836-100 Hopper, 0861-100 Timber Transport Car, 0865-400 MC Gondola, 0864-925 New York Central Boxcar, 0873 Rodeo Car, 0837-100 M&St.L Caboose, (5) sections 0988 18" radius curved track (18" long), 0976 curved terminal track (18" long), (3) 0909 straight track, 0950 Re-railer track, 0101 1 1/4 AMP DC/AC Power Pack	**325**

1965

17190	**Combination HO Raceway and Train Outfit** SRP: $40.00, 0055 Minn. & St. Louis Husky Switcher, 0865-400 MC Gondola, 0821-100 Pipe Transport Car, 0837-100 Minn. & St. Louis Caboose, (5) sections 0988 18" radius 18" long curved track, 0976 curved (18" long) terminal track, Wires and instructions, (2) Racing Cars, (2) 9" Straight Track, (6) curved track, straight terminal track, pair of lane change chicanes, (2) 6" straight track, Monte Carlo Scenic Background, Banking Pier Set, Railroad Roadway Crossing, Trestle Set, 2 Touch-A-Matic Speed Controller, Set of guard rails and flags, rail clips and road clips, power pack for supply to both HO train and raceway.	*
14240	**Four-Unit Freight** SRP: $20.00 0055 Minn. & St. Louis Husky Switcher, 0865-400 MC Gondola, 0821-110 Pipe Transport Car, 0837-100 Minn. & St. Louis Caboose, (5) sections 0988 18" radius 18" long curved track, 0976 curved (18" long) terminal track, 0103 Milliamp Power Pack	**125**
14260	**Five-Unit GP-9 Diesel Freight** SRP: $25.00 0594P Santa Fe GP-9 Diesel, 0836-100 Alaskan Hopper, 0865-400 MC Gondola, 0861-100 Timber Transport Car, 0837-100 Minn. & St. Louis Caboose, (5) sections 0988 18" radius 18" long curved track, 0976 curved (18" long) terminal track, 0103 Milliamp Power Pack	**175**
14280	**Eight-Unit Freight** SRP: $30.00 0636 LTS Pacific Locomotive and Tender with Headlight and Smoke, 0836-100 Alaskan Hopper, 0861-100 Timber Transport Car, 0865-400 MC Gondola, 0873 Rodeo Car, 0874-25 NYC Box Car, 0837-100 Minn. & St. Louis Caboose, (5) sections 0988 18" radius 18" long curved track, 0976 curved (18" long) terminal track, 0909 straight track, 0950 re-railer, 0103 Milliamp Power Pack	**225**

14300	**Nine-Unit Freight** SRP: $40.00 0646 LTS Pacific Locomotive and Tender with Headlight, Smoke, Whistle and Whistle Controller, 0815-50 Rocket Fuel Tank Car, 0836-100 Alaskan Hopper Car, 0861-100 Timber Transport Car, 0865-400 MC Gondola, 0873 Rodeo Car, 0874-25 NYC Box Car, 0837-100 Minn. & St. Louis Caboose, (5) sections 0988 18" radius 18" long curved track, 0976 curved (18" long) terminal track, (3) 0909 straight track, 0950 re-railer, 0101 1 1/4 AMP DC/AC Power Pack	300
14310	**Ten-Unit Freight** SRP: $40.00 0555P, 0535W, 0595 ABA Santa Fe ALCO Diesels, 0815-50 Rocket Fuel Tank Car, 0836-100 Alaskan Hopper, 0861-100 Timber Transport Car, 0865-400 MC Gondola, 0873 Rodeo Car, 0874-25 NYC Boxcar, 0837-100 Minn. & St. Louis Caboose, (5) sections 0988 18" radius 18" long curved track, 0976 curved (18" long) terminal track, (3) 0909 straight track, 0950 re-railer, 0101 1 1/4 AMP DC/AC Power Pack	325
14320	**Five-Unit Passenger Set** SRP: $30.00 0555P Santa Fe Powered A Unit, 0575 Santa Fe Dummy B, (2) 0733 Santa Fe Pullman Coaches, 0735 Santa Fe Observation Car, (5) sections 0988 18" radius 18" long curved track, 0976 curved (18" long) terminal track, 0909 straight track, 0950 re-railer, 0103 Milliamp Power Pack	275

1966

14240	**Four-Unit Freight Set** SRP: $30.00 0055 Minn. & St. Louis Husky Switcher with light, 0865-400 MC Gondola, 0821-100 Pipe Transport Car, 0837-100 Minn. & St. Louis Caboose, (5) sections 0988 18" radius 18" long curved track, 0976 curved (18" long) terminal track, 0103 Milliamp Power Pack	125
14260	**Five-Unit Freight Set** SRP: $25.00 0592 Santa Fe GP-9 Diesel with Headlight, 0861-100 Timber Transport Car, 0836-100 Alaskan Hopper, 0865-400 MC Gondola, 0837-100 Minn. & St. Louis Caboose, (5) sections 0988 18" radius 18" long curved track, 0976 curved (18" long) terminal track, 0101 1 1/4 AMP DC/AC Power Pack	175
14280	**Eight-Unit Freight Set** SRP: $40.00 In new set box with color pictures of components on the side, Cars are in individual boxes 0636LTS Pacific Steam Locomotive and Tender with headlight and smoke, 0836-110 Alaskan Hopper, 0874-25 New York Central Boxcar, 0861-110 Timber Transport Car, 0865-400 MC Gondola, 0873 Rodeo Car, 0837-110 Minn. & St. Louis Caboose, (5) sections 0988 18" radius 18" long curved track, 0976 curved (18" long) terminal track, 0909 straight track, 0950 re-railer, 0101 1 1/4 AMP DC, AC Power Pack	325
14300	**Nine-Unit Freight Set** SRP: $50.00 In new set box with color pictures of components on the side, Cars are in individual boxes 1. 0647LTS Pacific Steam Locomotive and Tender with Headlight, Smoke, Whistle and Whistle Controller, 0815 -50 Rocket Fuel Tank Car*, 0836-110 Alaskan Hopper, 0861-110 Timber Transport Car, 0865-400 MC Gondola, 0874-25 New York Central Boxcar, 0873 Rodeo Car, 0837-110 Minn. & St. Louis Caboose, (5) sections 0988 18" radius 18" long curved track, 0976 curved (18" long) terminal track, (3) 0909 straight track, 0950 re-railer, 0101 1 1/4 AMP DC/AC Power Pack	375
	2. * 0815-110 Sunoco Tank Car in place of 0815-50	550

14310	**Ten-Unit Freight Set** SRP: $50.00 In new set box with color pictures of components on the side, Cars are in individual boxes, 1. 0556P Powered A Unit, 0535W Dummy B with Horn and Horn Controller, 0595 Dummy A, 0815 -50 Rocket Fuel Tank Car*, 0836-110 Alaskan Hopper, 0861-110 Timber Transport Car, 0865-400 MC Gondola, 0874-25 New York Central Boxcar, 0873 Rodeo Car, 0837-110 Minn. & St. Louis Caboose, (5) sections 0988 18" radius 18" long curved track, 0976 curved (18" long) terminal track, (3) 0909 straight track, 0950 re-railer, 0101 1 1/4 AMP DC, AC Power Pack 2. *0815-110 Sunoco Tank Car in place of 0815-50	**425** **600**
14320	**Five-Unit Passenger Set** SRP: $30.00 0556P Santa Fe Diesel Unit with Headlight, 0575 Santa Fe Dummy B, (2) 0733 Santa Fe Pullman Coach, 0735 Santa Fe Observation, (5) sections 0988 18" radius 18" long curved track, 0976 curved (18" long) terminal track, 0909 straight track, 0950 re-railer, 0101 1 1/4 AMP DC, AC Power Pack	**300**

Accessories

Note: Several scenic accessories were offered by Lionel are Life-Like products sold in Lionel HO boxes. These are all rather difficult to find and in demand by the advanced collectors. Prices are given for boxed units only.

0110	**Graduated Trestle Set** with 46 piers, 58-66 central arch bridge	**25**
0111	**Trestle Set** 12 piers used to extend 0110, "L", 60-66	**20**
0114	**Engine House** w/Horn, horn often missing, 58-60	**75**
0115	**Engine House Kit** kit version of 0117, 61-63	**65**
0117	**Engine House** w/skylights in roof, plastic, 59, 60 windows along sides, passageways ends for two tracks	**60**
0118	**Engine House** with Whistle 58-62 whistle is often missing, 12" wide and 10" high	**80**
0119	**Landscaped Tunnel** 24 " long, 59-66	**50**
0140	**Banjo Signal** operating signal w/0145-200, 62-66 Contactor Track Section.Smaller version of O gauge accessory, however, not true HO scale	**95**
0145	**Automatic Gateman** 57-66 w/0145-200 Contactor Track	**60**
0197	**Rotating Radar Antenna** 58-61	**75**
0214	**Girder Bridge**	**15**
0221	**Truss Bridge with Two Trestles** 61	**20**
0222	**Deck Bridge with Two Trestles** 61	**20**
0224	**Girder Bridge with two Trestles** 61	**20**
0282	**Gantry Crane** manually operated, 61-63 shell is same as 0889 IC Wrecker Crane but numbered 0282, must have both crates	**120**
0310	**Billboard Set** 59-66 1. five plastic frames & five ad posters 2. Special set w/Lionel HO billboard	 **35** **100**
0430	**Six Tree Assortment** 59-62 w/pines and flowering shrubs	**75**
0431	**Landscape Set** w/box of lichen, 59-62 3' x 4' grass mat, path mats,1' x 4' rolls of earth	**85**
0432	**Tree Assortment** trees and shrubbery 59-62	**75**
0433	**HO Scenery Set** w/grass mat for 4' x 6' board, 59-62 1' x 4' roll of earth, bag of lichen and nine assorted trees.	**95**

0470	**Missile Launching Platform** w/Exploding, 60-62 Target Car, same as the O gauge accessory (470) except the HO 0847 target car replaced the O gauge (6470)	**90**
480	**Missile Firing Range** w/Camouflage &, 62,63 Target Car w/sealed bag of lichen, four small white plastic missiles and the HO gauge 0847 Target Car	**120**
0494	**Rotating Beacon** 59-63	**65**
0900	**Unloading Platform** 60-66	**35**

Transformer & Track Accessories

0100		**30**
0101	**Starter Transformer**	**10**
0102	**Power Unit** needs 0181 to control trains	**80**
0103	**Starter Set Transformer**	**10**
0104	**Two Train Transformer**	**100**
0145-200	**Accessory Activator Track**	**15**
0147	**Whistle/Horn Controller**	**30**
0150	**Rectifier** converts AC transformers for use with HO	**40**
0181	**Cab Controller**	**30**
390C	**Controller**	**15**
0919	**Re-railer Section**	**5**
0921	**Automatic Switches pair**	**20**
0922	**Switch RH**	**10**
0923	**Switch LH**	**10**
0930-300	**30 degree Crossing**	**5**
0961	**Illuminated Bumpers** pkg of six, 62,63	**100**
0962	**Non-Illuminated Bumper**	
0990-900	**90 degree Crossing**	**5**

Plasticville

Note: The only difference between Lionel Plasticville and regular Plasticville is the box. In order to be collectible, the set must be in a Lionel box. When purchasing Lionel Plasticville, make sure the dye lots of the colors match. Sometimes unscrupulous sellers will replace parts of Lionel Plasticville with parts from regular Plasticville. Prices based on far less than normal sampling and are just a very rough estimate as we have very few reports. Prices are based on boxes being in Excellent condition.

HO Plasticville

Note: Accessories 0410-0426 were packaged for Lionel in the appropriate Lionel HO boxes by Bachmann Brothers Inc. from their production of the popular Plasticville hobby kits. Prices are given for boxed units only.

0410	**Ranch House Set** 60,61	**60**
0411	**Figure Set** 59	**50**
0412	**Farm Set** 59	**50**
0413	**Railroad Structure Set** 59,60	**90**
0414	**Village Set** 59	**75**
0415	**Cape Cod Set** 60,61	**25**
0416	**Station Set** 60	**30**
0417	**Farm Set** 60	**30**
0418	**Industrial Set** 60	**40**
0419	**Rail Junction Set** 61	**80**
0420	**Railroad Set** 61	**65**
0421	**Farm Set** 61,62	**65**
0422	**Freight Set** 61,62	**70**
0425	**Figure Set** 62,63	**65**
0426	**Railroad Station Set** 62	**75**

O Plasticville

No.	Item	Rarity	Value
951	**Farm Set** Box Type I and Ia, 58 Truck, tractor, jeep, horses, cows, harrow, plow, wagon and footbridge. Sometimes found with incomplete or broken farm implements.	(2)	**225**
952	**Figure Set** Box Type I, 58 Townspeople, fire plug, fire alarm box and mail boxes. Sometimes confused with the 953 Figure Set. The 952 is harder to find.	(2)	**150**
953	**Figure Set** Box Type V, Va & Vb, 59-62 Same as 952 with paint brush, paint palette and styrene painting fluid and glue. Longest running single item in the series. The difference between a 952 and 953 is a paint brush, paint palette and painting fluid. Bros. instruction sheet for painting.	(2)	**75**
954	**Swimming Pool and Playground Set** 59 Box Type V, Playground equipment, patio set, pool, fences and shrubs. Same as Bachmann Playground Equipment Set with a fence and gate added.	(2)	**325**
955	**Highway Set** Box Type II, 58 Street signs, telegraph poles, auto and buses	(1)	**325**
956	**Stockyard Set** Box Type V, 59 Corral, cows and railroad signs	(4+)	**450**
957	**Farm Building & Animal Set** Box Type I & Ia, 58 Farm structures plus a fence, gate, pump, horse, fowl and cat and dog	(1)	**200**
958	**Vehicle Set** Autos, fire trucks, bus, ambulance, street signs, fire alarm box, mail box, fire plug and traffic light. There is a rare version included in a Sears uncataloged set 9807. This version came in a white box.		
	1. Box Type III, 58	(1)	**550**
	2. Box Type XII, 64	(5)	**1200***
959	**Barn Set** Box Type II & IIa, 58 Dairy barn, horses, fowl and domestic animals	(2)	**175**
960	**Barnyard Set** Box Type V & Va, 59-61 Farm buildings, vehicles & equipment, fowl, domestic and farm animals	(2)	**125**
961	**School Set** Box Type VI, 61 School, flagpole, busses, street signs, fence, shrubs & benches. Scarce	(4+)	**520**
962	**Turnpike Set** Box Type IV, 58 Interchange, stanchions, telegraph poles, street signs, autos, ambulance, bus	(3+)	**650**
963	**Frontier Set** Box Type VI & VIc, 59, 60 Cabin, windmill, fences, horses, cows and pump. Was not part of the Halloween General Set.	(2)	**250**
963-100	**Frontier Set** Box Type VIb, U60 Cabin, windmill, fences, horses, cows and pump. This version did come in the Sears' General Halloween Set and is the most desirable and valued of all the Lionel Plasticville line.	(5)	**650**
964	**Factory Site Set** Box Type VII, 59 Factory, auto, telegraph poles, and railroad signs. Almost as scarce as the uncataloged Frontier set.	(4)	**600▼**
965	**Farm Set** Box Type VIII, 59 Barn, farm buildings, farm equipment, fowl, dogs, cats and farm animals	(3)	**250▼**
966	**Firehouse Set** Box Type IV & IVa, 58 Firehouse, fire engines, alarm box, hydrant, ambulance, bus, auto, traffic light, street post and signs, bench, mail box, townspeople, telegraph poles and pine trees	(3)	**350▼**

No.	Description	Rarity	Price
967	**Post Office Set Box Type III & IIIa,** 58 Post office, mail box, townspeople, benches, street signs, street post, traffic light, truck and autos	(3)	**400▼**
968	**TV Transmitter Set** Box Type II, 58 TV station, fence, gate, townspeople, mail box, fire plug, jeep, autos and pine trees	(3)	**450**
969	**Construction Set** Box Type V, 60 House, construction material, workers and autos	(2)	**400▼**
980	**Ranch Set** Box Type V, 60 Loading pen, cattle, pigs, sheep, farm implements and vehicles	(2)	**350▼**
981	**Freight Yard Set** Box Type VIa, 60 Loading platform with carts, switch tower, telephone poles & RR men	(3)	**250**
982	**Suburban Split Level Set** Box Type VIIa, 60 Split level house, pine trees, auto, ranch fence, bench and people	(4)	**425**
983	**Farm Set, Box,** Type VIIa, 60, 61 Dairy barn, windmill, colonial house, horse, cows and auto	(4)	**400▼**
984	**Railroad Set,** Box Type VIa & VId, 61, 62 Switch tower, telegraph poles, loading platform, figures, railroad signs & acc	(3)	**250**
985	**Freight Area Set,** Box Type IX, 61 Water tower, work car, loading platform, switch tower, telegraph poles, autos, watchman's shanty, railroad signs and accessories. Thought to be the most scarce of all Lionel Plasticville.	(5)	**575**
986	**Farmhouse and Barnyard Set,** Box Type X, 62 20 pcs, New England farm house and barn with 18 domestic animals	(3)	**450**
987	**Town Set,** Box Type XI, 62 24 pcs, church, gas station, auto, 12 street signs, bank, 5 telephone poles and corner store. Hard-to-find and coveted.	(5)	**1200▼***
988	**Railroad Structure Set,** Box Type XI, 62 Railroad station, crossing gate and shanty, water tank, work car, hobo shacks, bench and figures. Another hard-to-find item.	(5)	**1200▼***

Postwar Catalogs

1945 4 pages (4) **20**

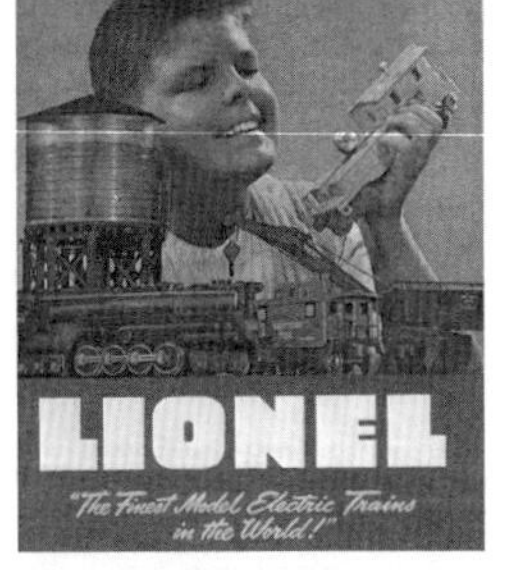

1946 18 pages (4) 75▲

1947 32 pages (4) 75▲

1948 36 pages (4) **50**

1949 40 pages (4) **100▲**

1950 44 pages (3) **200▲**

1951 36 pages (3) **50▲**

1952 36 pages (4) **50▲**

1953 44 pages (4) **45**

1954 44 pages (3) **40**

1955 44 pages (3) **35**

1956 40 pages (3) **25**

1957 52 pages (3) **30**

1958 56 pages (3) **30**

1959 56 pages (3) **35**

1960 56 pages (2) **20**

1961 72 pgs (3) **20**

1962 100pgs (2) **25**

1963 56 pgs (2) **20**

1964 24 pgs (3) **15**

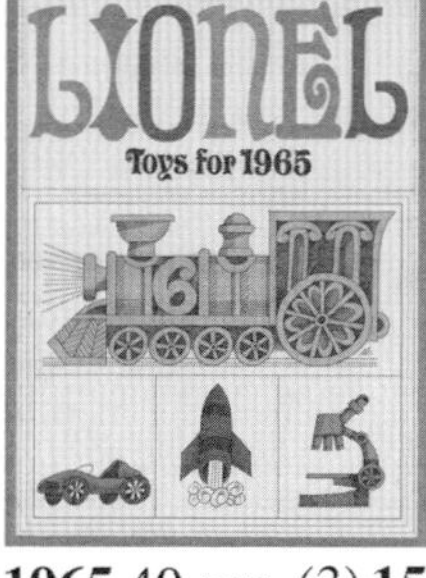

1965 40 pgs (3) **15**

1968 8 pgs (3) **10**

1966-67 40 pages (3) **10▼**

1969 8 pages (2) **10**

most collectible. Combine that with a guy passing a hobby shop and seeing a Santa Fe F3 in the window and boom (as Ari Gold would say) – another Lionel collector was born.

So the hobby expanded dramatically, fueled by the love of a quality toy that not only produced happy memories and immediate gratification, but was a good investment, increasing in value every year by 10-15%. All was rosy up through the turn of the century. Then the economy started to deteriorate and stagnation set in. The hobby had peaked, had begun to stall at the top of the hill, and start a slow slide down the hill.

Jump ahead to 2010. Economy is shaky. Most prices are down at least 20%, some as high as 50%. A very few have increased. Meet and hobby store sales are down, some stores have closed, and the number of ads in our hobby magazines are down.

For many items it is a buyer's market. If you are a disciple of the "buy low and have fun playing with toy trains" persuasion, get busy. Don't expect a bargain on everything, but many good-quality trains and accessories are available at reasonable prices.

No hobby or business is immune from the impact of a recession. Prices fall, areas of interests change, supply goes up and demand down, but through it all, train collecting will always survive because toy trains are quality and part of our recent history and there will always be a market for quality and history. And even the new trains of today are a refreshing alternative in a toy market dominated by virtual electronic reality. Toy trains, new and old, will always have a place in our culture.

So hang in, stay alert, visit your hobby store, go to meets, check out e-Bay, carry cash, and have fun. And remember, if you sell a train and use the money to pay a bill, you have nothing but a piece of paper moved from one pile to another. If you sell a train, and buy a new train, you have a new train. Hey, don't say we said that. It's up to you to convince your wife.

Allan Miller, Editor-in-Chief
O Gauge Railroading Magazine

We've been doing pretty well here at *O Gauge Railroading* magazine, despite the lousy state of the economy in general. I'm not sure if the same holds true for dealers across the nation because I continually receive mixed reports from them. Mom-and-pop dealerships, in particular, seem to be rather consistently falling by the wayside for a number of reasons, including retirements, health issues, the overall stagnant economy, and the impact of Internet buying and selling. Some dealers I've spoken with recently – old timers like me – just feel it's probably the right time to hang it up.

I have been holding the magazine to 100 pages for some months now because I want and need to keep things close to our preferred--meaning profitable – editorial/ad mix. When we add pages to any given issue of the magazine, we have to do so in multiples of 16-page signatures, plus the four-page cover sheet, and it requires additional ad revenue to support those pages. Thus far, I think it's fair to say that we've been providing a good variety of editorial content for our readers while consistently doing well against our competition when it comes to total page count.

I don't really have a crystal ball for determining what the future may hold for our hobby, but my guess is that the O gauge segment has probably peaked already and that, over time, we'll see manufacturing activity in this niche taper off a bit. After all, we have an aging demographic – those born just prior to, and in the decade or so after World War II-- that has long comprised the core population of this segment of the hobby. Many of those folks have reached their retirement years, and by now have pretty much completed their "must have" trains list. The O gauge market has been saturated with new product over the past 15-or-so years to the point where many hobbyists, regardless of age group, have simply satisfied their compulsive drive for new products or have become far more selective in what they do buy. This change in consumer habits will, I believe, almost surely continue to impact the industry side of the hobby, leading to more consolidation. The long term survivors, in my view, will be those who have diversified their reach into other scales and gauges – perhaps even other kinds of products – in addition to O gauge trains.

Our hobby is certainly in no danger of "disappearing," as some might fear. Trains and railroading are part of the fabric of our society, and folks young and old love trains of all types, real, model, and toy. The total number of participants in the O gauge hobby may shrink as time goes by, but there will always be an influx of new hobbyists who can't resist the lure of the rails and America's greatest and most enduring toys.

Tony Wallis
America's Best Hobby

cuboose@mail.com

The market is strong. I've seen more new faces in the store than ever before. A recession can be good for toy train sales. People cancel their travel plans and look for something to do around the house. We've had new customers come in and ask about building a layout. They want some activity the entire family can get involved in.

Lionel is appealing to all markets with starter sets like the Boy Scout, Lone Ranger, Christmas Story, Polar Express, etc. They're coming out with sets with more play value which is good because the new sets have a wide appeal and will capture more of the market. The FasTrack system has been a success and helps get new people involved. The younger guys are attracted by the new electronics. They don't want granddad's trains, they want new trains with the new electronics.

Some guys are selling off their Postwar and buying the new trains because that's the only trains their grandkids want to play with. The kids love all the sounds, bells and whistles. Lionel is also doing a good job appealing to the enthusiasts with their middle range engines and I hear the VisionLine is sold out. Accessories always sell well.

New kid shows like *Chuggington Choo Choo* and *Dinosaur Train* are very popular. So there's a lot going on to get kids interested in trains. It's up to us dealers to educate this younger market so they make the switch electric trains when they get older. I feel Lionel is giving us the ammunition to do just that. I'm looking ahead to an excellent fourth quarter.

David Dansky, Ridgefield, WA
David is owner of Train Heaven

trainheavd@comcast.net

I think the irreversible demographics of our hobby is contributing more to the downward trend than the economy. I call it the four Ds – death, downsizing, divorce, and debt. I get calls everyday from collectors who want to get out for whatever reason. So for every 100 collectors who want call it quits, there's only five or six new collectors ready to jump in so when supply exceeds demand, prices fall. But there are bright spots. Like New items with their box are holding steady. Ex+ 773 Hudsons still bring $1500-$1700 even thought the guides have them around $1200-$1400. The market for the rare variations has shrunk dramatically but there are still about 100 hardcore guys who want solid-shield Rutlands and the rare Mo-Pacs but those numbers are dwindling. The silver-based F3s like the Western Pacifics and Rio Grande are still bringing good money and the Texas Special, if the red is bright, is still good. The common stuff in average condition has taken a big hit. But that could be a bright spot because lower prices may get new blood in the hobby.

As far as prewar, it's too early to tell how MTH reproducing Lionel prewar trains will affect the market, but it certainly won't help. The reality of the situation is that our hobby consists mostly of guys between 60 and 80. You don't see many 20-30 somethings at meets. Look at the subscription numbers of the magazines and the membership numbers of the clubs. They're all down and the only way to reverse this trend is to get kids and young parents involved. The train videos and Thomas do fine job but by the time the kid is seven or eight he's twittering and tweeting and Facebooking. I feel it's sad because they're missing out on so much but it's a brand new world out there and us older folks are watching things fly by just like our parents watched stuff fly by them. It's the inevitable push of technological progress and those marvelous trains we love so much don't mean a thing to the younger folks.

David Dansky on the new Grading Standards
Perhaps I am just a Luddite, but the old standards seemed to work just fine. Thoreau said to simplify and simplify – our leading train organization must have missed that lecture. Whatever you set as a standard must be interpreted. There is a connotation to the C-7 and/or to Excellent or Very Good Plus. In the end it is all rather subjective; an unambiguous denotation is almost impossible to ascertain, except perhaps mint/sealed/boxed. The box standards now employed by some train organizations would confuse a Rhodes Scholar. There is no substitute for a seller with integrity and a buyer with experience. Nor for keeping it simple.

Note from TM: We agree. We're sticking with the old.

John La Lima
East Coast Train Parts

Today, more than ever, the economy drives the market. Collecting will always be what it was but time is passing. Our generation of collector are dying, retiring, or simply can not afford to keep up – but all is not lost. Our industry must realize is has to reinvent itself to appeal to the kid in all of us. Lionel is smart to come out with those special sets, the Boy Scouts, the Lone Ranger, Peter Potter, or whatever the heck the guy's name is – name trains like that bring new blood into the hobby and we need a major transfusion.

We have to survive until the economy gets better. Most people have no discretionary income, and our hobby lives on discretionary income. People go to meets, let the kids watch the trains run on the layouts, then they leave, maybe they'll buy a DVD but no trains. Lots of hobby stores are in trouble. Some are closing their doors.

But in spite of all this bad news, the really rare stuff in like new condition still commands goofy prices. Most of that good stuff only shows up in eBay or in auctions. Like the 910 uncataloged Submarine Base. One sold at auction recently for $12,000. The 60 Trolley with red letters. One sold for $14,000 and one sold for $12,000. A 2242 New Haven AB sold for $6000. Is that nuts? But all those items are really rare. There are still guys with money looking for the really rare stuff in top condition. I'm talking about a tiny segment of the market – maybe 3%. Boxes are another area that's hot. Record numbers are being paid. But the rest of the market, where most of us live, is soft. It will get better... I hope.

Late Changes/Additions

Received too late to include in text. If you have an item we missed or if you see a mistake, let us know. Email us at info@tmbv.com

About the 80N, 99N, 77N, 69N, 82N, 440N, 45N
Before 1936, accessories sold for Standard Gauge were identified by catalog number only, as in 80 Semaphore, etc. If the same accessory were also sold for O gauge, it was designated with an "O" before the catalog number, as in O80, etc. Each came with an appropriate track section. In 1936 and after, Lionel used "N" to designate accessories intended for both O and Standard Gauges, as in 80N, 99N, etc. The track section was no longer included.

Page 31
On both 265 and 265E Vanderbilts, check for original cab castings as they have a tendency to decay.

Page 40
In 1943 and 1944, Madison Hardware fabricated freight cars and accessories out of parts. Among them were a 2655 box, 2679 tank, and 2620 floodlight car (pictured on page 58). Madison also cobbled together three diner accessories out of parts. Two are pictured on page 58. The third was made from a Flying Yankee coach.

Page 43
0080 w/o whistle, 0080W w/whistle
First 00 set made by Lionel. 1938 only. Consisted of:
001 engine (with draw bar pin & chain), 001T tender (w/o whistle) or: 001W (with whistle), 0014 Yellow "Lionel Lines" Box Car, 0015 silver "Sunoco" Tank Car (the #0015 was in the decals), 0016 Gray "Southern Pacific" Hopper Car & 0017 "Pennsylvania Caboose" (red with maroon "catwalks"). It included 12 #0061 curved tracks and 4 #0062 straight sections. The 1938 catalog also listed a #0081K Locomotive & Tender in "kit" form; not believed to have been made.

Page 113
6410-25 Unlettered flat, 2 red autos (4) ?*

Photo Credits
The Early Period photos were supplied by Jim Flynn. Most of the Prewar photos were shot in John Potter's new train room (which, by the way, we left in post-hurricane condition). The shots of the unassembled, mint OO kits were supplied by Dick Kuehnemund. And most of the postwar items, including the mint sets in boxes, were from Craig Chidester's collection. Our sincere thanks to all.

Craig, by the way, who has a fine layout in addition to his incredible collection, will be featured in our *Lionel Nation, Part 5*.

Quick Reference

Prewar

Postwar